The Berlin Spies

ALEX GERLIS

THE BERLIN SPIES

CANELO

First published in the United Kingdom in 2019 by Studio 28

This edition published in the United Kingdom in 2020 by

Canelo Digital Publishing Limited
31 Helen Road
Oxford OX2 0DF
United Kingdom

A CIP catalogue record for this book is available from the British Library.

Print ISBN 978 1 78863 998 9
Ebook ISBN 978 1 78863 869 2

Look for more great books at www.canelo.co

Printed and bound in Great Britain by Clays Ltd, Elcograf S.p.A.

The Main Characters

(Where characters have an alias or change their names during the course of the story these names are shown in brackets)

The Recruits

Arnold Bauer (Tony Norton)

Mathias Hahn

Konrad Hartmann (Martin Page)

Lothar Meier (Christopher Vale)

Carsten Möller

Wilhelm Richter (Heinz Fleischhauer/Werner Pohl)

Christian Schäfer (Tom Hartley)

Otto Schröder (Bernhard Krause)

Horst Webber (Georg Stern)

Axel Werner

The Germans (Second World War)

Obersturmführer Feld SS Lieutenant at Magdeburg

Obersturmbannführer Frank SS Lieutenant Colonel, Freiburg

Obersturmführer Koch SS Lieutenant at Magdeburg

Sturmbannführer Krüger SS Major, Stutthof concentration camp

Obersturmbannführer Peters SS Lieutenant Colonel, Stutthof concentration camp

Brigadeführer Reinher SS Major General at Magdeburg

Obersturmführer Reiss SS Lieutenant at Magdeburg

Sturmbannführer Rottgen SS Major, 17th SS Panzergrenadier Division

Erich Schäfer Intelligence officer, Magdeburg

Manfred & Heike Weber couple in Berlin

Arno & Eva Stern parents of Georg

The British

Edgar retired British Intelligence officer

Andy MI6 officer, St Albans

Captain Canterbury (Dennis Field/ Bramley Arthur Sefton Bevan)

Ronnie Castle MI6 officer

Clive Cowley MI6 agent, Bonn (Julius)

Ken & Linda Frost Nazi sympathisers, London (1945)

Charles Kemp MI6 station chief, Bonn

Hugh Lassiter MI6 officer

Edward Law MI6 officer

Martin Paget Special Branch (police) superintendent

Christopher Porter retired MI6 officer

Richard MI6 officer

Walker MI6 Registry clerk

Williams security officer, British Embassy East Berlin

Martin Winter diplomat, British Embassy East Berlin

The Russians

Viktor Leonidovich Krasotkin veteran KGB agent, based East Berlin

Irma KGB East Berlin, partner of Viktor

Piotr Vasilyevich Kozlov KGB station chief, East Berlin

Yevgeny Yefimovich Mironov KGB station chief, Vienna

Andrei Volkov KGB Paris

Samuel KGB assassin, West Germany

Reinhard Schäfer KGB officer, East Berlin

The Germans (post Second World War)

Andreas homeless man, Cologne

Dieter Braun Red Army Faction member, Rome

Dr Manfred Berger doctor at the Uni-Klinik, Frankfurt

Elke BfV officer

Sabine Falkenberg (Ute von Morsbach) Red Army Faction member

Franz BfV officer

Frederick Red Army Faction contact, West Berlin

Frieda BfV officer

Hans Red Army Faction member, West Berlin

Max Lazerowitz friend of Viktor, East Berlin

Father Carl Lehmann Roman Catholic chaplain at the Uni-Klinik, Frankfurt

Peter Viktor's former agent, now in Frankfurt

Konrad BfV officer

The Saxon senior man at BfV

Alois Schmidt lawyer, Frankfurt

Red Army Faction (Baader Meinhoff) members

Andreas Baader (d October 1977)

Gudrun Ensslin (d October 1977)

Ulrike Meinhof (d May 1976)

Holger Meins (d November 1974)

Gerhard Müller (fate unknown)

Jan-Carl Raspe (d October 1977)

Prologue

'Good morning, Mr Hartmann.' A pause followed, during which time the caller abruptly cleared his throat. 'Will you kill yourself today, Mr Hartmann?'

Another pause, longer this time and lingering with all the menace it intended. The words ricocheted around the room with the velocity of a bullet. The man listening at the other end of the phone had neither the time nor breath to reply. He began to say 'I beg your pardon,' but all that came out was a silent gasp.

The caller repeated the message, this time even more slowly. 'Will you kill yourself today, Mr Hartmann?'

It was a male voice, speaking precisely, as if reading the message to ensure its accuracy. If pressed, the listener would have said the speaker was young rather than old, educated, and what the English called 'upper class'. He noted the perfect pronunciation of his surname, despite the obvious English accent. Two clear syllables: Hart-mann.

The line went dead, followed by a dialling tone for a few seconds and then a continuous electronic noise which went on for what must have been a good minute. During that time the listener found himself staring in disbelief at the telephone, and swaying. His mouth became very dry, his throat painfully parched. He placed the handset back on the cradle which in turn sat on a neat little shelf on the wall, next to a calendar with photos of cottages in various seasons. He had to steady himself against the wall for another minute, before slowly edging across the kitchen to the table, as if balancing on ice.

All this time, Radio Three was on in the background, the closing bars of a Mozart overture suggesting a cheerful day ahead. The man sat very still at the table, watching the sun stream through the narrow window set high in the kitchen wall, picking out countless tiny flecks of dust before illuminating the breakfast table, neatly laid the night before. A few beams of early morning sun broke through the drawn blind on the door, locked tightly against intrusions from the garden. He looked at his breakfast, meticulously arranged on the chequered tablecloth. The teapot, covered in one of the many cosies his wife had knitted; the three slices of toast in the china rack they had bought in Cornwall; the milk in an old chipped jug commemorating a doomed royal marriage; and the large packet of cereal, with a tiger grinning at him.

He needed to think, and leant across the table to turn down the radio to help his concentration. He noticed that his hands were trembling. His breathing was heavy and a cold sweat spread from his head down his back.

Think carefully... probably a terrible mistake... maybe my imagination... perhaps the new blood pressure tablets?

He had trouble removing his reading glasses from their case and, when he finally got them out, his shaking hands dropped them on the table. They caught the side of the Royal Wedding milk jug, causing one of the little pads that rest on the nose to snap off. He put them on anyway.

Write it down.

That is what his wife had always said. If you need to remember an important conversation, write it down as soon as possible. 'Makes it easier to complain later,' she would say, though she had long become used to the fact that it was not in his nature to complain, and he knew it was certainly not in his interest to draw attention to himself. He knew now that he couldn't possibly risk writing down what the man had said.

'Good morning, Mr Hartmann. Will you kill yourself today, Mr Hartmann?'

He was sure that was what the caller had said – and then said again.

'Will you kill yourself today, Mr Hartmann?'

He repeated the words to himself, trying hard to memorise them because despite how profound they were, he feared he would soon forget them. This was his life: important things he needed to remember would all too easily be forgotten, while memories whose sole purpose was to haunt him sat on his shoulder, a constant whispering reminder in his ear. He was damned.

He was in his fiftieth year though he knew he looked considerably older. He certainly felt older. He'd lived on his own since his wife died seven years previously and had no one to confide in, no job to go to since his redundancy two years ago. For days on end, sometimes even weeks, he had no real conversations and that suited him: it was safer that way. Recently, though, he had begun to worry about the effect this isolation was having on him. *Maybe this is a trick of the mind.* The thought failed to reassure him.

Ringing the police was, of course, not an option. So he sat and deliberated, even though no clear ideas came into his head.

I thought I had got away with it!

The noisy kitchen clock showed that it was nearly a quarter to ten. His routine was completely disrupted, but he was unable to move. His tea was stone cold, with an unpleasant film now gathered on its surface. The toast remained untouched in its chipped china rack and the cereal remained in the box, still guarded by the tiger.

Although he couldn't remember doing so, he had smoked four cigarettes and a fifth was alight in his trembling hand. He normally wouldn't touch his first until he sat down for his coffee after his morning walk. Even when he was getting through a packet a day he wouldn't have smoked five before ten o'clock.

He had once read in the *Daily Mail* how all the words and sounds ever made in the world did not disappear, but remained suspended silently in the atmosphere.

The words spoken on the phone had certainly remained in the room, clinging to the cornices and staring down at him like medieval gargoyles. They were there when he closed his eyes tight and even when he covered his ears. He turned the radio back on, but rather than the music drowning out the words, it only made them louder.

'Will you kill yourself today?' There was no doubt that was what the voice had said, twice. If that had been all the caller had said… well, he could just about have coped with that, even tried to dismiss it as a prank.

But: 'Mr Hartmann…'

No one had called him Mr Hartmann for over thirty years.

—

He walked into the front room as if in a trance. The room was reserved for special occasions, though there had been precious few of those. He couldn't recall when he'd last sat there but he came in every evening to draw the curtains just before it got dark, and the ritual was reversed every morning after breakfast. On Thursday mornings he would dust and vacuum the room, which meant it was the one time of the week when he could not avoid looking at the photos neatly arranged on the sideboard and the mantelpiece. It was the most painful moment of his week, each of them looking accusingly at him, reminding him of sins of which he was already well aware.

You don't need to remind me. And you don't even know the half of it!

That was his defence.

At least the room no longer contained the photos his wife had kept of him, from when they first met. He had destroyed those the very day she died. He'd looked so young in his late twenties. The photos had haunted him from the moment they were taken, his discomfort all too obvious in his reluctant pose, inching towards the shadows. Now that younger self no longer existed.

At least not until three hours ago '…Mr Hartmann…'

4

I thought I had got away with it!

For the past thirty years he'd lived in a state of constant fear. He fully expected every knock at the door or police car approaching to mean that he had finally been found out. Most weeks, there had been two or three occasions when he had been scared to death. What was it he had heard in a Shakespeare play on the radio a month or so back?

'Cowards die many times before their deaths.'

He went upstairs and, in the bathroom, turned on the small transistor radio which started playing something by Schubert. He thought he recognised the piece and if he wasn't in such a state he'd have been able to name it. After he finished shaving he opened the medicine cabinet and looked at the two shelves stuffed with his wife's medication. For seven years he had been meaning to take it all down to the doctor's surgery. That medication could solve everything now: he would lay down on the bed he'd last slept in the night before his wife died, listen to a cassette of Bach and wash a bottle of the strongest painkillers down with a large glass of whisky and water. It was not as if he hadn't thought about it before, many times.

But he began to rally. He was now having his doubts about the phone call. If someone was trying to scare him like this, why had they not rung back in the intervening three hours? Maybe, maybe… it was all a mistake after all, a hallucination… the blood pressure tablets?

At eleven o'clock, way behind schedule, he left the house for his daily shopping trip. Leaving the newsagent, he caught his reflection in the large window. For the first time in many years, it was Konrad Hartmann rather than Martin Page he saw staring back at him. He glanced round in case anyone else had seen that too, but the small parade of shops was deserted apart from an old man shuffling along, his head bowed with age and effort.

It was gone twelve when he arrived back home, and although he didn't normally eat his lunch until one he felt lightheaded, having missed breakfast, and was unsure what to do. *Stick to my routine* he decided, though he did allow himself a digestive biscuit.

He carefully put the lid back on the biscuit tin, a souvenir from a silent holiday in Scotland more than a decade ago. He then put on the light anorak he wore for the garden, and removed his slippers to replace them with the garden shoes he kept by the back door.

He had chosen this house so carefully all those years ago. It was at the end of a row, so with neighbours on just the one side. The roads to the front and side of the house were neither too busy nor too quiet. A garden with walls high enough to provide extra privacy, and a gate into the rear wall that opened into an alley. His wife had not questioned why these things mattered so much; she was more bothered by what was inside.

The garden was overgrown when they moved in and within months he had transformed it. Then, when there was suddenly no longer a need for the swing he had hurriedly removed it and turned the little lawn into a vegetable patch that soon took over most of the garden. One day, a work colleague of his wife's and her husband had visited and as his wife showed them round the garden he overheard the husband remark: 'It's all vegetables! Like those gardens people have on the continent.'

Evidently, turning the whole garden over to vegetables was not English, so within a matter of days the carrots were replaced by red roses, the rhubarb by white roses and the potato patch under the kitchen window became home to a large yellow rose bush. He disliked roses, he thought they were just one notch above weeds and certainly not worth all the trouble, but they served their purpose: they couldn't, he had decided, be more English. Never again would his garden be a cause of suspicion.

There was a large shed at the end of it. He unlocked the windowless shed door, along with two heavy duty padlocks. He closed the door carefully behind him then turned on the light. The inside of the shed was neat, but with little space between the garden tools and the dozens of boxes, all different sizes. He started to remove boxes from a stack at the back of the shed, half hidden behind a large deckchair and an old parasol. At the bottom of the stack was a wooden trunk: his heart beat fast as he opened it.

Every two or three months, for more than thirty years, he had been through this routine. Each time he would open the box half expecting that what he was looking for in it would be missing. The box was full of inconsequential items: old cutlery, souvenirs from cheap holidays long forgotten, yellowing magazines, books now rendered unreadable by mildew. Their only purpose was to conceal a tightly-wrapped plastic package at the bottom. It was there. It always was.

He hesitated, standing very still to catch any noise in the garden before unwrapping the package and placing its contents on the lid of the now-closed trunk. He held the barrel up to the light and checked the mechanism. He removed the bullets from their case and polished them, as he always did, inspecting them carefully for any sign of rust. He kept the pistol in good condition. There was nothing to suggest that it would not work, but he had no idea as to whether it would fire correctly or if anything had happened to the bullets.

Twenty years ago, in a moment of madness, he'd fired the gun. His work had taken him to Cornwall and he'd decided to stop on Bodmin Moor where he reckoned it would be deserted enough to test the revolver. He'd parked on the side of a quiet road and then walked for an hour, during which time he saw not a soul. He found a small lake, sheltered by a ring of low hills, placed a can on a nearby rock and fired at it. The gun worked perfectly, but the echo of it firing and the clatter of the can reverberated for what felt like an eternity and as the noise began to fade away he was convinced he heard a dog barking. A dog comes with an owner and if the dog heard the gun then the owner would have done so too.

He'd hurriedly put the gun away, retrieved the can and even managed to locate the casing from the bullet. Expecting the brows of the hills to fill with uniforms any minute, he hurried back to the car. He'd resolved never to test the gun again and never to remove it from the shed unless absolutely necessary.

Now, he decided, it was absolutely necessary.

That night, his daughter came to visit him.

She had been an occasional visitor in the months after his wife had died. At first she came as often as twice a week, but in the past five years or so she'd visited no more than three or four times a year. Her visits initially provided a kind of brief comfort, but that was replaced by being uneasy and unsettled for days afterwards.

This visit was as before: she stood in his bedroom doorway, backlit by the dim light that he always kept on at the top of the landing. He had no idea how long she had been standing there, her small hand clasping the doorknob, strands of her long fair hair caught by the light. She made no noise, of course, but he awoke as always with a start and propped himself up in the bed, waiting to see if she would come to him, which she never did. He would wait a while, and then start to speak. He hesitated because sometimes she would leave as soon as he began to speak. But at other times she remained, her small head moving very slowly as she allowed him to have his say.

'I'm so sorry... I had no idea. If I had realised I would have called the doctor... your mother pleaded with me to do that, but I just thought it was a high temperature and you'd be fine in the morning. I didn't want to make a fuss. You know how I feel about people coming to the house...'

And if she still remained after that, which was rare, he would tell her how his wife – her mother – had never forgiven him, even though she hadn't once uttered a word about it. And that his wife had died of a broken heart, just five years after her daughter.

'But it was me that was being punished, for everything I've done. It was so cruel, you were only seven!'

That night he'd hesitated for longer than usual before saying anything. He knew she wouldn't leave until he said something or until it began to get light. She was capable of standing there for hours. He always had the same thought: maybe she'd forgive him and run to the bed and throw her arms around his shoulders as she used to, her warm cheek pressed tight against his, his ear damp as

8

she whispered something into it. So that night he felt able to tell her.

'It seems they've found me, you know, after all these years. Does that help? Does it make you feel better?'

But it didn't. She remained for another minute, her body swaying slightly. At one stage the light caught her eyes, but they didn't seem to be looking at him. They looked so much darker than he remembered. And then she disappeared.

He was unsettled when he got up the following morning. Not just from her visit, but also at the memory of the phone call. If they are going to call again, it will be at the same time, he had decided, with an uncertain logic. He smoked three cigarettes waiting for the call, but seven fourteen came and went and there was no phone call. He was able to drink his tea and eat his breakfast and although all was still very far from well in his world, it was certainly better than the previous day.

He was able to resume his routine. He visited the shops at his normal time, returning home at nine thirty as usual, double locking the front door and attaching the chain. He could now have his cup of coffee, read the *Daily Mail* and life would have returned to normal.

The kettle was just beginning to whistle when the phone rang. He was inclined at first to ignore it, to let it ring. But then he realised it would be cathartic to receive a normal call, to talk to someone trying to sell him something, or one of the friends of his wife who called very occasionally out of a sense of duty to see how he was.

'So, Mr Hartmann, did you enjoy your morning walk? The queue at the newsagent not too much of an inconvenience, I hope.'

The same voice.

'Who is this?'

'Evidently you didn't manage to kill yourself yesterday, did you? Today would seem to be a good day for it, don't you agree, Mr Hartmann?'

9

'Please tell me who you are. My name is not Hartmann.' But he was quickly aware that he was now talking to a dialling tone.

Near Magdeburg, Germany, September 1944

The small rip in the blackout blind was just wide enough to allow a narrow beam of moonlight into the room. Konrad Hartmann been staring at the ceiling for hours, and couldn't decide whether the shape the moonlight projected onto it looked more like France or Poland. Or at least, what was left of them.

As far as he could tell, the other two boys in the room had fallen asleep. Despite his exhaustion, he was quite unable to do the same. Every time he closed his eyes images of his family came to him, and they only faded if he opened his eyes again.

And when he did open his eyes, it was no better. He couldn't stop thinking about the night before. He had never experienced anything like it. What was it that teacher in his school was supposed to have said just after the war started?

Animals. The Nazis behave like animals.

He hadn't heard the teacher say it, of course, and none of his friends had either, but everyone swore they knew someone who had heard it, apparently muttered in a corridor to another teacher.

Animals.

How could he say that, or even think it? Konrad had been outraged, and was pleased that justice was served when the teacher was dragged away by the Gestapo, never to be seen or heard of again.

Animals. That word had stayed with him since then. So much good was being done in this country, indeed across the whole world. How could they be compared to animals? It was so unfair!

But still, the one thought to come into his head last night and remain there was what the teacher was supposed to have said. The Nazis behave like animals.

He tried again to sleep, gently shutting his eyes and turning onto his side. Now he could clearly see his father walking up the small path to their front door, with both dogs leaping around him.

He paused at the entrance, turned round and self-consciously waved at him. Then his mother opened the door, a beaming smile on her face and there, behind her, were his two younger brothers, scrapping with each other as usual. They all gathered in the doorway: his parents, his brothers and the dogs. Behind the house he could see the Thüringian forest rising, a perfect shade of dark green brilliantly picked out against a deep blue sky. Far in the distance, the first hint of the white-capped mountains. Outside the room he could hear occasional heavy footsteps, walking slowly, pausing outside the door and waiting there for a minute or two before moving on.

He opened his eyes again and turned onto his back, propping his lumpy pillow up against the iron bedstead. The boy in the next bed was awake now, staring silently at him. They looked awkwardly at each other for a moment before the other boy turned his head away. Konrad must have slept for a while because when he woke up the moonlight had been replaced by a bright shaft of early morning sun.

He closed his eyes tightly, but the images of his family were no longer there. He turned onto his front and buried his head in the pillow, willing the images to return, but he struggled even to remember what they looked like.

Act as if you've died and been reborn. It's the only way you'll cope.

That is what he had told himself as he lay in bed. The only way to survive what was coming was to accept that your previous life was over. Like being killed and then coming back to life.

Forget the past.

But the past, it seemed, was forgetting him.

And what was it the officers had said to them just before they were dismissed a few hours ago? 'Remember, boys. You are soldiers, being told to do what soldiers do. You are being sent into battle.'

Since he was eleven or twelve he had assumed he'd become a soldier, and as soon as he had joined the Hitler Youth four years ago he'd realised that he may be killed once he was sent to fight.

He understood that. He understood that a soldier goes into battle, fights with the enemy and runs the risk of being injured or killed or being taken prisoner. But what they had talked about the evening before was no ordinary battle. The battles he understood lasted hours, or days, maybe weeks or even months, like Stalingrad.

But this battle wasn't going to be like that.

This battle was going to last the rest of his life.

–

'Cigarette?'

It didn't sound like a generous offer, more like one made out of a grudging sense of obligation.

They'd left the camp outside Stettin in the early hours of the morning, when it was still dark. It was dark now, but the darkness of the other end of a long day. This was only the second or third time the SS officer sat alongside him had bothered to address him directly. Until then, his utterances had either been to the driver or to the world in general, usually gazing out of the window as he spoke. To the driver, he had barked out instructions: 'You need to go faster… You need to slow down… Is this the best route? … Make sure we get through the next roadblock faster… This car is nothing compared to the Daimler.'

The world in general did not get off so lightly. 'I don't trust any woman, certainly not my wife – not even my favourite mistress… Never trust a woman who says she loves you… The Wehrmacht are so disloyal… traitors… The *Führer* can only trust the SS… I wouldn't be surprised if there are secret Jews high up in the Wehrmacht. That would explain Stalingrad. And the food shortages – have you noticed the food shortages?'

He was convinced it was a trick to catch him out. Food shortages were not an advised topic of conversation with anyone, let alone an SS officer.

'No, sir. At the camp they feed us very adequately. I have not seen any problems in the towns either, sir.'

'Oh, haven't you? Very good. Very obedient. You'll make a good member of the SS.'

His voice was a mixture of sarcasm and boredom.

And so it had continued. 'The British deserve everything they're going to get… The Russians are not human, none of that lot are… A year from now, there'll be no Jews left in Europe – can you imagine that? … The Italians are a complete joke… As for the Luftwaffe… well, they may as well have women flying the planes. And please, don't even mention the Navy… You can excuse the French because of their women – and their wine. And their incompetence.'

The drink had done much of the talking. The officer's hip flask had appeared soon after they'd left the camp and he had refilled it from a bottle in his knapsack at least twice. But he had sobered up at the first signs of dusk and with them the inevitability of Allied air raids. They would need to be well clear of Berlin. The RAF had a habit, the officer assured the driver, of dropping their bombs early and in consequence the suburbs and smalls towns around the city took many hits.

They were past Potsdam and somewhere to the south of Brandenburg. It was hard to tell their precise location in the near dark and with the absence of road signs, but the driver had a map open on the empty seat next to him and had been updating the officer. Wave after wave of Lancaster bombers, with their distinctive tail planes, were passing overhead. The driver had pulled off the autobahn and joined a main road, but the officer was not happy.

'We're still too exposed,' he insisted. His voice had a nervous edge to it now. So they had dropped to a smaller road, not much more than single track. The driver killed the headlights and their speed, but the officer was still not happy.

Pull in here.

So now they were parked under a canopy of trees, the car banked at a steep angle on the verge and darkness and silence around them, apart from the distant crumple of bombs falling, anti-aircraft fire to the east, and the constant drone of planes above. There was a smell of freshly ploughed fields, and a silent breeze caused the hedgerow around them to sway.

'Cigarette?'

He wasn't sure what the right answer was. 'Yes' could seem too familiar. 'No' could appear rude. He held up his hand as if to say 'No thanks,' but the officer persisted. He pulled a cigarette out of a metal case and handed it to him and followed it up with a lighter with a large flame that illuminated the interior of the car. A heavy sweat on the officer's brow glistened in the flicker of the flame.

The cigarette tasted good, much better quality tobacco than he was used to. He inhaled slowly, allowing the smoke to float around his mouth first so that he could taste it properly. It was so strong that he soon began to feel lightheaded, and his throat tightened.

The officer unwound the window, staring up at another black wave of Lancasters, muttering something under his breath. He began to talk quickly and seemed now a bit more relaxed towards Konrad, even slightly friendly. Perhaps he was nervous. Some people behaved like that when they were nervous, he'd noticed: excessively friendly.

'Have you been in an air raid?'

'No sir. I have been near one, but not actually in one.'

'Huh! Everyone in Germany's been near an air raid.'

He looked at the officer; unsure as to whether this hint of indiscretion was all part of whatever it was that was going on. He had no idea where he was being taken, or why. He didn't reckon he was in trouble, he would have been treated differently if he was, but for a junior recruit to the SS to have a car and a driver and an officer to escort him, something had to be up. He noticed that the officer's hand was trembling as he held his cigarette out of the window, flicking off the ash.

'How old are you boy?'

'I am seventeen, sir. Eighteen in three months.'

The officer nodded slowly, as if he had guessed as much. So young.

'And tell me boy, have you ever had a woman?'

How was he meant to reply?

'Of course, sir!' As soon as he said it he realised his answer had been too quick to sound convincing.

'Best lay I ever had was in Magdeburg, not far from here I suppose. She was seventeen – five times in one night: wonderful. Maybe she's still there. Perhaps I ought to look her up. She's probably only able to manage four times a night now!'

The officer laughed heartily at his joke and Konrad joined in, grateful for the opportunity to relieve the tension. He was concerned that the officer might quiz him about his own experiences. He would have to make something up. And he was intrigued: five times in one night. Was that really possible? Surely, once a night would be enough, maybe twice – but five times… but would an SS officer lie?

As he shifted again in his seat he caught the driver's eye in the rear-view mirror, not a sign of life in them, but looking directly at him without appearing to blink. And then, the tiniest nod, as if to warn him.

Be careful.

It was so quiet now that he could hear the officer inhaling his cigarette. It had been a good ten minutes since the last plane had flown overhead, so the officer felt able to leave the car. He walked into the middle of the road, gazing up into the night sky, studying it for a few minutes. He walked to the side of the road, relieved himself against one of the wheels and climbed back into the car.

'It's safe now,' he said to the driver. 'How long do you reckon?'

'An hour, if we're lucky, sir.'

The officer repeated the driver's words, mimicking his rough Berlin accent, speaking softly but loud enough for them all to hear, even as the engine of the Mercedes coughed into life.

'Lucky? Haven't you heard luck's also rationed now?'

Chapter 1

Moscow, 1949

As the lift took him to one of the upper floors in the headquarters of the Ministry of Internal Affairs in Moscow, Viktor
Leonidovich Krasotkin was worried. Not as worried as he'd have
been had they descended to one of the notorious basements
beneath Zhitnaya Street, but worried nonetheless. From the lift,
his escort led him down a well-lit corridor with paintings of
heroic workers on the walls, and numbered brass plates on the
doors. The escort knocked on one of the doors and opened it
without waiting for a response.

There were three men behind the table, two of whom he
recognised. Ponomarenko was his latest boss, a thin, worried-
looking man with a weepy eye that he constantly dabbed at with
a dirty handkerchief. Klimentov was also there, Ponomarenko's
boss. Viktor had time for Klimentov: he'd fought in the Red
Army during the war, unlike so many of the others who'd spent
it behind their desks in Moscow and then fled the city at the first
sound of distant German artillery in 1941. The third man he didn't
recognise; younger than the other two, good-looking with a dark
complexion and a well-cut suit, not the kind made in a factory.
Viktor was relieved to see his escort hadn't followed him into the
room. So far, matters were not nearly as bad as they could have
been.

Klimentov spoke first, a long rambling tribute delivered in
a soft, not unfriendly tone with a distinctive southern accent.
'Distinguished service… unequalled skills… personal sacrifice…

unending gratitude of the Party and the State... Comrade Stalin himself...' Viktor had heard it all before: just words, usually delivered before a reprimand but at least he'd probably leave the building alive. 'Interrogating Nazis... not a pleasant task... we recognise that... year in, year out... nevertheless...'

'Nevertheless,' repeated Klimentov, his voice no longer soft and now distinctly unfriendly, 'what the hell are you up to Krasotkin?'

–

Viktor had met Carsten Möller two months earlier, in mid-September, at a German prisoner of war camp near Rostov. It was one of the larger camps, now half empty, and he'd interrogated prisoners there on many occasions. One of his team had been there recently and reported that a prisoner was insisting on speaking to 'someone very important'.

He arrived at the camp on a cold morning, a wind from Siberia attempting to blow him back to Moscow. The camp commandant cut an obese figure, stuffed behind a desk piled high with files, the tops of a couple of bottles poking out behind them.

'He is twenty-three and from Munich,' said the commandant, who sounded asthmatic. He paused to light a cigarette, not bothering to offer one to Viktor. 'He was a junior officer in a SS unit defending Leipzig when the city was taken by the Americans in April 45.' The commandant was straining to read the notes in the file, wafting away cigarette smoke. 'We took over Leipzig from the Americans in the July which was when Möller became our prisoner. He was transferred to the Soviet Union a month later.'

The commandant shut the file. And that's that.

'I've come all this way for you to tell me that?'

The commandant looked put out. 'He said he wanted to talk to someone important. Apparently I'm not important enough. Insolent young Nazi...'

'Before I go and see him, what else can you tell me?'

'Not a lot: he's young – one of the youngest SS prisoners that we have left here. He would only have been eighteen when he was captured. By all accounts he was a fairly hard line Nazi at first but in the last year or so has been much quieter. He has become increasingly disillusioned and depressed as other prisoners have been sent back to Germany. I'm not sure what he wants to talk to you about but my instinct tells me it's important. Otherwise I wouldn't have brought you here.'

–

The commandant took Viktor to an interrogation room where the prisoner was handcuffed to a chair with a guard either side of him. Across the desk from him were two empty chairs. The commandant lowered himself into one of them.

Viktor told the guards to remove the handcuffs and leave the room. 'You too,' he told the commandant. 'I'm sure you have plenty to get on with. All those files on your desk, you must be so busy…' The commandant hesitated, clearly reluctant to leave, especially after having made such an effort to sit down.

Once he was alone with Möller, Viktor walked around the room. Although he couldn't be sure, it was not unusual for these rooms to be bugged and even the thought of it inhibited him. The Russian picked up his chair and put it next to the German's, although facing the opposite way. The two men were sitting shoulder to shoulder.

Carsten Möller looked younger than twenty-three, his fair hair no doubt bleached by the hours he'd spent outside. His blue eyes fixed on Viktor, following him around the room at first and then studying him closely when he sat down.

'You wanted to talk to someone important, I'm told. I'm that person.' Viktor spoke in German and he could tell from the younger man's reaction that he was wondering whether Viktor was a native speaker.

'And who are you? I need to know your name and what you do.'

Viktor folded his arms across his chest. 'Son, I am afraid you're not in a great position to call the shots. I'm as important a person as you'll get to speak to. I've come all the way from Moscow, so you'd better tell me everything.'

'If – when – I am sent back to Germany, can it be under a different identity?'

'That depends…'

'I don't know what the situation really is in the Federal Republic but from what we're told here, it seems ex-Nazis now run the place. Maybe the East would be safer…'

Viktor snorted. 'It's not much better there, I can tell you! You're thinking too far ahead, Möller. Your story…'

Viktor removed his leather notebook from his jacket pocket and sharpened his pencil with a knife. For the next two hours, Carsten Möller told him his story. Viktor stopped him on more than one occasion so he could re-sharpen his pencil.

Möller told of how he'd joined the SS at the age of seventeen, and soon after had been taken to a remote house in the country-side near Magdeburg, along with a dozen or so SS recruits of a similar age. The one thing they had in common was a fluency in English, which was crucial to their mission. He described how, after their training, they would be attached to units with the eventual aim of being taken prisoner by the British or Americans and brought to Britain as prisoners. He provided details about their training, and the brutality of some of the things they were required to do shocked Viktor.

Möller's story ended with an account of how he was captured. The remains of his unit had been scooped up by the Americans, and he thought everything was going to plan, but then Leipzig was allocated to the Soviet zone and he found himself a prisoner of the wrong Allies. His story then stopped abruptly, and the young German broke down, sobbing uncontrollably for a few minutes. Viktor said nothing. He was more than familiar with this emotion: the relief after someone had unburdened themselves of a story which had haunted them for so long.

Viktor leaned back in his chair and closed his eyes against the harsh light of the cell. Since 1945 he had interrogated thousands of Nazi prisoners, some of them for just a few minutes, others for days at a time. What they had to say tended to blur into one endless stream of professed innocence and self-pity. But sometimes, a small line or fact from a story struck a chord or triggered a memory from something he had heard before. As Möller's sobs receded, Viktor realised that the story of young, English-speaking SS officers deliberately looking to be captured was similar to something he had heard before – a few years previously, in the prison at Gdansk, in a room not unlike this one. It had been told to him by another Nazi officer, this one just days away from his execution. Viktor patted Möller's knee in a friendly manner. 'You are correct to share your story. If it makes you feel any easier, you can be repatriated to the East, if you express a preference for being sent there. Not many do, mind you. Tell me though: can you remember the names of any of the other recruits who gathered at Magdeburg?'

Carsten Möller took the handkerchief Viktor offered him, and composed himself. 'I don't remember all of them, by any means,' he said. 'There was an Arnold and a Lothar. I remember the names of the two I shared a room with: Konrad Hartmann and Mathias Hahn. But the one I remember best was Wilhelm Richter.'

Viktor said nothing as he wrote in his notebook. 'Can you repeat the last name please?'

'Wilhelm Richter.'

'And you said you remember him best… why is that?'

Carsten Möller was quiet for a few moments. 'Since I joined the SS five years ago I have encountered many evil people. But Richter is the most evil person I have ever known.'

–

'I beg your pardon?' The atmosphere in the room in the MVD headquarters on Zhitnaya Street had suddenly changed. Viktor knew how to handle his superiors when they turned on him. He made sure he sounded confident and aggrieved, and addressed his remarks at Klimentov, who had just spoken to him.

'You heard me, Krasotkin, I said: what the fuck are you up to?'

'You'll have to be more specific than that.'

Ponomarenko and the other two shifted uncomfortably in their seats as Klimentov slammed his fist on the table. 'Don't be insolent, Krasotkin. You're not half as indispensable as you'd like to think.'

'I've been interrogating Nazis for the past four years, day in and day out. I doubt I've had more than ten days off in that time. I have never,' his voice was louder now, 'had either my competence or my loyalty questioned, comrade.'

'No one is questioning your loyalty—' Ponomarenko's words were cut short as Klimentov placed a hand on his arm.

'I'm not questioning your loyalty; I'm questioning your… judgement. This prisoner you've been enquiring about…'

'Which one? There are thousands!'

'Wilhelm Richter.' This came from the man at the end of the table, the man Viktor had not met before. He spoke with an authority that suggested he was senior even to Klimentov.

Viktor made a good show of pretending he was struggling to recall that particular name.

'Come on Krasotkin,' said the man. 'You've been asking about Richter for the past couple of months, checking records and asking around the camps.'

'Him, yes… his name came up in an interrogation. He may have committed a war crime. I was checking the story out. That's my job.'

'Well,' said the same man, 'you can forget about him. His name came up before and he was investigated. Don't waste your time.'

'In any case, Richter's dead. He was held at a camp near Perm where he died of typhus.' Klimentov was beginning to get up as he spoke. 'Just keep your head down, stick to your job and forget about Richter, understand?'

'I understand. One question though: when did Richter die?'

Klimentov stared at Viktor, his eyes filled with indignation. He turned to Ponomarenko who shrugged his shoulders. No idea. The good-looking man with the suit which hadn't been made in a factory replied quietly.

'1947.'

For just a brief moment Viktor was aware his reaction betrayed his shock, as he gripped the side of the chair and he started to perspire.

Chapter 2

The priest had some difficulty finding the correct ward. The University Hospital – *Uni-Klinik*, as everyone called it – was so vast that even staff who'd worked there for many years struggled to find their way around.

The doctor was young, almost as young as the priest. It took a while for them to find an unoccupied room. 'It is a most unusual situation, Father... I'm sorry, I should have remembered your name...'

'Lehmann. Carl Lehmann. Father Lehmann.'

'Dr Manfred Berger. Let me explain the situation, Father Lehmann. Bernhard Krause...' the doctor had opened a file in front of him and removed a pair of glasses from his shirt pocket. 'Bernhard Krause is forty-two years of age and works as a clerk with a law firm here in Frankfurt. He is not known to have had any previous medical problems apart from a bad leg: according to an X-ray his ankle was broken many years ago but was almost certainly not reset properly at the time. As a consequence, by the time the break healed, the leg was deformed. We asked him about it, but he would not discuss it. He has been an in-patient here for three weeks. He was admitted with advanced bone cancer which has metastasised extensively. Apparently he kept his symptoms to himself for some time before he finally went to his doctor, which was only recently. He must have suffered considerably. Of course, his condition is incurable: I would be surprised if he lasted another month. He must be a very tough and resolute man to have survived this long.

'Herr Krause has had no visitors since he's been here, and says he has no family. He is all alone. All we can do is ensure he's as comfortable as possible, and he is unfortunately in a lot of pain – but he won't let us give him proper pain relief. He is absolutely insistent we don't give him morphine or anything else. I don't know why. Maybe because of his condition, he doesn't trust us. A serious and painful physical illness will sometimes trigger psychotic features, like paranoia. Could you try to persuade him, perhaps?'

'I can try, but if you haven't been able to…'

'He is an unusual patient. Very private, and although he behaves properly, he clearly does not trust anyone. Even with you – you are aware of the situation?'

'I understand there is something about him not wanting to see any of the other chaplains?'

'Oh, he saw plenty of the other chaplains all right, but none of them were good enough for him, I don't know why. He saw the Lutheran chaplain, a couple of Evangelicals and even your senior Catholic priest here, Father Roth. But he wouldn't talk to any of them. He said they were all too old, and asked me to find someone under thirty. He was quite insistent, and as he was getting so distressed about it I felt I had to do what I could.'

'Why do you think he's so insistent?'

'Who knows, but it was the same with me: he didn't want to be treated by one of the older doctors. One of my colleagues said he had come across this before, especially in patients of this age, around their early forties. He no doubt fought in the war. Maybe that's something to do with it: he possibly associates people over the age of forty with the war, and so doesn't trust them. That could also be the reason he is so reluctant to take morphine. Some men of that age are terrified that it will make them disinhibited, and they'll get themselves into trouble on their deathbeds. So they won't take the one drug that could help. As a consequence, they die painful deaths. Maybe they think that's what they deserve.'

24

Everything in the room appeared to be a different version of grey: the floor a shiny, dark grey, the walls a light, speckled grey, the blinds a dirty grey and the blankets on the bed – bluish grey. Greyest of all was the man propped up in the bed, under the bluish grey blankets. Beneath a thick mop of untidy silver-grey hair was the face of a man looking considerably older than his forty-two years, his pallor distinctly sickly, skin pulled painfully tight over his skull.

The priest tiptoed towards the chair by the window. The patient appeared to be fast asleep, his body not stirring. He was propped up on a number of large pillows.

'You are the chaplain?' The man's voice was hoarse. His head had lolled in the priest's direction and he was looking at him through grey blue eyes, the only part of him which appeared to be more alive than dead. 'You will need to come closer. Even my hearing is affected now.' A white hand slowly waved him over. 'Come even closer.' This time the long white hand beckoned him to bend down. 'Tell me your name and your age.'

'My name is Father Lehmann. I'm a Roman Catholic chaplain here at the *Uni-Klinik*. I am twenty-eight years old.'

'So what year were you born?'

'1941. Here in Frankfurt.'

The man in the bed furrowed his brow, trying to work out whether the priest had given the correct age. 'I am not a religious man, Father. I cannot remember the last time I went inside a church. I don't even believe in God.'

'I quite understand, for many people a time like this—'

'I am dying,' interrupted the man. 'They try to keep me comfortable. I sleep and I think and I stare out of the window and then I sleep again. I am in a waiting room.'

The priest followed the old man's gaze out of the window, and for a moment they both watched a long black barge heading slowly north through the brown waters of the Main.

'You know what is happening in here?'

Father Lehmann shook his head, unsure where 'in here' was. Did Krause mean inside his head? Krause raised a shaking arm and pointed straight ahead of him. At the same time a long tongue, quite grey in colour, emerged from his mouth to lick his lips, the end of it curving to rest on his top lip for a while. The shaking arm was still pointing at the wall.

'I'll tell you what is happening in here, Father. Every time I go to sleep, the walls close in a little. Not by very much, just a few centimetres each time, but I know it is happening. Eventually, they will close in on me completely and I will be gone.'

Outside the window was the sound of a long, muffled hoot from the barge. A trolley rattled past in the corridor, squeaking loudly. The priest ran a finger under his tight collar. The temperature in the room was now almost unbearable and he was beginning to feel lightheaded: it was early August but the heating was on.

Krause had sunk back in the pillow, his arm returned to his side. There was a long silence, during which the patient closed his eyes once more. Father Lehmann looked round the room and could appreciate what Krause meant. In the short time he had been in the room, it did appear to have become smaller. 'Are you in any pain?'

'Some, but nothing they cannot look after. They want to give me morphine, you know. I wouldn't be surprised if they asked you to persuade me to take it.'

'If it helps you should—'

'But I don't need it!' For the first time his voice rose above a loud whisper. 'I'd fall asleep and never wake up. Or rather, if I did wake up, I wouldn't realise it. So I won't take it. Now, I want you to listen carefully. I want to tell you the real reason I asked you to come along. In the cupboard over there are a few possessions of mine, Father. Would you please go and bring over the briefcase?'

The wardrobe contained a few items of clothing which would never be worn again, and behind a pair of highly-polished black shoes was a scuffed leather briefcase, which Father Lehmann brought over to the bed. With some difficulty, the patient hauled himself into a more upright position and removed a large bundle from the case, wrapped in a white plastic bag and heavily sealed with strips of shiny brown tape. Attached to the front of the bundle was a white envelope with an address on it. Exhausted by the effort, he sank back into the pillows, clutching the bundle to his chest. He took a minute or two to regain his breath.

'You will take this to the address on the envelope, you understand Father? You will find more specific instructions inside the envelope. You give me your word as a man of God?'

Even though you don't believe in him. The priest took the parcel and looked at the address: it would require a special journey, perhaps he could go by train. 'Of course, Herr Krause. Perhaps—'

'But you must wait, until I'm dead. That will not be long. What did Dr Berger say?'

The priest shrugged, unwilling to answer.

'A few weeks? That is what he usually says. Take the parcel, keep it somewhere safe and remain in contact with Dr Berger. When you hear I have died, you will deliver the parcel.'

'I will do what you ask. Have you thought about your funeral?'

The man glared at the priest, his eyes flashing angrily before he allowed them to close again.

–

It was a Tuesday in the middle of September when Father Lehmann was informed that Herr Krause had died the previous night. The priest waited a week before travelling to Bonn, where he managed to negotiate his way into the main reception of the British Embassy on Friedrich-Ebert-Allee. Being a priest had helped so far, but it did not appear he was going much further.

'As I say, sir: leave the parcel with me and I will ensure it gets to the right department. I am afraid you cannot go up there, especially not without an appointment.'

'Well, maybe if I could see someone from that department?'

Half an hour later the priest was sitting in a small waiting room on the ground floor with a young man in British Army uniform. The man had begun to open the parcel the priest had handed to him.

'Please. My instructions are that the contents should be opened in a secure room. And they are to be handed first to someone here who works in intelligence. I was given this by a dying man and these are his strict instructions. Surely it is not too much to ask for his wishes to be respected?'

The man in uniform looked part aggrieved, part mystified. He promised to do his best.

Chapter 3

After this, they would have to take her seriously. There'd be no more making fun of her because she hadn't heard of Gramsci or any other obscure Marxist philosopher or read anything by Engels – actually she had tried to read him but he was almost impossible to follow. They'd stop the jokes about how she only had a poster of Che Guevara on her wall because she fancied him or telling her she was just playing at being a revolutionary, because she was so beautiful. She couldn't understand the logic of that, especially as whoever was telling her usually had his hands all over her as he did so. Now she was about to show them how seriously they'd have to take her. They would have to start treating her with respect.

The courier left the bank on Potsdamer Strasse just after eleven o'clock, as he did every morning. He glanced around as he left the bank, as he also did every morning, but in a rather casual manner – more to check the weather than for reasons of security. Then he headed south, walking quickly despite a pronounced limp. The limp made her feel even better about what she was about to do: it would be a war wound, she'd decided, which meant he'd be a Nazi.

He swapped the briefcase from one hand to the other a couple of times, so she knew it wasn't attached to his wrist with some kind of security chain, which she'd assumed it would be when she first started to plan this. They'd be so pleased with her, spotting crucial details like that. He glanced round once more as he turned right into Pohlstrasse, and didn't spot her despite the fact she was now just a few yards behind him. Then he entered the cake shop, as she'd watched him do every morning for the past week and which she assumed he wasn't allowed to do. This was the first morning she actually followed him into the shop, and she was pleased that the shop was as crowded as ever. As he reached the counter she edged in behind him.

'Very well, I shall have two doughnuts!' This was followed by a confident chuckle, and the woman in the white hat behind the counter smiled politely. It sounded as if he probably said the same thing every morning. It was the first time she'd heard him speak: quite a pleasant voice actually, softly spoken and certainly not a Berlin accent. Now was her opportunity. As he reached inside his jacket for his wallet, he wedged the briefcase between his legs on the floor. She knew she had a matter of seconds and in one move bent down, grabbed the briefcase, and pushed her way out of the shop, almost in a crouching position. She was in the street before she heard shouting, and sprinted as hard as she could. An elderly couple were in the middle of the pavement, blocking her, and she ran straight through them, sending both flying over.

She carried on running, round the block and then to Goeben-strasse where she caught a tram and, once on board, she slipped the briefcase into a large shopping bag she had folded up in her coat pocket. They would be so impressed at the precautions she'd taken. She got off the tram near the cemetery on Blücherstrasse and walked through Kreuzberg before entering the apartment on Alexandrinenstrasse.

–

Not for one minute had she expected such a furious reaction from the comrades. Rather than taking her seriously and treating her with respect, they were actually incandescent with rage, especially Andreas Baader who was screaming at her, his face no more than an inch from hers.

'You stupid fucking bitch! You've put us all at risk for… this!' His hand swept along the top of the table, sending the contents of the courier's briefcase flying onto the floor: a few letters and a number of documents, but no money.

'You had no authorisation to do this, Ute, none whatsoever. What have you done? Stolen a few worthless pieces of paper and then come here, no doubt leaving a trail of clues along the way. You know I'm on the run, Gudrun too. I'm surprised half the fascist police in West Berlin aren't breaking the door down already. They could be here any minute: when they arrive, you stand behind the door and take the first shot, understand?'

She was trembling violently and sobbing. There were perhaps a dozen of them in the apartment. Gudrun Ensslin was also there – she and Baader had been on the run for the past few months – but she was uncharacteristically quiet. The others were the typical crowd, some she knew by their first name only, others whom she'd not seen before. For a while there was silence apart from her sobs. Although no one said it, they were all thinking the same thing: she'd been back in the apartment for over an hour and if the police were going to come, they'd have done so before now.

'I'm sorry, maybe I made a mistake but we all agreed we have to do everything in our power to dismantle the state. There are so many former Nazis in positions of authority; I thought this was a perfect way of attacking them. I...' Her voice trailed off, unsure of what to say. Her defence of her actions sounded feeble and she feared she was about to be rejected by the group. That would be calamitous: she'd rejected her family to be here and now her friends – her comrades – were about to reject her.

'Go with Hans,' said Baader. 'Give us a minute to talk.'

Hans was a young guy from Hamburg who'd joined the group after he'd escaped from a juvenile prison. He didn't appear to know too much about politics, but everyone liked him. She'd slept with Hans a few times and was quite fond of him. It was evident his job now was to keep an eye on her. They sat on the bed in the room she sometimes slept in, both smoking. Hans said a few times in his soft voice that she was not to worry, and started to stroke the inside of her thigh. Just as she was thinking they may as well go to bed, the door burst open and Ensslin walked in.

'Out,' she told Hans.

'You – stay here.' When they were alone she spoke in a more reasonable tone than Ute had expected. 'Don't be too upset about Andreas,' she gestured with her lit cigarette behind her, in the direction of where Andreas would be. 'We're all nervous, Ute: we could be arrested any minute. Look, he's not the intellectual brains of our group but we need him to...' she paused to inhale and come up with the right words '...organise us and motivate us. He sometimes overreacts. What you did today was stupid, but it shows your heart is in the right place. Marx said history is nothing but the actions of men in pursuit of their ends and at least you're doing something and are obviously committed to the cause. Andreas – and I – think we can trust you. But we need you to trust us too.'

She got up from the bed where she'd been sitting alongside Ute and walked over to the window before turning round to face her. 'Your family are in Augsburg, yes?'

Ute nodded and felt a wave of nausea sweep over her.

'We need you to disappear for a while. We'll be getting a new identity for you. A few of our comrades are doing this. We don't know what your mission will be yet but, after the nonsense of today, just remember to do what you're told. Trust us. Don't come up with any more clever ideas of your own. Understand?'

She nodded. 'And when will this be?'

'I'm not sure, but the way things are going I don't imagine it will be too long.'

Chapter 4

'I've never liked the French.' He stared suspiciously into his coffee cup, tilting it and then swilling its contents around carefully as if checking for evidence of poison. 'Never liked them, and trust them even less – a duplicitous lot. Anyone you speak to who was here during the war says it was a wonderful posting, even easier than being in the Reich – until the first signs of the so-called liberation and then suddenly the French all claimed they'd been in the Resistance, that rabble…'

Two men in a bar in Paris, at the intersection of Rue d'Hauteville and Rue la Fayette in the tenth arrondissement, the imposing Église Saint-Vincent-de-Paul framed in the rain-splattered window where they sat. The man who'd never liked the French was the younger of the two, perhaps in his early forties.

The other man was noticeably short, even when sitting down, and appeared quite a few years older than his companion. 'Maybe you should keep your voice down,' he told the younger man. 'What the hell's the matter with you? It's bad enough that we're speaking German in Paris. It wasn't that long ago—'

'I could hold a decent conversation in French, Schäfer. You're the one who only speaks German.'

'And Russian: I'm fluent in Russian, you know that.'

'Well that certainly wouldn't draw attention to us would it? A conversation in Russian… you'd better remind me of your cover story.'

'Swiss, from Zurich – I'm here for a business meeting. We're old acquaintances, bumped into each other, decided to have a drink, you know the story… you look worried.'

The younger man swivelled round to check no one was in earshot. 'Worried? Of course I'm fucking worried Schäfer! Turns out Otto Schröder spotted me in Frankfurt less than two years ago… Jesus Christ, Schäfer, if it were you you'd be worried enough—'

'Keep your bloody voice down. Remember that I am mentioned too, though admittedly only in an historical sense. I told you, we've been able to confirm that Schröder – or Krause as he called himself – is now dead. As for that bloody document he wrote, well – we were lucky. The British Embassy in Bonn are only interested in Communists so they sent it to London and it went straight to my man in MI6, which is how I got it and why we have nothing to worry about.'

'Easy for you to say, but I can't afford to be so confident.'

Schäfer gripped the other man's wrist. 'Look, stop being irrational. Don't you realise – if anyone was going to act on this document, they would have done so immediately? The fact that the British got it three – four months ago and still nothing's happened shows that no one attached any importance to it. You have nothing to worry about.'

'And that bloody Jew in Berlin, what about him, a real turn up for the books, eh Schäfer? You managed to recruit a fucking Jew into the SS – in Berlin, in 1944: some achievement that…'

The barmaid was glancing in their direction.

'That's enough – and keep your voice down. If we do anything about him it would create too much attention and we can't have that. He doesn't want anyone knowing about his past, any more than we do. I want to reassure you that there is nothing to worry about. It was a close shave, but no more than that. We need to concentrate on the work we do now. What do you have for me?'

Schäfer felt something push against his legs under the table. 'It's all in there,' said the younger man. 'Nothing that will get you the Order of Lenin or whatever they give your lot these days, but useful to have anyway. Background briefings rather than anything top secret – oh, and there's another report on the Vietnam War.'

'Saying?'

'Not very much… troop withdrawals, that kind of thing. They don't think they're going to win the war. Or lose it, for that matter. Nothing you probably don't know already.'

'Source?'

'All US Embassy.'

'All useful though, thank you. Anything else?'

'Apparently the British are very excited about a new agent they have at the Polish embassy in Bonn.'

'Who?'

'Tadeusz Wójcik: he's the senior Polish intelligence officer in the Federal Republic, the MSW head of station at the Embassy.'

'Wójcik! Fuck. Been in post for just under a year. I'll have to tell Moscow straight away. Good work. What's the matter? You look unhappy.'

'Everything I give you, Schäfer, it all benefits the Soviets. That's not what I'm meant to be doing, is it? What about our mission? I never hear anything about it these days.'

'Be patient, Goalkeeper, it's all about being patient. I keep telling you, everything you give me helps establish how important and how credible you are and, when the time comes, that will stand us in good stead. In any case I was about to tell you something important, I…'

'I don't know, Schäfer. Here I am, an officer in the Federal Republic's security service – your man inside the BfV – and you're just not using me properly. I know you tell me to be patient, about our mission and all that, but in the meantime I have expenses. Everything I give you, it all comes at some kind of price.'

'The usual sum was paid into your account in Zurich this morning.'

'That's convenient.'

'You can check if you like.'

'I believe you. You can't afford not to pay me, Schäfer. After all, I give you so much and get so little in return.' He paused. 'What was it you were going to tell me that's so very important?'

'No need to be sarcastic. You'd better order us more coffee.'

Schäfer waited until they'd been served, and moved his chair closer. 'Have you ever come across the Military Liaison Office at the BfV?'

He shook his head. 'Never heard of it. Are you sure that's what it's called?'

'Of course I'm sure. It's so secret most people in the BfV won't have heard of it. It reports jointly to the President of the BfV and the Chief of Staff of the Federal Defence Forces. Its job, as the name suggests, is to provide a line of communication between the BfV and the armed forces. We need you to get into that section—'

'Which is so secret I've never heard of it. What do I do, go and knock on the door and ask when I start?'

'Shut up and listen for once, Goalkeeper. There's a specific reason we need to get you in there. All top secret NATO material is handled by the Military Liaison Office. NATO has a plan called Operation Open River, which is concerned with the defence of Western Europe. Essentially, it lays out what it calls 'the trigger points' – what NATO would interpret as hostile actions by Warsaw Pact states against NATO members in Europe. As you know, NATO's policy is that if one member is attacked, then NATO itself will respond. Operation Open River goes into very specific detail about this policy: it identifies areas of weakness along NATO's eastern border, and locations which it regards as being especially sensitive from a military and strategic perspective. As far as Andropov is concerned, it is essential the Soviet Union gets its hands on this document.'

'And the BfV is the only source for it?'

'It's not a straightforward situation, Wilhelm. Operation Open River is updated every quarter, and it's vital we have access to current versions. There are master copies of course – at NATO headquarters in Brussels – but we have reason to believe that our cell there – it may have been compromised. We need to see copies from more than one source to see if they corroborate each other, that we are not being fed disinformation. We especially need access to the plans for Operation Open River which have been sent to those NATO states which have land or sea borders with the Warsaw Pact, these plans are known to be especially detailed and are specific to each country. As far as Greece, Turkey, Norway and Italy are concerned, we have very good sources: we see every version of Operation Open River. But for Denmark and West Germany, it is more problematic. If you can get into the Military Liaison Office then that will give us access to another, more reliable, source for Operation Open River.'

'And help the Soviet Union... it's like I was saying before, it's all about helping those fucking Communists!'

'You need to understand this: if the Soviet Union can lay its hands on the Operation Open River plans, then the chances of a war in Europe between the east and west are greatly increased. The Soviet Union will have a better idea of where to attack. And when that happens there'll be chaos in Europe, and we'll be ready to step into the vacuum. All the people like you, who went undercover at the end of the war, will come together... it will all be as planned, Goalkeeper, people will understand that the *Führer* was right all along, a new Reich will emerge, we...'

The man who'd been called Goalkeeper no longer looked so angry. He nodded as Schäfer spoke and by the time he'd finished even appeared excited. 'But if this military liaison office is so secret, how do I get into it?'

'You take your time. This has to be a long-term aim. Remind me: how long have you been with the Operations Department?'

'Four years... getting on for five. Why do you ask?'

'That's long enough: should request a transfer. Isn't here's something called a Rotation Team?'

'Yes... the people on it are moved around different departments, to where they're needed. You usually spend six months or so in each department.'

'If you get onto the Rotation Team, sooner or later you'll be transferred to the Military Liaison Office. The fact that you won't have applied to go there will be critical. It could take two or three years, maybe even longer, but Moscow is prepared to play the long game.'

'And in the meantime?'

'In the meantime you just keep your head down. Don't take any risks, don't draw attention to yourself.'

'So no spying?'

'Don't worry, we have another project to keep you occupied. The Red Army Faction—'

'You mean that gang of students playing at bank robbers and pretending to be anarchists and Maoists?'

'Presumably the BfV has an interest in them?'

'The BfV has an interest in them? That's an understatement, Schäfer: they're becoming obsessed with them. It is the BfV's job to be interested in groups like that.'

'Moscow is beginning to take quite an interest too. We need to know more about them.'

'If you want my opinion, I think people are getting unnecessarily excited about a bunch of middle class kids from the Free University who smoke marijuana and pretend to understand Marx. They're just kids and in a year's time they'll probably all be studying to become accountants.'

'In Moscow's opinion...' Schäfer shifted his chair even closer and lowered his voice, 'the Red Army Faction has the potential to destabilise the Federal Republic, which is to be encouraged. The organisation is not without its flaws. It has certain bourgeois tendencies and lacks discipline, and its influences tend to be revolutionary and anarchist rather than Marxist Leninist. But nonetheless it has impeccable anti-imperialist instincts. Moscow wants to know more about them.'

'I'm not sure what this has to do with me – I've told you what I think of them. I've not had to deal with them at work.' There was a pause, during which he shrugged his shoulders and looked disinterested once again, his fingers drumming on the table.

'Moscow want me to put someone on to them – you.'

'Hang on, hang on… you look after matters in the DDR, and I work for you. What about the KGB station in Bonn, surely the Federal Republic is their responsibility? I'm busy enough as it is, Schäfer, I sometimes think you forget that. I work full time at the BfV, then there's my work for you, and now you want me to take on this…'

'This will be part of your work for me, Goalkeeper.'

–

They left the bar minutes later. One of Schäfer's rules was that agents should always stay together for a while after a meeting. He was convinced splitting up too quickly aroused suspicion, even if staying together did make things easier for anyone following them.

So the two men walked slowly down the narrow Rue d'Hauteville before turning left into Rue de l'Échiquier and then along Rue de Metz before turning into Boulevard de Strasbourg. By then they knew they hadn't been followed, so continued towards the Strasbourg – Saint-Denis metro station, before parting at its entrance.

The younger man went down the steps into the metro, and Schäfer waited for him to disappear from view before crossing the road and heading south down the Boulevard de Sebastopol. He would need to get the intelligence about Tadeusz Wójcik to Moscow as soon as possible.

Despite this good bit of intel, he was uneasy. He played over in his mind what Goalkeeper had said. Everything I give you Schäfer, it all benefits the Soviets. That's not what I'm meant to be doing, is it? What about our mission? I never hear anything about that these days.

This wasn't the first time he had made a remark like this. For the past few years, almost every time he'd seen him, he'd said something along these lines. But this was by far the most explicit. For all his greed, impatience, impetuosity and sheer nastiness, he was still an excellent source and a clever and resourceful agent. He'd never made the mistake of underestimating him, but now he'd need to be even more careful.

Despite this, he felt the meeting had been a success. It would take time for him to get in the Military Liaison Office, but Moscow was prepared to be patient. He could only hope Goalkeeper would be patient too.

Chapter 5

They were on their own in the open bow of the pleasure cruiser La Suisse as it slowly fought through the wind and the rain on Lac Leman. Geneva had long since disappeared behind them, and the few other passengers were wisely below deck.

'So you managed to get on to the Rotation Team?'

'Yes, it wasn't exactly difficult. It's not the most popular part of the BfV.'

'But you've only just started there, Wilhelm. Remember, this is about the long game, be patient. Now then, do you want to hear what your other mission is – or are you just going to be difficult?'

'Rob a bank…? Chuck a few stones at a newspaper office?'

'A few weeks ago a young man calling himself Dieter Braun walked into the TASS news agency office in Rome, and asked to speak to someone about a sensitive political matter. The KGB resident there met with him and Braun told him he was wanted by the police in West Berlin, and admitted he was working for the Red Army Faction. He was a bit all over the place but, from what the resident could gather, Braun was mainly after money – funding for their organisation. The resident thought he was rather naïve, assuming the Soviet Union would be an easy touch. The resident took all his details and told him to come back a few days later. He thought Braun was another walk-in who wasn't to be trusted, and he wanted to drop him, but Moscow took the view he could be a way into the Red Army Faction, and came up with an idea.

'Braun is apparently rather gullible; he's prone to believing what he wants to believe. So the resident appeared to take Braun into his confidence. He told him it wasn't up to the Soviet Union to fund the Red Army Faction – it was too risky – but that there were in any case many people in the Federal Republic who were secretly sympathetic to his group, and who could be a good source of funds if the Red Army Faction were to approach them. Braun was eager to get names, and the resident appeared very reluctant to let him have any, but eventually let slip about one wealthy businessman who is sympathetic to the Red Army Faction and could be very generous towards them, if approached in the right way.'

'Don't tell me, Schäfer, this businessman is—'

'You, Wilhelm.'

'You want me to be a businessman—'

'Just listen.' Schäfer leaned back and ran his fingers through his hair. 'There is a woman called Ute von Morsbach. Her family used to live near Brandenburg but fled to the west when the Red Army arrived in '45. They settled in Augsburg and Ute was born there in 1948, so she's now twenty-two. Her father is a wealthy industrialist: we don't know whether the 'von' means genuine nobility or is an affectation of it. From what we've been able to gather, she doesn't get on with her parents. They're rich, right wing and religious, none of which go down well with the Red Army Faction…'

'It's probably what drove her into it.'

'Indeed. We know she went to West Berlin in '67 and enrolled at the Free University, so she was there for the Shah protests and all the '68 riots and everything, which is when she became involved with the people who now make up the Red Army Faction. We don't know if she's ever been involved in any of their actions but she's close to some of those at the top and very well informed about what they're up to. She's certainly more important than Dieter Braun in Rome.

'As far as we know, she disappeared earlier this year. We believe she is one of a small group of members who've been encouraged to change their identities, keep a low profile and avoid any public links with the Red Army Faction until they're needed. The KGB resident at TASS told Dieter Braun the wealthy businessman spends a few days each month in Aachen – and guess what's happened now? They've taken the bait: Ute von Morsbach has resurfaced in Aachen, using the name Sabine Falkenberg. She's clearly been sent there to find the businessman. Aachen's good for you, isn't it?'

His companion shrugged, as if he couldn't care less whether it was or it wasn't.

'I mean, how far is it from Cologne – an hour?'

'More or less, but isn't it also close to Bonn?'

Schäfer turned his collar up against the spray from the lake, and removed a folder from his briefcase. 'Listen carefully. You'll go to Aachen and make contact with Sabine Falkenberg. In here is your new identity. You'll be Werner Pohl, a wealthy businessman with access to plenty of cash. Moscow has opened a very generous account for you at the main branch of Commerzbank in Frankfurt, with special facilities in Aachen. Moscow has also opened an account at Bank Leu in Zurich: this is where they'll channel the money to. You will have access to both accounts, and you can use them to fund the Red Army Faction. You should always be secretive about your business and where the money comes from. Your political sympathies will be hard left—'

Wilhelm laughed loudly. 'And you don't think Sabine Falkenberg might spot a certain paradox here – a wealthy businessman with hard left politics? Come on, Schäfer, what's up with Moscow these days? That's a pathetic cover.'

'But it's not an obvious one, is it? It will enable you to allude to the fact that much of your wealth is inherited, and you resent your family for it. That ought to strike a chord with Sabine. But more than anything else, she'll be interested in the money. We've rented you a flat in Jesuitenstrasse, off Kleinmarschierstrasse, near the cathedral – it's a very smart area. The records show the flat has been rented by Werner Pohl for two years, so if she looks into it she shouldn't be suspicious. Your story is you work all over the world, but Aachen is where you go for some peace and quiet every so often – which makes sense, it is a spa town after all. Get to know her, but don't be open, be secretive and evasive – as enigmatic as possible. You'll only be around for two or three days a month—'

'Which is hardly enough time to—'

'It will be enough. There's a photograph in the folder, have a look at it.'

Wilhelm opened the envelope and pulled out the photo of Sabine Falkenberg, shielding it against the wind. He nodded approvingly and smiled. He looked interested for the first time since they'd started talking.

'Twenty-two, you say? This mission is beginning to appeal to me now!'

'You'll behave with her, Goalkeeper, no violence this time. It is possible to have… relations… with a woman without needing to be rough. You've caused enough problems in that respect…'

'Hah! So you're a relationship expert now are you, Schäfer? You said the resident in Rome told this Dieter Braun that I could be very generous if I was "approached in the right way". What did he understand by that?'

'I think you probably know what that means. Sabine Falkenberg is twenty years younger than you. She is a very attractive young woman. She will understand you have certain tastes… desires…'

Wilhelm nodded, much more interested than he had been at the start of their meeting. 'And tell me Schäfer – how I get to meet Sabine Falkenberg?'

'Go to Aachen the weekend after next. Dieter Braun has been given your name and address, and told you'll be in Aachen then.'

'And then what do I do?'

'And then she'll find you.'

–

On the Friday of the weekend in question, he arrived at the Aachen apartment just before seven in the evening. He showered, and changed into the kind of outfit he thought a wealthy businessman such as Werner Pohl would wear: a smart but understated dark jacket and cream-coloured trousers, a tailored white shirt, Italian shoes and a Cartier watch he had insisted Schäfer purchase when they were in Geneva.

And then he left the apartment, turning left when he exited Jesuitenstrasse and heading north to the cathedral, which he slowly circumnavigated, pausing to light a cigarette and enjoy the warm evening.

If it was me I'd just watch on the first night. Follow, but not approach. Watch where I go and that I live where they say, and don't meet up with anyone…

But he couldn't count on an anarchist in her early twenties having quite the same degree of street craft as an experienced agent like himself. So he carried on: through the square between the cathedral and the town hall and then into Rethelstrasse, and into a French restaurant he'd found the previous week. Expensive, but not outrageously so; classy rather than ostentatious and not so quiet that anyone following him would be noticed. And, most importantly, a *maître d'* whom he'd tipped very generously on his previous visit – generous enough to ensure he remembered him and made a fuss of him. Herr Pohl…

He ate alone, just a hors d'oeuvre and a main course, followed by a leisurely stroll more or less in the direction of his apartment. On Krämerstrasse he stopped at a bar called the Magnuskeller he'd been into the week before, which was an ideal venue for 'Sabine' to bump into him. It had a mixed clientele – some students, a few tourists, and a fair number of professionals in their thirties and forties. It wasn't too crowded either, and had lots of small alcoves.

He spent an hour in the bar, moving around, having conversations with a couple of strangers in the way you do in bars. Anyone watching would assume he was a regular – there meeting friends. He found out the names of all the bar staff and tipped them generously.

By eleven o'clock he was back in the apartment. If she had been following him she'd been good, because he hadn't spotted anyone obviously tailing him and none of the many young blondes he'd seen looked quite like her photograph.

The following morning he returned to the Magnuskeller for coffee and croissant, settling into an alcove with a copy of that morning's *Aachener Volkszeitung*. He hadn't been there for much longer than ten minutes when a young woman walked past his table, and then again, glancing at him each time she passed. On the third occasion he managed to get a proper look. He was sure it was Sabine Falkenberg even though the hair was lighter than in her photo, she was taller than he'd expected and, although pretty in the picture, in real life she was beautiful.

But Sabine Falkenberg didn't join him then as he expected. He'd made it so easy for her: the bar, the alcove... so he ordered another coffee to show he was in no rush. Ten minutes later he left the Magnuskeller and walked a short distance to a small park, where he found an unoccupied bench and sat down with his newspaper.

'Excuse me, do you know where Theaterplatz is?'

She was standing in front of him, wearing sunglasses, and he couldn't help noticing how short her skirt was and how long her legs were.

'Theaterplatz? It's about five minutes' walk from here, in that direction.' He gestured south, barely looking up from the Aachener Volkszeitung.

'Thank you. Are you from Aachen?'

He peered at her, blinking in the sun and managing to appear mildly annoyed at being disturbed. 'Pardon?'

'Are you from Aachen?'

'No.'

She hesitated, looking awkward and a bit nervous. He was worried he'd scare her away, which would be hard to explain to

Schäfer, so he smiled and folded up his newspaper, using it to pat the empty space next to him on the bench. 'I'm sorry, I must appear rude. Come dear, sit down. My name is Werner by the way.'

She sat down, looking relieved now. 'Thank you. I'm Sabine.'

'And where are you from Sabine?'

She hesitated for a moment, as if trying to remember a script. 'West Berlin. I'm from West Berlin.'

'Really? Your accent sounds more southern to me.'

'Well, yes… I spent time in the south but more recently in West Berlin. And you?'

'Well, I'm from everywhere! Everywhere and nowhere. But I have an apartment here. It's where I come when I want to get away from everything, unfortunately not nearly as often as I'd like to. And what do you do here in Aachen, Sabine – are you visiting?'

'No, I'm a student here.'

'And you don't know where Theaterplatz is?'

'I live near the university. I don't come to the centre very often.'

'A student, eh? You probably can't afford to come to the centre, eh? Every student I meet tells me how poor they are!'

–

And so it began. It was so easy he found it enjoyable, helped unquestionably by how attractive Sabine Falkenberg was and the rising excitement of what lay ahead. He had to work hard to keep his enthusiasm in check. He was, after all, a wealthy businessman who'd met a student half his age in a park – he didn't want to seem too eager. They remained in the park for half an hour, chatting about the history of Aachen on which he was able to profess some expertise, and for which information she was duly grateful, his visits to countries around the world, West Berlin, films… anything uncontroversial. He did allow one political remark: 'Willy Brandt may be a social democrat but as Chancellor he's more like a Christian Democrat!' And then a reassuring pat on the knee and an apologetic smile to indicate he shouldn't have talked politics.

The he stood up, and Sabine followed.

'I have to go now, and you obviously need to get to Theater-platz. It has been a pleasure meeting you, Sabine. I don't suppose…' he hesitated, looking sheepishly at the ground, his hands clasped behind his back, 'I don't suppose you'd join me for dinner this evening?'

–

She joined him at the French restaurant on Rethelstrasse where he'd dined the previous night. The *maître d'* was, of course, most attentive and Sabine would have been in no doubt Werner Pohl was a regular and respected patron. She let him do the talking. His family had made money – he didn't say how, but managed to convey the impression he'd rather not talk about it. His job was to invest that money in interesting and lucrative projects around the world. He felt guilty at the amount of wealth he had and how it had been acquired – again, no details – so he looked for projects that as well as offering a high return had some social value to them. No, he said in reply to her question, he rarely saw his family these days: his father was dead, his mother was in a very expensive nursing home in Switzerland and his two sisters and their families, well… at this point he looked round in case anyone was within earshot – their politics were very different to his.

'What do you mean?' Sabine sounded a bit too eager.

Herr Pohl didn't answer as he chewed on a mouthful of fillet steak – he'd ordered it *saignant*. He waited a moment longer, drank from his glass of Burgundy, and replied in almost hushed tones. 'Let me just say they are well to the right of me. But then…' a pause while he chewed some more, 'most people are.' The last phrase was said without so much as half a smile. It was intended as a statement of fact, taking her into his confidence.

There'd been a marriage he said, quickly – as if to get this out of the way, but it had been distant: 'in more ways than one.' She'd have to work that one out. 'But please, I am so boring. Why would a pretty young student be interested in the life of a middle aged man! Tell me about yourself.'

Sabine didn't tell him very much. She lived in Maastrichter Strasse, north west of the city centre, near the university.

'What do you study?'

'Philosophy. In fact, a Masters in Philosophy.'

'Why do you look embarrassed?'

'Because my family say philosophy is useless.'

He assured her it wasn't useless, it was important young people developed an intellectual and questioning approach to life. He said he wished that in his younger days he'd devoted himself to studying philosophy or politics or a similar subject, rather than giving in to family pressure to make money. 'But you must realise, it was just after the war… things were different.'

And then he talked about the philosophers he admired and, of course, the greatest of them all – and again, he turned round to check no one was listening – Karl Marx. But he didn't elaborate, that would be for another time he said. It was getting late, he said, and he had to be in Brussels early the following morning for a flight to New York. He'd be there for a week and then in Zurich for another but he expected to be back in Aachen sometime in May. 'Maybe we can continue our conversation then?'

She agreed, and also agreed to his offer to order a taxi to take her back to where she lived in Maastrichter Strasse. 'That's so nice of you. I will only accept your offer if you accompany me. Then we can have coffee.'

–

The small apartment on the top floor of a large house didn't look enough like a student apartment, it was too tidy: no Che Guevara poster over the bed or books on the floor or empty bottles on a cluttered table, unwashed dishes and pans flowing out from a dirty sink.

She came to sit next to him on the sofa as they drank their coffee, clutching the cup with two hands in an attempt to conceal her trembling. He could tell what thoughts were preoccupying her, the instructions she would have been given by the Red Army Faction leadership. 'We are told this Pohl will be very generous towards us if he is approached in the right way... apparently he has certain tastes, desires... it is your duty to do what we ask...'

She placed a hand on his thigh, held it there for a moment and then slid it up, leaning over to kiss him. He pulled out of the embrace after a while and stroked her cheek, gently. 'Are you sure about this Sabine? I honestly have no expectation of anything, I...' But she knew what she had to do and stood up, leading him by the hand to the bedroom. Once they had started, after a bit of awkwardness, she'd turned out to be an enthusiastic lover and he'd behaved himself, curbing his natural instincts – the tastes or desires she'd have been told about. But after they'd finished she'd left the room and when she walked back in, still naked, she was smoking what looked like a large and misshapen cigarette with an unusual, almost sweet aroma. She offered it to him.

'It's a joint,' she said, laughing at the fact that he was clearly a novice. At first he was wary of feeling so uninhibited, worried he might say something he regretted.

But after she showed him how to smoke it properly he found he didn't really care about anything, and when they finished the joint – him smoking most of it – he grabbed her by the wrists and she giggled. She stopped giggling when he forced her down and climbed onto her, one hand gripping her hard by the jaw throughout. She squealed a couple of times and looked frightened and when he finished she pulled the sheets over herself and lay very still, her eyes filled with tears.

When his head had cleared he went and made her a coffee and then said he was sorry if he was a bit rough, he must have got carried away. If she wanted him to leave he would do so immediately and he wouldn't contact her again. 'I'm really not sure what got into me. Maybe it is because you're so beautiful.'

But she sat up and wiped her eyes and said not at all, it was just she wasn't used to it, but it was fine and she liked him very much and would love to see him again.

Chapter 6

Aachen and Mönchengladbach, West Germany, April to May 1972

'Sometimes it's as long as two months, Werner, and I hear nothing from you – not even a postcard!'

'I keep telling you Sabine, I go to boring places on boring business. What do you want me to do, send you a postcard of an office building?'

They both laughed and she finished her joint. He restricted himself to just an occasional puff these days, he needed to ensure he kept a clear head. But for Sabine it was different: as soon as they had finished sex, she would light up a joint already rolled up and kept by the bed.

It was a Saturday afternoon in the middle of April, and they were in bed in Sabine's apartment in Maastrichter Strasse. She was rubbing her wrists, soothing the red marks where the rope had been tied.

'Did I hurt you?'

'Just not so tight next time, Werner, but I always tell you that. And you promised you wouldn't hit me again…'

'I told you, I get carried away. It is not meant to hurt you, it's… meant to be affectionate.'

She looked away from him, towards the window. 'And you still don't tell me where you go…'

'I have business around the world, you know that.'

'Capitalism.'

'It's capitalism, Sabine, that keeps you and your comrades in funds.'

'Talking of which, Werner…'

'I'm going to make another transfer next week, I told you. I'll be in Zurich then.'

'How much?' She had leaned over to him, her head resting on his shoulders, her fingers drawing an intricate pattern on his chest.

'Probably 400,000 Deutschmarks.'

She said nothing but moved her finger away from his chest.

'That's a lot of money you know, Sabine, it's nearly half a million Swiss Francs.'

'Of course I'm grateful, but you know how much money we need to fund the cause. I told you what Andreas said.'

'I understand, but you should know me well enough by now to know how passionately I believe in the cause too. That is why I have given you so much over the last two years. Do you even know how much it comes to?'

'I have no idea, the money doesn't come anywhere near me. Gudrun seems to be in charge of it. She controls the accounts, though now they've started dividing them up.'

'What do you mean?'

'They're worried about losing control of the accounts if people are arrested. So when the money comes in – your money and all the other funds we get – Gudrun moves it around into other accounts. Meinhoff controls an account even though Gudrun doesn't want her to, and Jan-Carl Raspe looks after another one. There's another one in Hamburg, but I'm not sure who has control of that, and probably others which I know nothing about.'

'Not Baader?'

'Are you being serious? If Andreas had access to an account with even a few thousand Deutschmarks in it he'd go crazy, like a child in sweetshop. He thinks we should concentrate on robbing banks.'

'Hah! And get caught? You say Ensslin and Meinhoff aren't getting on. Why is that?'

So Sabine told him, happy to unburden herself of the tensions within the Red Army Faction, which the press was now calling the Baader-Meinhoff Group. It was also an opportunity to share gossip – Werner was skilled at asking her questions which did not appear prying. He was able to tease vital information out of her while at the same time appearing uninterested, as if he was in fact doing her a favour by letting her talk.

She told him about the different relationships within the group, who was sleeping with who, who was exercising the most influence, and about any newcomers. It was through her that Moscow had found out that a group of them, including Baader, Meinhoff and Ensslin, had gone to a Palestinian training camp in Jordan. Moscow didn't like the PFLP – it was too revolutionary for them, too unwilling to accept any form of control – and they were pleased when Wilhelm was able to report that Sabine had said the trip had gone badly. Baader had had a row with them, complaining that he didn't see why they should be trained for fighting in the desert, and saying that PFLP didn't like their attitude and their casual attitude to wearing clothes.

And then Wilhelm would gently lead her into telling him what actions were planned – the inevitable bank robberies, and the increasing number of bombings and attacks on individuals: American servicemen, police officers... a few months earlier Schäfer had told him this was what Moscow wanted to see more of. He was to do his best to encourage it, make suggestions of targets. Be subtle, but also make it apparent that it's a condition of the money you're giving.

'There's a problem though, Werner.' She had propped herself up on her elbows, her face very close to his, noses touching, the smell of cannabis still strong on her breath.

'What's that?'

'They say I don't do enough.'

'Who says?'

'The others, but mostly Andreas. He says I'm leading a comfortable life here in Aachen, not getting my hands dirty. That's how he puts it.'

'But if it wasn't for you they wouldn't be getting my money.'

'That's not how they see it. They think I need to take part in an action. They've talked about it for a few months, but now they're insisting. The other day Baader told me he was beginning to suspect I may be a Government spy.'

'That's ridiculous...'

'Of course it is, but at times he's not rational, and he holds such a sway over the others. Meinhoff may be the brightest of them, the real brains behind the organisation, but Andreas can control it through his emotions. I've been ordered to plant a bomb.'

She was sitting back against the pillows now, the sheet pulled tight to her shoulders. She looked horrified saying the word 'bomb'. 'Can you imagine, Werner – me? Plant a bomb? I can't even operate the cooker properly.'

'Do you know the target yet?'

'Hah! On top of everything, they want me to suggest a target. I wish I'd never got involved with them sometimes. Maybe we should just disappear, Werner, you and I? I could change my name, I've done that before. I'm tired of this. We could go and live somewhere away from all this...'

'Hang on, Sabine... hang on. You can't give up now. If they're saying you have to carry out a bombing, you won't be able to run away. You must do what they say. Maybe when you've carried it out – then you can—'

'But where, Werner? What should I suggest? A supermarket? An old folks home for Nazis? And there's something else, Werner.'

'What's that?'

'I think this could be to do with you...'

'Go on...'

'They said to me they're having trouble manufacturing bombs: they are too amateur. They want to start a major bombing campaign and they asked me if any of my contacts could get hold of professional bomb-making equipment, especially detonators and timers. Does that make sense, Werner?'

'It could do... they're the most sophisticated parts of a bomb. It's not too difficult to get hold of explosive and casing, but good detonators in particular are very difficult to get hold of.'

'And could you help?'

'Me?'

'Who else do I ask? Maybe they think because you have so much money, you'll be able to get hold of this equipment, I don't know…'

'Let me see what I can do, Sabine.'

–

He'd got a message through to Schäfer the following night, via a dead letter drop in Cologne. He said he needed to meet urgently. He was going to be in West Berlin for work that week, could they meet while he was there, perhaps?

He was tied up in meetings in West Berlin until the early evening, and he couldn't risk leaving early, meaning Schäfer had to come across in the afternoon and wait for him. He wouldn't be able to go back until the following morning, so he was in a bad mood when they met.

They were on the top floor of a brothel on Kurfürstenstrasse, in the heart of West Berlin's red light district. If he was followed – which was quite possible, the BfV liked to keep tabs on its staff from time to time, especially when they were away from base – a visit to the red light district at least provided a plausible excuse.

He took a tram to Potsdamer Strasse, got off a stop early, at the junction with Lützowstrasse, and walked from there, taking a circular route, including Kluckstrasse, the name of which always amused him. By the time he entered the brothel he was sure he hadn't been followed, but he knew Schäfer would have had him watched anyway.

Despite the warmth of the evening the room had its heating on, and Schäfer was wearing a coat. He was sitting, enveloped in a large velvet armchair of a dull, deep red which was stained, like the walls, the curtains and the bed cover. He gestured for Wilhelm to sit on the bed. The ceiling was one large mottled mirror.

'Did you request this room, Schäfer – or are they all like this?'

'You said it was urgent, Wilhelm, get on with it.'

So Wilhelm did get on with it and, from the way Schäfer nodded and then removed not just his coat but his jacket too, he could tell his companion agreed – it was indeed urgent.

'This is very good. Detonators and timers you say?'

He nodded, and Schäfer looked pleased. 'We were expecting them to run a proper bombing campaign.'

'Can you get hold of them?'

'Is that a serious question? Of course we can get hold of them. That's the least of our problems. We could fill an Antonov 22 with them, but I doubt they'd clear customs very easily. Where are they to go to?'

'As far as I can gather, Baader and Raspe are in Frankfurt. Sabine's been told to go there in two weeks. It sounds like this might be where they're making their bombs.'

Schäfer stood up and paced the room, gazing disapproving at the ceiling. 'Tell her to tell them you can get hold of what they need, but it will take a couple of weeks. Ask where they are to be delivered to. If they have any sense it will be somewhere away from Frankfurt, but who knows? And you say they want her to suggest a target?'

'It seems they want to see how committed she is.'

'That makes sense. Actually, I can suggest an excellent target. Listen carefully.'

Half an hour later it was time to leave. Schäfer said he'd stay there that night, and cross back in the morning.

'On your own tonight, eh?'

'Yes, Wilhelm, on my own. Unlike you I'm able to control myself. You'd better get going.'

'So soon? I was hoping you'd be able to get me a discount...'

–

They left Aachen at one o'clock on the last Saturday in May. If everything went according to plan they'd be back in the city by early evening.

He'd discussed the plan with Schäfer, who seemed unusually anxious. 'Of course you'll have to go with her. What will happen if she's caught? It's too risky. I can't see why they want her to do this on her own, it seems like a bad idea.'

'I told you why: they've been watching the place and apparently pretty, young, German women drive in and out of it all the time and they're never stopped. They think if she does this on her own then it will be easy. I have to say, it makes sense to me.'

'No, no, no… if she's caught she'll blow the whole operation and expose you.'

'All she knows about me is that my name is Werner Pohl and I have an apartment in Jesuitenstrasse in Aachen, where I stay for no more than a few days a month. She knows nothing else about me. Werner Pohl will disappear the moment she's caught. There's nothing to worry about. It would be a lot worse if I go with her and I'm caught too. I wouldn't look forward to having to explain what a BfV agent is doing planting a bomb in—'

'You will accompany her,' said Schäfer. The discussion was over.

Sabine had travelled to Frankfurt on the second Monday of May for her briefing. She'd met Andreas Baader and Jan-Carl Raspe in an apartment on Inheidener Strasse, in the Bornheim district of the city. The apartment was now, to all intents and purposes, a bomb factory. While Baader paced the room, agitated and angry, Raspe calmly explained her mission to her.

'We're very pleased with your attitude, Sabine, and the suggestion you came up with was excellent. It will be your target. We are also delighted with the detonators.'

Sabine nodded in acknowledgement. Baader came up to her, a lit cigarette stuck between his lips. The sight of a cigarette in a bomb factory unsettled her.

'I – we – need to know exactly where you got them from.'

'Aren't they good enough?'

'Of course they're good enough. They're exactly what we need – they're military grade for fucks sake! That's the point: how come your man is able to get hold of such top quality material? And the drop, Sabine – in the middle of the country, yet we never saw him come, we never saw him go.'

'You know as much about him as I do, Andreas. His money is good, isn't it?'

Raspe came over and placed a hand on Baader's shoulder. 'Leave it, Andreas. We mustn't complain.'

'But he's so… I don't know the word – Ulrike would have the right word for it. He's like a ghost – he suddenly appears in Aachen and then disappears. I just need to be sure he's not dangerous.'

'He is,' said Sabine. 'But fortunately it's not us he's dangerous for.'

'Now listen. We're starting a new bombing campaign this week. The plan is for this phase to last until the end of the month. Then we'll see. We have the Olympics starting soon in Munich, we need to think about that. For your mission you'll travel to Mönchengladbach by train. When you leave the station, turn left, and on Goebenstrasse you'll see a row of three telephone kiosks. You are to telephone this number.'

He handed her a slip of paper which she glanced at, folded, and put into her pocket.

'That's not for you to keep, it's for you to memorise. When someone answers the phone you are to ask if Manfred is there. If they reply that Manfred has gone away, you are to abort the mission. Return to the station and get the first train out of Mönchengladbach, even if it is not going in the direction of Aachen. Are you following this?'

She nodded, her eyes half closed in concentration.

'However, if they reply, "this is Manfred speaking," you are to say, "this is Karin, I was wondering if I could visit this afternoon?" If the reply to that is "yes" then you go ahead with the mission. The person will then tell you where to go to collect the car. You have all of this?'

'I think so, Jan-Carl.'

'Don't worry, we have two hours. By the time you leave you'll be well prepared. Now we need to brief you, and show you how to set the timer. You'll need this by the way.' He took a package out of a drawer and handed it to her.

'Open it, Sabine. It's a Weihrauch revolver, quite easy to use and a good size. Hold it for a bit, get used to handling it. Don't worry; it's not loaded – yet.'

–

Werner had arrived in Aachen on the Friday. Over the preceding fortnight the Red Army Faction had carried out six bombings: Frankfurt, Augsburg, Munich, Karlsruhe, Hamburg, Heidelberg. A handful of people had been killed, dozens wounded and there'd been plenty of damage to property. Mönchengladbach was next.

When Sabine told him what her instructions were he shook his head. 'It's a flawed plan, Sabine.'

'Why? I thought you said it was a good target?'

'It's an excellent target, Sabine, which is why I suggested it. They deserve everything they're going to get. But sending you on your own is ridiculous, and going by train is too risky – railway stations are the first place the police will go to afterwards. And then the getaway… I find it remarkable they should even suggest such a plan, unless of course they want you to be caught.'

'Of course they don't, Werner.'

'Just tell me once more.'

'As soon as I've parked the car and set the timer I am to walk towards the bus stop. They say that at that time of the afternoon there is a bus every half hour to the centre of the city. If I park the car at a quarter past four and set the timer immediately, then the explosion will occur at a quarter past five: apparently the area will be very busy at that time. There is a bus to the city centre at four thirty. I'll be on a train before the bomb goes off.'

He laughed, throwing up his hands at the ridiculousness of it all. 'And if the bus is late, or cancelled – or the timer doesn't work properly? I've never heard anything so crazy… look, Sabine, I have a better idea. I will drive you to Mönchengladbach. I'll drop you at a side entrance to the station. It's likely they'll be watching the telephone kiosks, which is why they've specified that you should use one on Goebenstrasse. You'll go into the station, wait until a train arrives, and then leave with the other passengers. Make the call, go to where they tell you to collect the car, and drive to the target. Once I've dropped you at the station I'll head in that direction. Pass me that map. Look, I'll park here and wait for you. Once you've parked and set the timer, walk this way and leave through one of the pedestrian gates, then come to the car. We'll be back here in Aachen in just over an hour. None of that bus nonsense.'

They took Autobahn 44 as far as Mündt and then wound their way towards the centre of Mönchengladbach by staying on the Landstrasse, the country roads. It was a long, indirect route so it was close to two thirty when he dropped her off in a side street near the station, and almost a quarter to three when she emerged from it and dialled the number she'd memorised at one of the phone kiosks on Goebenstrasse.

Manfred, it turned out, would certainly like to see Karin that afternoon. 'Take a bus from the stop opposite where you are now and go to the Bökelbergstadion. Do you know what that is?'

'No.'

'It's the ground of Borussia Mönchengladbach, the local football team. The stadium is in the district of Eicken, it's in the north of the city. There's no match on, so the car park will be almost empty. Close to the main stadium entrance you'll see a maroon Opel Kadett, with Volkswagen vans on either side of it – one green, one white. There'll be a copy of this week's *Stern* magazine on the dashboard. In the front driver-side wheel arch of the green VW van you'll find the keys to the Opel. You've got all that?'

'Yes.'

'Good. It's now ten to three – there's a bus to Eicken at three, it will stop at the Bökelbergstadion. By the time you get to the car it will be close to three twenty. In the glove compartment there are some identification documents for you. It's unlikely you'll need them but, just in case you get stopped, make sure you know the date of birth on them – oh, and memorise the registration number of the car. It's a lot, isn't it? Don't worry, you'll be fine. You'll have plenty of time to get used to the car: aim to arrive at the target at around ten past four. Set the timer at four fifteen, as you've been told. Understand?'

'I hope so.'

'The answer needs to be yes, Sabine. Repeat everything I've said, and then you'd better go for your bus. Remember to wear gloves the whole time.'

It was just before four thirty when he spotted Sabine, walking down the road towards the old Mercedes sedan he'd hired in Cologne the previous day – for quite a lot of cash, and no questions. She walked too fast and glanced behind her too often, but the street was deserted and no one would have noticed her. 'Everything go as planned?' He waited until he'd started the car and pulled out before asking her. She didn't react, other than to frown as if to indicate she wasn't sure. They were both silent as they headed south-west out of Mönchengladbach and drove along the smaller roads close to the Dutch border. They reached Aachen just after six. They'd had the car radio on throughout the journey but there was no news about any bomb, just endless talk about the Olympics in Munich. They were in his apartment when the news came through at six thirty.

Reports coming in of an explosion at the British army base at Rheindahlen in Mönchengladbach... Understood the explosion may have been caused by a car bomb... British army truck parked next to the car took the full force of the blast... Some damage to nearby buildings... Believed there are no serious casualties... No group has claimed responsibility for the bomb. The Red Army Faction has recently targeted American military bases, and the Provisional IRA has previously attacked British bases in Germany.

'They'll be furious with me, Werner. They'll say I failed, they'll probably think I did this deliberately! I tell you, there was no truck there when I parked the car. I did what they told me, I parked it in what looked like an open space.'

'You need to call them, Sabine. Go in to Kleinmarschierstrasse, there are a few phone kiosks there. If you don't call them it will look suspicious.'

She was a lot calmer when she returned; there was even a spring to her step.

'They're not unhappy at all; actually they are pleased we managed to get a car bomb into the British base and for it to go off. They say there's nothing that could be done about the truck, that's just bad luck. They say it is important we've shown we can get into a key target like this. They're going to put out a statement this evening claiming responsibility. Apparently they'd attached a small plate with a series of numbers on it to the engine block, which would withstand the blast. They will quote those numbers to prove it was the Red Army Faction which carried it out. They were just waiting to hear that I'm back safely.'

'Well done Sabine, well done. I think we now need to celebrate.'

Chapter 7

Martin Winter hadn't worried too much at first. He suspected he'd made a mistake, but at least he hadn't fallen into one of the traps Williams – the security chap at the embassy – had warned him about so graphically.

'Avoid the Grand and the Metropol on Friedrichstrasse, and the Palace on Karl-Liebknecht-Strasse,' Williams had told him, before leaning across his cluttered desk, lowering his voice and adding with a knowing wink and the beginnings of a smile, 'especially the Palace.'

'And why's that... sir?' Winter had hesitated before adding the sir, still unsure of where he came in the embassy hierarchy in relation to Williams.

Williams loosened his collar, leaned back in his chair and linked his hands behind his head, revealing dark patches of sweat under his arms. He was clearly pleased the younger man had asked the question. 'All three are where the Stasi like to keep an eye on foreigners. They have very sophisticated surveillance systems in those hotels. But the Palace is where...' he paused and leaned towards Winter again, lowering his voice once more. He had a lascivious look creeping over him, and Winter caught a full on whiff of alcohol. 'Have you heard the term "honey trap"?'

'I'm afraid not, sir.'

Williams loosened his collar further. A few beads of perspiration had formed on his forehead. 'A honey trap, Winter, is when the other side get an attractive young lady to entice you into bed. There have even been instances where they've used attractive young men, would you believe. The idea is to compromise you and get information or suchlike out of you: blackmail. They record the whole event, if that's the right word for it. I'm told the films are most explicit. What some of these women get up to... well, it's hard to believe.'

–

That was five months previously, in London, a week or so before his posting to the British Embassy to the German Democratic Republic. So many meetings, so many briefings. Now Martin Winter had been summoned to what he had been told was a very important meeting with an Edward Law. 'Don't make any jokes,' he'd been warned.

'Jokes about what?'

'About his name... Law. And whatever you do, don't ask who he works for.'

He'd arrived at the building in Holborn which had the names of various obscure Government agencies on brass plates in the doorway. By the time he found the room he was looking for, he felt as if he'd walked to another part of London – down one corridor, along another one, up in a lift and then along a strange tunnel-like bridge that seemed to have taken him into another building altogether. Then more corridors, another lift and then through a series of doors, the last one of which had a man in a dark, shiny suit standing guard. He very politely told Martin Winter he needed to search him, after which Martin was instructed to leave his briefcase with the guard. Martin was shown into a mostly bare room, containing only a long wooden table with two chairs on either side of it. The fluorescent light on the low ceiling made the small room uncomfortably bright.

It was a good five minutes before the door opened and the man he assumed was Edward Law burst in. He inspected the empty chair to see if it was clean enough to sit on and, after deciding it was, spent a minute arranging a file and a notebook on the table, along with a cup of coffee and a couple of pens. Only then did he look at Martin Winter, quizzically at first and then with the very faintest hint of disdain. He had fair hair that came just over his ears and across his forehead, and he was quite possibly younger than Martin.

'Martin Michael Winter. M.M. Winter.' He spoke with an accent that Martin had come to recognise as public school and Oxbridge. Winter nodded. Edward Law continued to study the file, licking his forefinger to turn over the pages. Winter was surprised at how thick the file appeared to be.

'Born in Exeter… Only child… Parents both teachers – parents are always bloody teachers, eh? Grammar school… Birmingham University… Years?'

'I beg your pardon?'

'What years were you at Birmingham University from? Come on, we're not even on the difficult questions yet!'

'1967 to 1970.'

'And you studied German, I see…'

Martin Winter nodded. He wondered if Edward Law was looking at his file for the first time.

'What confuses me, Winter,' said Law as he closed the file abruptly, 'is that in all the time you were at university you apparently showed no interest in politics, none whatsoever as far as we can make out. And this covers 1968, remember: Paris, Grosvenor Square riots – all that nonsense. Everyone who was at university was interested in politics then, even the bloody chemists. But evidently not Martin Winter.' Edward Law had clearly not been looking at the file for the first time after all. Law raised his eyebrows to make it clear that he had just asked a question, and was waiting for an answer.

Winter shrugged. 'I just wasn't terribly interested.'

'So what I need to know is: what were you interested in? Girls… or boys, maybe? That was becoming all the fashion then, wasn't it?'

'Not an awful lot outside of my studies. Cricket, I suppose. I was in the third eleven, bit of an all-rounder – and I was a member of the university choir, but never got beyond the back of the chorus.' Martin Winter laughed nervously. Law didn't even smile.

'And I presume you never touched drugs, eh? Teetotal, I presume?'

'I was never offered drugs, and I'm not teetotal. I've even been drunk a few times. I expect you'll find the dates in that file. I'm not sure of the relevance of all this...'

'The thing is, Winter, I am paid to be suspicious, you understand? Now then, if you'd gone and joined the Communist Party of Great Britain or one of its variants, that would make me fairly suspicious. If you'd smoked a few funny cigarettes and gone off the rails – that would make me fairly suspicious too. If you'd withheld your rent for a few weeks because you didn't approve of what the South African Government was up to or because of what the Queen was wearing at Ascot – also reasonably suspicious. But as for showing no interest in politics whatsoever, and leading such a virtuous life... well that makes me very suspicious.'

Martin Winter said nothing. 'He'll try and provoke you,' he'd been warned. 'Ignore it: just play a straight bat, don't get rattled. And remember, no questions.'

'So you graduated in 1970 with a 2:1 Honours degree and joined the Department of Trade and Industry. From 1972 you were based in the export division, and now you're about to start a two year attachment to our Embassy in East Germany which, somewhat paradoxically, calls itself the German Democratic Republic.'

Edward Law stood up to remove his jacket. When he sat down he had also removed a gold-coloured packet of cigarettes from one of the pockets and was fussing with a gold lighter. He pushed the packet towards Martin Winter, who shook his head.

'Despite some of the questions I've been asking you, the purpose of our little chat this afternoon is not to see whether you can be trusted to be sent to East Germany. If you hadn't passed security clearance in the first place you wouldn't have got the attachment.' Law patted the file in front of him. 'I just want to get a sense of what makes you tick – or not. And most importantly, I need to warn you about some of the dangers you're likely to face in East Germany.'

Edward Law paused while he finished his cigarette, dropping the remains of it into the coffee cup. The only sounds in the room were the fizz as the cigarette hit the coffee and the intermittent hum of the fluorescent light.

'This attachment idea of the Foreign Office – plucking chaps like you from the more innocent parts of Whitehall and sending them off to embassies around the world... I don't know... I can see its attractions, I suppose. But why can't they send you to less bothersome places? New Zealand, for instance – Canada, Switzerland. But East Germany for fucks sake – what were they thinking?'

'I think it's because our embassy only opened in 1973 and they feel the export opportunities are ripe, and...'

Law held up his hand to stop Winter. 'It was a rhetorical question, Winter. I know why you've been sent there: it's an untapped market as far as exports are concerned, and you speak decent German. I've read the file. You're here because I need to give you a warning. It comes in two parts. I hope you're listening carefully. Part one: resist the temptation to think that just because you're in East Germany you are a de facto spy. We see it all the bloody time – junior diplomat is posted to a controversial part of the world and the next thing we know they're making notes of the numbers they see on the side of military vehicles, producing copies of railway timetables and imagining they're being followed.

'Some chap smiles at them in a queue and they think they're about to run an agent for their foreign service. I blame those bloody James Bond films. Life is not like that. I imagine you're thinking nothing could be further from your intentions but, I can assure you, things change when you're out there and you're a bit bored. So resist the temptation. You're not being sent out there to spy – you are not a spy. You're hardly even a bloody diplomat for that matter. Just do your job, play with yourself when you feel

68

the urge coming on – though probably not in the Embassy – and take plenty of good books. Got it?'

Winter nodded, aware he was blushing.

'Part two: and this is the more serious part. Notwithstanding what I've said about you hardly being a diplomat, you will nonetheless be of interest to the East Germans. You could well be a target for them. Williams will brief you once you arrive there, but just keep this in mind. It is extremely easy for you to sit here today and assure me that you have absolutely no intention whatsoever of being a naughty boy, that you'll keep your trousers zipped up at all times and that you will resist temptation in a manner that would make a monk appear unduly virtuous. However…'

Law paused to inhale more of his cigarette and lean back in his chair, running his hands through his fair hair.

'It's easy enough to have good intentions, quite another to keep to them. It is girls you're interested in isn't it, Winter?'

Martin Winter nodded, aware he was blushing again.

'Splendid. Now we've all fantasised about our ideal woman, haven't we? Well, imagine such a paragon approaches you when your defences are down? Very hard to resist, Winter. Happens all the bloody time. Just be aware of it. If you so much as spot the most beautiful girl you've ever dreamed of heading in your direction, walk away. Easier said than done, I know. But remember, the East Germans are smart. In our opinion the Stasi are more sophisticated than any of the other East European security services, with the possible exception of the Czech StB.'

–

It hadn't happened as Law predicted, nor in the way Williams had warned him. She was not the most beautiful girl he had ever dreamed of and he hadn't seen her heading in his direction, at least not in a way he was aware of. And they went nowhere near the Grand, Metropol or Palace hotels.

It was the third occasion on which he'd bumped into her, though each of the first two encounters seemed so spontaneous they certainly gave no cause for suspicion. The first time had been in a café on Unterwasserstrasse, by the Spree canal. It was hardly bohemian in the West Berlin sense of the word, but it felt less utilitarian than most other places in the east of the city, and the coffee was almost palatable. He'd been sitting at a bench in the window, overlooking the canal and she'd come to sit next to him.

What followed was hardly a conversation, more an exchange of pleasantries. 'It's cold enough for there to be ice on the canal… You and I are the only people in here not smoking… I've walked so far today I feel as if my feet will refuse to go one more step…'

They'd not exchanged names and she hadn't remarked on his accent, which people usually did. It was so innocuous he decided against reporting it to Williams, as he was supposed to do for all encounters with DDR citizens.

The second time was a fortnight later, at an art exhibition by the Berliner Dom. It was disused church hall which had been turned into a temporary gallery. One of his colleagues at the embassy had said the exhibition was worth a visit, which was a measure of how little there was to do in this side of the city. He didn't know much about art, but if you ignored the obligatory paintings of the struggle of the proletariat there were some interesting works, some of which were seventeenth century. He was approaching the end of the exhibition when they bumped into each other.

'Didn't we meet at the café by the canal? What a happy coincidence!'

Martin Winter had agreed that it was indeed, and introduced himself.

'So you are American? Your German is excellent.'

'Thank you, but I am British.'

The conversation that followed was hardly scintillating and her questions certainly not probing. Her name was Clara, and she was a lawyer. She had two children and was divorced. On the days when her ex-husband collected the children after school, she liked to wander around the city for an hour or two.

They had talked for ten minutes and still he did not think it worth reporting this encounter, although he was aware he should have done. He made a note of it in his diary at work to cover himself.

A week later, on a Tuesday evening, he had left the British Embassy on Unter den Linden late, close to a quarter to seven. Outside he had paused to button up his coat against the cold and rain, regretting having brought neither his hat nor umbrella but deciding not to go back into the embassy to get one of them. He ought to have headed south to the small apartment he had to himself just off Leipziger Strasse. But he needed to buy some food and there was a place nearby which was almost unique in East Berlin in closing as late as seven, so he turned right and then right again into Neustadtische Kirchstrasse and was alongside the Foreign Ministry when someone walked past him, lightly catching the side of his head with their umbrella. The person stopped, turned round and apologised and he replied to say it was no problem, not to worry.

'Goodness me, it's you – Martin!'

He hesitated for a while, struggling to recognise her in the poor light. 'Ah, Clara! How are you?'

'Where are you going? Didn't you say you lived near Leipziger Strasse?'

He explained he was heading to a shop on Clara-Zetkin Strasse, and she said she was heading that way too and would walk with him. It was only later – much later, when it was too late – that he thought about what she had said, and realised he had never told her he lived near Leipziger Strasse.

By the time they turned left into Clara-Zetkin Strasse the rain had become very heavy and she walked close to him, holding the umbrella over both of them. As she did so he caught her scent. It was strong and even though he was no expert, it didn't smell cheap. Like her accent, it had a refined quality to it.

Just before the shop was a turning into Schadow Strasse and she asked him if he would mind accompanying her to the front door of her block. Once there she led him into the block and told him – sweetly but quite firmly – that he should come up to her apartment.

Some thirty minutes later, he was lying naked on his back on a large bed, still trying to catch his breath. They had already made love once and now Clara was kneeling between his legs doing things he'd only ever dreamt about. He was, despite the very considerable distractions, struggling through a mental checklist to work out whether he had made any of the mistakes either Law or Williams had warned him about. Clara had told him that she was lonely, which was reassuring and also that he was an attractive man, so much more appealing than East Germans. He'd have to report this, of course; he had to do that if he was involved with a DDR citizen. He'd undoubtedly gone further than was permitted. The report would read like one of those pornographic novels which used to be passed around the sixth form common room and he'd probably be sacked for writing it. When, half an hour later, he informed Clara that perhaps he ought to leave he was relieved she seemed happy for him to do so. This was not one of Williams' honey traps after all: maybe there was no need for the pornographic report.

Perhaps we can meet again. They had both said that.

Clara said she would use the bathroom before he left. Martin Winter lay naked on the bed, the sheets gathered on the floor, and feeling satisfied in more ways than one. He had always been shy with girls, unsure how he would perform when the big moment – which he had dreamed of for too long – finally arrived. He was convinced his inexperience would let him down. Now it seemed he had nothing to worry about – on the contrary, it transpired he had a natural aptitude for it. Clara herself had more or less said so, remarking on how skilled he was – 'You made me feel like a woman, Martin!' His feeling of joy in the encounter outweighed his doubts about whether he had broken any of Williams' or Laws' rules.

It was feeling which lasted less than another minute.

When the man entered the room, Martin Winter was too shocked to react. He remained naked on top of the bed, convinced he was about to be shot or arrested. The man looked well into his seventies, but moved deftly for someone of his age and size. He came over to the bed and threw a sheet over Winter before pulling up a chair and angling it so that he was close to Winters' face. His own face was heavily lined, but betrayed no emotions. He looked neither happy nor angry. There was no look of disgust or shock. Instead he studied Martin Winter carefully. When he spoke it was in fluent German, but with an accent Winter recognised as Russian.

'You liked Clara?' he asked, gesturing with his head towards the bathroom.

Winter found himself nodding more enthusiastically than perhaps he should have done in the circumstances.

'I thought you would. You were eager, weren't you, eh?' He winked at the British diplomat, but without smiling. 'We have photographs, by the way – if you should want a souvenir!' The man laughed loudly, genuinely amused by his joke. Winter found himself staring at an array of gold teeth. The older man said nothing more for a while, as he removed his heavy overcoat and took a leather-bound notebook from his jacket pocket. From another pocket he removed a pencil, and from yet another a flick knife with a long blade, which he used to sharpen the pencil.

'You've not been in Berlin too long, have you, Martin Michael Winter?' He pronounced the three components of his name as if they were one word and his surname as if it began with a 'V'. MartinMichaelVinter. 'And they warned you about this, yes? They always do, and people almost always fall for it – even some of our people!'

'Look, perhaps—'

'And what will they do to you, eh? Send you back to London, obviously. And will you lose your job at the Department of Trade

73

and Industry, or will you just be warned? Whatever happens, this is not good for you at all, is it, MartinMichaelVinter?'

The Russian paused, waiting for an answer from. The only sound was of the bathroom door opening and then, a moment later, the front door of the apartment opening and closing.

'Clara,' said the Russian, by way of an explanation. 'Now then,' the Russian was rubbing his hands together and sounding almost jovial – upbeat, even. 'You will be feeling now that you are in the most terrible predicament, that your career is in ruins, your life too. But it is not as bad as it seems, MartinMichaelVinter. As it happens, you have a choice. If you do as I ask, nothing of what happened here tonight will ever be revealed. Otherwise…' The Russian spread out his hands in a gesture of hopelessness. 'I want you to be a messenger. That's all: nothing that will compromise you. You will not be putting yourself in any danger, I am not asking for secrets or information or anything like that. I simply want you to be a messenger. I suggest you get dressed before we talk properly, maybe you'd like to wash too.'

–

The small lounge was comfortable but with a typically East German utilitarian feel. When Winter entered the room, the Russian was sitting on a shiny sofa smoking a small cigar. He patted the space next to him, indicating that Winter should sit down. As he began to speak the Russian leaned forward, his arms resting on his knees. Winter moved forward into the same position.

'There is a retired politician in your country, a man called Edgar. Have you heard of him? If it helps, this is a photograph.'

'Yes, I've heard of him. Quite distinguished in his day, wasn't he?'

The Russian smiled. 'I understand he was a Member of your Parliament and retired in 1970. You are so civilised, allowing people to retire like that. My information is that Edgar now lives in a place called Door Sat. Have you heard of it?'

'Door Sat?'

'It is a region in England; on the south coast I am told.'

'I think you may mean Dorset. It is a county in the south of England.'

'Not like Siberia then, that's where our people retire to!' The Russian laughed, revealing flashes of gold teeth. 'I understand you're due to return to England next week for your annual leave, correct?'

Winter nodded, wondering how on earth the other man knew this.

'You are to go to Door Sat. I will give you Edgar's address. Be discreet please. Do not let anyone know you are going to visit him, or even going to that area. Do not warn him you are coming. When you approach him, please make sure he is on his own.'

'And what am I to say to him – how do I know he won't treat me like a complete fool?'

The Russian stood up and walked to the window, pulling the curtains back just far enough to be able to observe the street below. After a silent minute he allowed the heavy curtain to fall back into place, but remained standing, facing it.

'The first thing you say to him is that Baron Otard is trying to contact him. Baron Otard. It is most important you say this clearly and correctly. Baron Otard. Once he hears that, you will have his full attention, I can assure you. I am now going to give you the details of the message. You must memorise it, nothing can be written down. Once you have given him the message and leave, your role is over; you will have fulfilled your obligation. You can resume your career.'

'And if he asks who gave me the message…? Are you Baron Otard?'

The big man turned round, looking exasperated before speaking carefully. 'Be clear: you are to say a Baron Otard is trying to contact him. That is enough.'

Chapter 8

Martin Winter returned to England as planned. He was due in London for the first few days of his leave, for meetings and to catch up with friends, then to travel to Exeter on the Friday to stay with his parents for a week. He told his friends he had to leave for Exeter on the Wednesday, thereby creating a couple of days he wouldn't need to account for. The subterfuge, he found, was quite exciting. Perhaps Edward Law had been right to warn him about the attractions of espionage.

On the Wednesday morning he hired a car and headed south. The Russian had given him an address in the small town of Wareham. Just before noon he found Edgar's house, over the River Frome on the southern edge of the town, on a small lane off the main road to Stoborough. Martin walked to the end of the lane, which had a dozen or so large cottages on one side, concealed behind high hedges and long drives. The other side of the lane was open fields.

When you approach him please make sure he is on his own, the Russian had instructed, which was easier said than done. If he hung around the lane for too long he would draw attention to himself. He walked to end of the lane again and then, on the way back, allowed himself a few steps up the gravel drive to get a clearer view of the house. On the lawn in front of the house he saw a tall man watching a small dog running in circles. The man looked up.

'Can I help you?'

Winter recognised Edgar as he walked towards him. The older man was eyeing him suspiciously, standing upright with his hands clasped behind his back.

'I have a message for you.'

'Oh yes – and who would that be from?' Edgar was peering beyond Winter, checking he was alone.

'You are Edgar, aren't you?' The other man said nothing and just raised his eyebrows quizzically. 'It's just that the message is for Edgar: only Edgar.' Winter worried his voice a bit too high pitched.

'Yes, I'm Edgar.'

'The message is that a Baron Otard is trying to contact you.'

Edgar's eyes betrayed no hint of shock. He stared at Winter for few seconds, looking him up and down.

'I'm supposed to be taking Harry for a walk. Come with me. We'll go into the fields. No need to talk until we're there.' Edgar spoke in the manner of a person used to giving instructions. They walked along a narrow grassy path on the edge of a ploughed field, the dog haring off in all directions, chasing birds into flight.

'I have to ask you who you are, if you please.' Another instruction. Winter produced the identity card which showed that he worked as a trade attaché at the British Embassy in East Berlin.

'Foreign Office?'

'Department of Trade and Industry,' said Winter. 'On attachment.'

'And you were given the message about Baron Otard in Berlin?'

Winter nodded, unsure whether he was allowing Edgar to lead him into saying more than he should.

'East or West?'

'East.'

Edgar walked along, hands clasped behind his back, looking down at his shoes. 'And this was all away from the embassy, eh? No one else knows about it?' Edgar paused to remove his gloves and pick up a piece of wood to throw for the dog. 'Honey trap, was it?'

Winter didn't answer.

'Wasn't worth it, eh? Never heard of one that was.'

Winter resisted the temptation to say that it was, actually. 'The man who gave me the message—'

'Describe him,' interrupted Edgar.

'Very large chap, but well built rather than fat if you know what I mean. I would say he is a bit older than you. He spoke excellent German but I recognised his accent as Russian, one hears an awful lot of that in East Berlin. He also made—'

'You'd better give me the message.'

'Will you want to make notes?'

Edgar looked at him as if he were mad, so Winter carefully explained how Edgar was to get into East Berlin, where he was to go to when he got there, and how to know it was safe to approach the address.

They had reached the end of the path; ahead of them was a small wood. Edgar walked towards it and then turned around, to address the field rather than Winter. 'Last saw him in Vienna, May '45. And you know what surprises me? Not that he's still alive – if anyone could survive it would be him. No, what really surprises me is that he took thirty years to get in touch.'

—

'Tell him to use a West German identity but *not* a West Berlin one. He'll understand. He should enter West Germany through the Netherlands. He is advised to stay in West Berlin for a couple of days before he crosses over, to ensure he's clean, but he'll know that anyway.

'Whatever he does, he must not – I can't emphasise this strongly enough – use either Checkpoint Charlie or Friedrich-strasse station. Those are where foreigners come through: they have the sharpest border guards. Chausseestrasse and Invaliden-strasse crossings are just for citizens of West Berlin, so avoid them too.

'Now, this is important. I think the safest place to get into East Berlin is the border crossing at Heinrich-Heine-Strasse, in the south of the city: Checkpoint Delta. It's for citizens of the Federal Republic. He'll come through Kreuzberg, that's in the American sector. If he doesn't like the look of it when he gets there – he'll know what I mean – then he is to wait a day and then try the Bornholmer Strasse crossing in Wedding, in the French Sector.

'You've got all that? That's the easy part. This is what he's to do when he gets into the East…'

–

There was no question that Edgar had a certain spring in his step after Winter's visit. His wife certainly noticed it.

'And who was the young man you were walking with in the field?'

'Just some chap out on a walk – said he had a dog just like Harry when he was younger.'

'Well, he was wearing the wrong kind of shoes for a walk across the fields.'

Edgar said nothing. He should have spotted the shoes. Maybe it would have been better to walk along the lane.

'And this has nothing to do with you going up to London for the week?'

Edgar explained again, in a manner that made clear this would be the end of it: there was some tedious business the Service needed him to look over, old files, the usual sort of thing. He'd be away for a few days, perhaps a week.

When his wife went out, later that afternoon, Edgar climbed into the loft and opened the small safe hidden under a box of old books in the eaves. Inside were half a dozen passports, each in its own envelope and wrapped in a plastic bag. He had used Karl Albrecht before; it was one of his most reliable identities. He had first used it to get into Germany on a desperate mission in April 1941, and had made a point over the years of keeping it up to date – he had last renewed it in 1970. He had even obtained a *personalausweis* – an identity card to match the passport. Karl Albrecht was a businessman from Hanover, and this suited Edgar. He had spent a year at university there and was comfortable with the refined Hanoverian accent.

The following day he caught the train to London and, using a British passport in the name of Paul Barker and buying his ticket with cash, took the night ferry from Harwich to Amsterdam. A few hours after it docked, Paul Barker was on the midday train from Amsterdam Central, arriving in Hanover just after four in the afternoon. He took a left luggage locker at the station, where he deposited his British passport and anything else that could identify him as being British. He found a small hotel just off Burgstrasse, checked in as Karl Albrecht, and took a room at the rear of the hotel, overlooking the River Leine.

As anxious as he was to get to Berlin, he knew he mustn't rush. He needed to spend some time in Hanover, to acclimatise himself to the city in which he was meant to be native. For the next two days he spoke to as many people as possible, ensuring his fluent German had the correct Hanoverian ring to it. He went shopping too, buying clothes, toiletries and even a small suitcase from local shops, and depositing his English clothes in the left luggage locker at the station. He made one other purchase, made almost on the spur of the moment as he walked past a specialist shop, which put the idea in his mind. After that he found a busy bar in Ostadt, where the owner seemed to know everyone.

'I'm looking for a lift to West Berlin; my car's just broken down. Would you know anyone who's driving there in the next couple of days? I'll pay for the petrol and a bit extra on top…'

The bar owner said to come back the following day and, when Edgar did so, he handed him a slip of paper. 'Ring Helmut – he drives to West Berlin every few weeks, his mother lives there. If you're generous with him he'll drive you there and back. You can be generous to me too.'

They left Hanover early in the morning in Helmut's old VW Squareback and it wasn't until they were on Autobahn 2 that

Helmut spoke more than the odd word. 'I presume you're looking for an easy journey?'

Edgar nodded.

'I do this journey all the time. We'll enter the DDR at the Marienborn crossing. Our timing is good because by the time we get there they'll be starting to get busy and they like to keep things moving. We'll be searched of course. You aren't carrying anything they won't like, are you?'

Edgar replied that of course he wasn't.

'I know many of the East German guards, most of them are Stasi. They know I'm always clean. I leave a few packets of French cigarettes for them in the boot, they like those. If they ask, we'll just say we're friends, eh?'

It took them an hour to get through Marienborn, which Helmut said was quite good going. The half a dozen packets of Gitanes in the boot had helped. From Marienborn it was another three hours to Berlin on the autobahn. They were in East Germany but not permitted to stop, as if they were driving through a tunnel. They went past Magdeburg, south of Brandenburg, and bypassed Potsdam before reaching West Berlin in the early afternoon.

'You'll want a lift back, I suppose – how long will you need here?'

Edgar asked if three days was all right, and had to slip Helmut some more money to make sure it was. The VW Squareback dropped him outside Kurfürstendamm station and they agreed to meet at the same spot in three days.

Chapter 9

East Berlin, March 1976

Edgar checked in, as Karl Albrecht, at a hotel just off Potsdamer Strasse in West Berlin. He found a telephone box a few blocks away and rang the West Berlin number Winter had given him.

'*A female voice will answer. She will repeat this number. You are to ask if Klaus is there. If she replies to say there is no Klaus, do not attempt to cross over. Otherwise, she will tell you when Klaus will be there. Most likely she will say 'tomorrow,' but be prepared for it to be a day or two later. That's when you cross.*'

Viktor. So thorough: quite the best agent he had ever encountered, on any side.

The female voice told him Klaus would be there tomorrow, so he was up first thing the next morning and took a tram to Kreuzberg. All the other passengers appeared to be exhausted Turkish workers. He left the tram on Lindenstrasse and walked for fifteen minutes, though not directly towards the border. When he was certain he hadn't been followed, he approached the border down Prinzenstrasse. Ahead of him was the vast expanse in front of the Heinrich-Heine-Strasse checkpoint.

'*Be clear that you're only there for the day; any longer and you'll have needed to apply for a visa beforehand.*'

It took the best part of an hour to get through. The queue inched slowly, then he encountered the first official, and then a second, who took away his passport and brought it back twenty minutes later. Why did he want to visit East Berlin?

'I am getting very old now and I rarely leave Hanover. I used to visit Berlin before the war. I am in the West visiting friends and would dearly love to see parts of Mitte again… one last time.'

The official looked unimpressed, and told him to wait. The third official was a woman who asked a series of questions and painstakingly wrote down the answers. Edgar recognised the technique: the same questions, but asked in subtly different ways. An inexperienced person could be caught out. At the end she looked disappointed.

'You understand this visa is just for today?' She stamped his passport. Edgar nodded. 'You can only exit through this crossing. Make sure you're back here by five at the latest.'

After that there was a thorough search, with particular interest paid to the labels of his clothes. He was glad he had bought new ones in Hanover. And then the currency exchange at an obligatory punitive rate.

He knew that once he was through the checkpoint he'd be followed, so taking a circuitous route or going down too many side streets would only arouse suspicion, as would other standard evasive techniques like doubling back. This was where the item he'd bought in Hanover came into its own. He remembered how, when he used to follow targets, what was most infuriating was when they were too slow. It made it hard to maintain a discreet distance. But a target needed a good excuse to move so slowly. Fortunately the East Germans would have seen that Karl Albrecht was seventy-seven. Edgar had avoided shaving that morning, and held himself less upright. As he shuffled along with the aid of the walking stick he'd bought in Hanover, he convincingly looked his age.

He walked to the end of Heinrich-Heine Strasse, turned left into Neue Annenstrasse, and eventually joined Breite Strasse. Edgar felt immediately as though he had walked not just into a different city in a different country, but also into a different era and a different time of year. The contrast with the West was stark: the small number of cars, the presence of so many people in uniform, the lack of colour and noise in the streets, the apparent absence of advertising, and the profusion of political posters. The pervasive smell of lignite – the cheap brown coal they used in the east – was noticeable, and he began to feel it at the back of his throat. Fairly soon he was away from the looming presence of the wall. It was no more than twelve feet high but it still felt ubiquitous, as if it cast a grey pallor over the city.

He crossed Französische Strasse and in Marx–Engels Platz spent some time slowly moving around the vast square, constantly in the shadow of the vast Palast der Republik. The home of the Volkskammer, the East German parliament, also contained a concert hall and art galleries where Edgar spent half an hour, taking an apparent interest in an exhibition of contemporary Bulgarian art.

Back in the square he sat on a bench and took stock of his situation. The pair who had initially followed him appeared to be down to one: a tall, bored-looking man who constantly wiped his nose with a large handkerchief. He knew if he was patient then sooner or later his tail would be removed altogether.

An hour later, he'd walked down the Unter den Linden towards Pariser Platz. Just before the Brandenburg Gate he turned back and, now sure he was no longer being followed, walked back down the Unter den Linden, turning left into Schadow Strasse.

–

Viktor had embraced him so tightly that Edgar wondered for a few uncomfortable moments whether he had fallen into a trap. It had all gone as per Winter's instructions: a small 'x' had been scratched on the side of the door to the apartment block on Schadow Strasse, the same mark repeated just inside the doorway. In the damp entrance hall, he spotted a copy of the previous day's *Neues Deutschland* in the pigeon hole for the flat, and when he climbed to the top floor the final sign all was safe was in place: a black umbrella with a bright brown handle propped up beside the door.

A middle-aged woman let him into the apartment. He had barely stepped into the small lounge before the Russian threw his arms round him.

'Edgar, Edgar,' he said as he released the Englishman from his embrace, and held his shoulders in his outstretched hands, admiring Edgar as one would a growing child. 'So we've both lived long enough to reach old age. What were the chances of that when we last met, eh? You have not changed, my friend. It is so good to see you. Come, sit down. Irma, bring us a drink. Edgar I hope you weren't insulted by my instructions. I knew I could trust you, but being so careful and taking so many precautions – that's what's kept me alive!'

Anyone observing the scene would imagine the two were old friends, rather than adversaries going back thirty years. The last time the two had met was in the NKVD headquarters in Vienna, in the May of 1945, shortly after the Red Army had liberated the city. Edgar had entered Vienna clandestinely, to find out what had happened to one of his agents whom he suspected of also working for the Russians. He'd been arrested by the NKVD, and Viktor could have done anything with him. But, to the Englishman's great surprise, Viktor not only let him go but actually helped him with his mission.

And when Viktor explained why, Edgar understood immediately. One day I may need your assistance Edgar. I may have to contact you indirectly. I would like you to give me your word that if I do, you will do what you can to help me.

Edgar had asked how he would know it was a genuine approach. The Russian spymaster had looked around the room and picked up a nearly empty, pear-shaped Cognac bottle, a Baron Otard.

'*Should you ever get a message that a Baron Otard is trying to contact you, you will know it is genuine, that it is me. You understand?*'

–

The two old spymasters sat opposite each other: the Russian on a shiny settee, the Englishman in an armchair which appeared to be made from a type of plastic. The woman Viktor had addressed as Irma brought in a full bottle of brandy on a tray.

'Three years ago my doctor asked me how much I was drinking,' said the Russian as he poured two very large measures. 'I said maybe two bottles of vodka a week and you know what? He told me to stop!' Viktor paused, long enough to allow Edgar to absorb the sheer injustice of it. 'Which I did, of course, who disobeys a doctor? But he never said anything about brandy, eh?'

The two men laughed heartily and drank their brandy. It had a rough edge and Edgar was concerned they'd only just started.

'So, you survived, Viktor!'

'You mean after what my doctor told me?'

'No...' Edgar hesitated, looking for the right words. 'I mean after the war, Stalin, the purges... all that kind of thing one heard so much about.'

Viktor shrugged. 'And so did you, Edgar.'

'Survival was possibly more of an achievement in your case, am I right?'

Viktor shrugged again. 'You became a politician I hear?'

Edgar nodded. 'I stayed in the Service for a while, but it wasn't the same. I had an opportunity to go into politics and I was a Member of Parliament until 1970. I decided to retire then, I was seventy. But I have remained involved with the Service over the years, helping out with the odd case, reviewing files and notes, people coming to see me about agents I ran – that kind of thing. You never really retire from our world, do you?'

The Russian said nothing as he carefully studied the glass of brandy he was holding. He took a tin of small cigars from a jacket pocket, extracted two, gave one to Edgar, and lit them both. 'My doctor told me to stop smoking too. I decided he meant cigarettes, not cigars!' He paused.

'In our service very few people retire, as such, apart from a small number who became too old or too ill. The remainder either stay on forever, like me, or they are sent away.' There was another pause. Viktor pointed his lit cigar towards Edgar. 'They spend what is left of their lives – which is usually not very much – in some miserable camp somewhere in the east.

'When the war ended I was forty-five years old. I had been an agent for the Soviet Union since I was twenty, would you believe. Since the age of thirty-two I'd been operating clandestinely in Europe: I did that for thirteen years. Along the way I got married, got divorced and had a child, who I've not seen for forty years. That I survived for so long away from the Soviet Union was remarkable. You know a bit of what I was up to, Edgar; you have to admit I was good...'

'You were extraordinary Viktor. Our hardest opponent...' Both men fell silent, reflecting on the past: on the regrets, nostalgia and memories that came with looking back on one's younger days. Edgar found it hard to overstate his admiration for Viktor. The Russian was such a large and distinctive character, yet he'd been able to move silently and safely around Nazi-occupied Europe. He disappeared when he needed to and when he re-emerged he effortlessly took on the role of a native of whichever country he was in. He had been a brave spy, and a dangerous opponent.

'They didn't trust me, the idiots who'd stayed in Moscow throughout the war or fled as soon as they heard the German artillery in '41. I was recalled to Moscow in May 1945 – not too long after we met in Vienna. When I arrived I discovered that my boss, Ilia Brodsky, had been executed. Brodsky was a brilliant spymaster, but Comrade Stalin never much liked his Jews.'

There was a pause as the Russian undid his shoelaces. 'Brodsky was very good at his job and the last thing Stalin needed once the war was over was a good intelligence chief. I thought I was also done for, I can tell you. I had been in the west for so long that they were convinced I had developed bourgeois tendencies. But at first that didn't seem to matter, because there was a big operation on – some crazy plan of Stalin's to invade France and Italy once the war was over. Because of my experience in France and my contacts there, I worked on that for a few weeks – and even went to France – but that's another story. After a couple of months this operation was suddenly dropped, and I really thought by then my luck had run out. But two things counted in my favour... Edgar, you must have more brandy, what's the matter with you? It's Bulgarian.' The Englishman covered the top of his glass with his hand as the Russian attempted to fill it. 'Don't tell me, you have one of these doctors too?

'The two things in my favour were my record – as you say I was very good: I had run agents throughout Europe and the intelligence I sent back was first class. I had been loyal and brave and they knew that. But those idiots in Moscow could never be accused of sentimentality – my record did not count for much, and Brodsky's record hadn't helped him. No, what really saved me was my experience of Nazi-occupied Europe, Germany in particular, and my fluency in German. By the end of the war, I not only spoke it like a native but I understood every nuance of the language. There was an old professor at Sciences Po in Paris, I ran him as an agent in the thirties, who told me something I have never forgotten: it is far easier to speak another language than to understand it. What he meant was to understand it like a native, pick up on the little inflections or tics that show you whether someone is telling the truth, or lying. By 1945 I could do that in German. Now then, Edgar, I have a question for you. How many German prisoners of war do you think the Soviet Union held in 1945?' The Russian leaned back in his seat, folding his large arms across his chest, a gesture that said, 'go on, guess...'

Edgar thought for a moment and shook his head. No idea. 'A million? I recall it was a lot.'

Viktor smiled. 'Closer to three million and let me tell you, Edgar, many of them never made it back to Germany: they either froze to death or starved. More brandy, perhaps some cake? Irma!'

There was a pause as Irma served a fruit cake along with coffee. Edgar noticed Viktor following her every move with his eyes and smiling at her affectionately. As she left the room she gently ran her hand over Viktor's head, letting it rest briefly on his shoulder while he leaned over and kissed it.

'You didn't meet Irma in Vienna, did you?'

Edgar shook his head.

'Irma worked for me in Vienna and I fell in love with her. Her husband was an officer in the Wehrmacht and when he was unexpectedly released by the Americans I had to get her out of Vienna in a hurry. I managed to get her a job in our embassy here. It has worked out well, in more ways than one. She's been safe in East Berlin. This is her apartment, by the way. I trust her more than I trust myself. She knows everything. Now then, where was I?'

'You were talking about there being so many German prisoners of war in the Soviet Union.'

'Yes. The official line was they were all Nazis, but we knew that we had to differentiate between the ordinary conscripts, the Nazi Party members and the war criminals. They all needed to be questioned, we had to find a way of processing them and, frankly, it was an overwhelming task. To do it properly we required fluent German speakers, ones who could be trusted – and I can tell you, the Soviet Union was not exactly awash with them.

'So my ability to speak German fluently saved me. For the next ten years I ran a unit which went round the camps, interrogating prisoners of war. We began to send back prisoners in large numbers around 1950, but still held on to many tens of thousands after that. The final prisoners of war were not repatriated to Germany until 1956. Stalin died in '53, so by then I was safe, I had survived the purges.'

It was now quite warm in the apartment, so Viktor removed his jacket and loosened his tie. He filled up his brandy and tipped some of it into his coffee cup – a habit, he explained to Edgar, he'd picked up in Spain. There was a further pause as he lit another cigar and savoured it for a while, before addressing Edgar from behind the wisps of grey-brown smoke. The Russian bent over and kicked off his shoes before swinging round to lay across the settee, now at an angle to Edgar, the patient to Edgar's psychiatrist. For a while he said nothing, as he finished his cigar and dropped the lit stub into the coffee cup.

'Naturally, no German we interrogated admitted to being a war criminal. But I became very good at knowing who was telling the truth and who was lying. I became something of an expert on war crimes. My team and I were sent all over the Soviet Union to interrogate German prisoners. We were sometimes also sent into the countries that had come under our control. In June 1946 I was asked to go to northern Poland – Gdansk.'

'The Germans called it Danzig, didn't they?'

'They did indeed. There was a concentration camp near Gdansk, called Stutthof. For much of the war Stutthof was for non-Jewish Poles, though by the end of 1944 it housed mainly Jewish inmates. According to the Poles, around 100,000 prisoners passed through Stutthof during the war, of whom some 60,000 were murdered. The Red Army liberated the camp on 9th May. I'm going to have some more brandy, Edgar. I think you're going to need some now.'

Edgar poured large measures for both men, and removed his own jacket.

'I was called to Gdansk,' he continued, 'because the Poles had arrested a large number of SS officers and other camp staff from Stutthof, and had just completed the first of a series of war crime trials. One of the SS officers who had been convicted and sentenced to death told the Polish prosecutor something very interesting, which he thought I ought to hear. I met the prosecutor and he arranged for me to meet this officer, whom I interrogated at the main prison in Gdansk. His name was Werner Krüger and he had been a *Sturmbannführer*, more or less equivalent to a major in the army.

'Now, as I've already said to you Edgar, I was good at knowing who was telling the truth and who was lying. I expect you are too. Well, from the moment I first met him I was convinced Krüger was telling the truth. He had been found guilty of his crimes, and was due to be executed at the beginning of July. He knew he had committed war crimes and he wasn't trying to squirm out of his sentence, like so many of them, with all that nonsense about only obeying orders. Krüger was no fool, he wasn't pleading for his life or anything like that. But he told me a terrible story, which is why we're here today.'

Viktor had hauled himself up in the settee and was now speaking in a quieter, more portentous voice. The atmosphere in the room seemed to have chilled. Edgar noticed Irma standing in the doorway, her head bowed.

'In late January 1945 some 5000, or possibly more, Jewish inmates from Stutthof – mainly women – were evacuated. They were being marched north east, towards Konigsberg – which we now call Kaliningrad. Krüger was the officer in charge. The march was chaotic: some 2000 prisoners died en route, and the Red Army posed a constant threat. According to Krüger, they came to a fishing village on the Baltic coast and found they couldn't move on. Evidently the overland route was blocked, and it seems there was some confusion and disagreement as to what to do. Krüger told me he had a young officer under his command, by the name of Wilhelm Richter. He was an *Untersturmführer*, a junior lieutenant. Krüger said this Richter had only been with the SS at Stutthof for a few weeks but had shown himself to be especially vicious and brutal. He'd tortured and murdered many prisoners and was a fanatical Nazi, still convinced they would win the war – which few of them believed by that stage. Krüger said he went into a house in the village to send a message back to Stutthof, to see what they should do, when he heard shooting. When he came out he saw that his men were marching the prisoners into the sea and machine gunning them – on the orders of Richter.

'He described how he found Richter and asked him what was going on, and how the younger officer called him a Jew-lover and dared him to stop the attack. By the time they had finished, there were hardly any survivors. He described how young Richter waded through the edge of the sea wildly firing his pistol, laughing as he did so.'

'So he was blaming another officer for the war crime of which he'd been convicted?'

'Yes, but he was not seeking to exonerate himself. He knew he was guilty. But listen, Edgar, I've not finished yet. Krüger told me something very strange about Richter. When he'd arrived at Stutthof the month before, Wilhelm Richter reported directly to an *Obersturmbannführer* Peters – a Lieutenant Colonel, and obviously senior to Krüger.

'Krüger said it was most unusual for a junior officer to be so close to such a senior officer. However, Krüger and Peters were friends: both men came from Bremen. One night Peters got drunk and confided in Krüger. He told him Richter was on a top secret mission and he – Peters – was responsible for him and it was making him sick with worry. Apparently Peters' instructions were to ensure Richter was captured by the British or the Americans, because there was a plan for Richter to be part of some future Nazi movement. Richter was supposed to be sent to a unit fighting in the west, and Peters was trying arrange it, but Richter was resisting Peters' attempts to have him transferred because he was "having too much fun" at Stutthof. Those were the words he used.

'According to Krüger, after the massacre they all returned to Stutthof. They remained there until the Red Army was a day or so away and then fled. Peters was desperate to get Richter to where the Americans or British were, as per his orders – but they'd only got as far as Poznan when they were caught by the Red Army. All of them were taken back to Gdansk as war criminals but, to everyone's amazement, Wilhelm Richter – the man responsible for the massacre in the Baltic – managed to persuade the Germans to send him to the Soviet Union as a prisoner of war. Krüger also said *Obersturmbannführer* Peters apparently committed suicide just before their capture. According to Krüger he was alone in a shack with Richter when there was a gunshot. Krüger naturally had his doubts as to whether it was suicide.'

'And his reason for telling you all this…? Revenge?'

'I imagine it was, that's as valid a reason as any other. Krüger thinks Richter may have persuaded a Red Army officer he was innocent of any war crimes because of his age, he was only eighteen or nineteen. Krüger wanted us – the Soviets – to know the truth because Richter was our prisoner of war. Who knows, maybe Krüger felt passing on the information would give him some peace of mind? I took down everything he said and resolved to investigate it. Krüger was executed at the beginning of July. Just before I left Gdansk, the Polish prosecutor there told me that Richter's name kept coming up in his investigation: not just from survivors but also from other SS prisoners and *kapos*. He pleaded with me to try to find him. He was determined to put him on trial.'

The Russian said nothing for a while, as if he had reached the end of his tale. He had an unlit cigar in his hand.

'And that's it?'

'No, no... When I returned to the Soviet Union, I made some enquiries. But, as I told you, Edgar, we were overwhelmed. There were millions of prisoners at this stage. I was working ten – twelve hours a day, often seven days a week. I had no time to look for Richter. I forgot about him. And then, three years later – in 1949 – I was called to a camp near Rostov, where a young SS officer was insisting on talking to someone important. His name was Carsten Möller. He was worried about being repatriated to West Germany, because he had heard it was controlled by Nazis. Instead he wanted to be sent here, to the East, which was a most unusual request, I can tell you. He told me a long story, about how he had been part of a group of young SS recruits who all spoke perfect English, and were trained at a remote place near Magdeburg with the aim of then allowing themselves to be captured by the British or Americans. The story rang bells of course. It was more or less the same as the one Krüger had told me in Gdansk. After capture, the boys would be brought to England, where they would escape and eventually lead a revived Nazi movement.'

Viktor hauled himself up and slowly walked over to the window. He gently pulled the net curtain aside while standing well to the side of it, a move familiar to Edgar.

'Möller told me how, a few months earlier, he'd been taken to a special camp near Kazan, the purpose of which was to assess prisoners to see if they could work for the Soviet Union. He was only there for a week or two: he was deemed unsuitable. He said the camp was divided in two. There was an assessment centre, where he was held, and then a training camp, nicknamed the 'hotel', for those who'd actually been recruited. One day he caught a glimpse of a group coming out of the hotel, and amongst them spotted one of the other recruits from Magdeburg: Wilhelm Richter. He described him as the most evil person he'd ever known.

'I would have left it at that, but of course the mention of the recruits and of Richter in particular pricked my conscience. I'd promised the Polish prosecutor I'd look for him, and I never had. So after meeting Möller I started to look for Richter again. I thought that in my position it wouldn't be hard to find out what had happened to him and where he was. But I was surprised at how difficult it was. I eventually found one file about Wilhelm Richter, but purely by chance – it had been kept in the wrong section, and I came across by chance while looking for another file. According to Richter's file he'd had an SS rank of *Untersturmführer*, had been brought to the Soviet Union in June 1945 as a prisoner of war, and was eighteen at the time of his arrest, as Krüger and Möller had both said. The last entry in the file said he'd been sent to a camp near Kazan in 1948, where he was being assessed for "rehabilitation and training", as they put it, which was a euphemism for working for the Soviet Union.

'Now, I knew the commandant of that camp, and rang him. He was a friend of mine, but his reaction to my enquiry was not friendly. He told me to drop the case and forget about it. The next thing I knew, I was summoned to Moscow, to the headquarters of the Ministry of Internal Affairs on Zhitnaya Street. Forget what you hear about the Lubyanka, Edgar – worse things happened in much less famous buildings in Moscow. They still do. Anyway, at this meeting I was warned off Wilhelm Richter in no uncertain terms. And I may have gone along with it, had they not made a serious and very telling mistake.'

The Russian lit another cigar. Edgar noticed his hands were shaking. 'They told me – almost as an afterthought – that Richter was dead. I asked when he'd died, and they said in 1947.'

Viktor jabbed his lit cigar in Edgar's direction, his face red with anger. 'The fucking idiots couldn't even get their story right! I had Möller's sighting from earlier in 1949, and I'd seen a file that told me that Wilhelm Richter had been in the camp near Kazan in 1948, a year after he was supposed to have died. So, unless it was his ghost...'

'And since then?'

'I haven't finished yet, Edgar. I decided to drop it, for the time being at least. I was no fool, it wasn't worth the risk. I'd intended to resume the search for Wilhelm Richter when it felt safer. The fact that he'd disappeared, and my bosses had lied about him – well, that made him interesting, don't you agree?

'A few months after this meeting at the Ministry of Internal Affairs – this would now be 1950, perhaps in the spring – I was back at the camp near Rostov where young Carsten Möller had been held. I was there to see another prisoner but I did ask about Möller, and was told he'd been found dead in an outhouse the previous November, not long after I'd met him. His body had been found hanging from the rafters.'

'Suicide?'

'That's what I assumed, but the commandant said if it was, Möller had managed to do it with his hands tied behind his back. Actually, he'd wondered if I'd been involved somehow.

'Over the years I did wonder what had become of Richter. Whenever I got the chance I would look through the files, but all trace of him had disappeared, which was most unusual. Even the one file I had originally discovered – showing that he was in Kazan in 1948 – had disappeared when I went back to look for it. After the last German prisoners were sent back in '56, I had a series of desk jobs: intelligence analysis, training new agents – that kind of thing. I missed being in the field, and it was difficult for me to travel out of the Soviet Union. But it was not all bad. I had a small flat all to myself in Moscow – no shared kitchen or bathroom – and the use of a *dacha*, and Irma was allowed to travel to Moscow, so I was certainly one of the privileged few. For twenty years, I kept my head down. Gradually life became a bit easier and I was permitted to travel more freely, only within the Eastern bloc of course. Then in 1974, a man I had trained in the '60s – Yevgeny Yefimovich Mironov – became our deputy station head here in Berlin. The head of station is a fool called Kozlov, and Yevgeny arrived to find things in a mess. He decided to give our intelligence operation in the DDR an overhaul, and he thought I'd be a good person to help him with that.

'Over the past couple of years I have been based here more or less full time. My main role is ensuring we have good systems in place, though I do also get to review our operations, and study the quality and quantity of the intelligence we're getting. It's a bit like the old days, except I'm at a remove from the agents in the field. I do miss that contact, which perhaps explains what happened next. You want some more brandy… no?'

Viktor poured himself a glass and studied it for a while. 'I began to notice we were getting very high-grade intelligence from West Germany. Truly outstanding material, much of it coming from one source, with the codename "Goalkeeper". I was intrigued about who "Goalkeeper" was and, frankly, investigating him was far more interesting than coming up with new systems to help Yevgeny. It felt a bit like running an agent again, like the old days. So, more out of curiosity than for any other reason, I started to look into "Goalkeeper" in more detail. Actually, I asked Irma to look into it for me. Tell him, my dear.'

Irma straightened her skirt with her hands before speaking, quietly, her Viennese accent still noticeable despite her thirty-year absence from the city.

'I am well-trusted in the Embassy. I have been working there for a long time, and there have never been any questions mark about my loyalty. After all, I had been a Communist in Vienna during the war – hardly any of the Germans working there have credentials as good as that. Nor, for that matter, do many of the Russians.

'Since the late 1960s I've been based in the KGB section of the embassy. I am a senior clerk, I suppose you could say: I look after files and records, and encrypt documents. I have the highest level security clearance for someone of my grade. When Viktor asked me about "Goalkeeper" I tried to find out more, but it became clear this agent really was a top secret source, so any files relating to him would be kept by the most senior German in our department: Reinhard Schäfer. Apparently Schäfer was an ordinary police officer here in Berlin during the war, but had been, all the while, a secret Communist.'

'Two months ago,' said Viktor, patting Irma on the shoulder, 'Schäfer was on leave for a week. Until then Irma couldn't get anywhere near his "Goalkeeper" files. But while he was away his senior clerk was ill, and Irma had to cover for her. This gave her a chance to look for the information we wanted.'

Irma held up her hand in a 'stop' gesture and shook her head. 'No, no, Viktor, I have told you this before: I did not see the main file – Schäfer would never allow his senior clerk to have access to that. What happened was: I had permission to go to the registry in the basement of the Embassy to look for some of Schäfer's files and records there. They are kept in large, secure cupboards and a guard has to be present in the room whenever they're open. I was keeping an eye out for anything interesting, and I noticed an old card index box, dated 1971, so I glanced through it. Sure enough, there was a card for "Goalkeeper" in there. Everything on the card was in Schäfer's own handwriting. Mostly it was a series of numbers – file references and dates, going back to 1958 I think I recall. And alongside the last file reference were the letters BfV.'

Viktor leaned forward and looked carefully at the Englishman, speaking in little more than a whisper. 'You know what the BfV is,

Edgar? The Federal Office for the Protection of the Constitution – it is West Germany's equivalent of your MI5.'

'Of course I know what the BfV is,' said Edgar.

'So it seems that Goalkeeper works for the BfV. It would certainly fit with the type of intelligence we are getting from him.'

'Why on earth are you telling me this, Viktor? This is one of your own agents—'

'Because there's more, Edgar, just listen. Carry on, Irma.'

'You know Viktor,' she smiled and patted his arm. 'This revelation was not enough for him. He insisted I went back for more intel. I only had another few days before Schäfer returned to work, but fortunately I had another opportunity to go to his secure cupboards in the Registry.'

'From what I knew of him,' said Viktor, 'Schäfer would have kept any files relating to Goalkeeper in his own safe, to which only he would have access. The card index box being in the registry was possibly an oversight, but they are very bulky, which is why I imagine this one was deposited there – and why others would be there too. So I told Irma to look through all the other card index boxes.'

'When I returned to the registry,' said Irma, 'there were two other clerks taking items from the cupboards and just the one guard, so it was a bit easier. In total Schäfer had eight card index boxes down there. The first one covered 1958 to 1962, and the others either covered a few years or just single years. I looked through the box for 1958 to 1962 and, sure enough, there was a card for Goalkeeper, with everything in Schäfer's handwriting like before. It seemed to be just file references, but on the reverse of the card, written in pencil, was "Wilhelm Richter, Dresden, November 1926".'

During the long silence that followed, Edgar closed his eyes to absorb this information. He was beginning to understand why he had been summoned to East Berlin.

'So Goalkeeper is Wilhelm Richter. Wilhelm Richter is a Nazi war criminal. I failed to catch him in 1949. Looking for him almost cost me my career, maybe even my life.' Viktor was now red in the face, his voice raised. 'And now it all makes sense: the bastard is one of our agents, though I have no idea when he became one. And in case you're wondering, Edgar, why I'm so worked up about this, I don't like the fact that a Nazi war criminal working for a western intelligence agency any more than I imagine you do. That bastard may be one of our agents – and a good one too – but I don't care. As far as I'm concerned he's a Nazi war criminal who I've been trying to bring to justice since 1945. So, you know what I want you to do…?'

'You want my help to find out his real identity out and expose him, eh?'

Viktor started to speak then stopped, pausing to think carefully. 'It's not as straightforward as that, Edgar. I don't want you to expose him – not yet at any rate.' The Russian paused again. He appeared on edge as he filled his own brandy glass and moved across to once more glance through the curtains, his face now flushed, beads of perspiration prominent on his forehead. 'I could have killed you in Vienna in '45, Edgar. You know that, don't you?'

Edgar nodded. It had been a clandestine mission, one borne out of desperation. If he had disappeared no one would have known what happened to him. Viktor had unquestionably spared him.

'So you owe me this, Edgar. First, try to find out what you can about Richter and what name he is operating under now. Then…' Viktor paused. 'Irma, please would you go and make Edgar a hot drink before he leaves?' He waited until she'd left the room and then dropped his voice, leaning over to grip Edgar's forearm. 'But then tell no one, please Edgar: you tell me first. Find out Richter's identity and who he really works for, and then tell me. You can promise me that?'

Edgar felt a shiver run down his back. The fear in Viktor's voice was unmistakeable. 'But I thought you wanted him exposed? If I inform our people that one of the top men in the BfV is a Soviet agent, they'll ensure the book is thrown at him.'

'No, Edgar, no! There's a reason for being discreet, which I will tell you in due course, but not now. Don't tell your people before you tell me! Trust me: you'll soon realise I'm about the only person you can trust. I can't trust anyone on my side, Edgar, and I'm sorry to tell you but you can't trust anyone on yours. In due course you'll understand why I'm asking you for your help. In time, it will all make sense.'

'But—'

'I'm not telling you any more now. Once you've found out Goalkeeper's identity, and told me – and no one else – give me a month. If nothing happens in that time then he's all yours. Promise me that?'

Chapter 10

England, April 1976

Edgar was waiting at Waterloo station for his train to Dorset when a seven-year-old memory suddenly struck him.

Christopher Porter had been his immediate superior throughout most of the war, and had remained in the Service long after it, not least because he had nowhere else to go. Porter had never been much of a practitioner, as such, in the world of espionage. He was more of a manager in it: the person who uncomplainingly went to all the meetings, who managed budgets, found funds and other resources for various operations, who covered up Edgar's mistakes and indulgences and who would read and analyse the interminable detail of countless reports. Porter was good at reports, at reading them as well as writing his own. This all meant that Edgar had always rather taken him for granted. He had often been, to his regret, less than polite to Porter – even disobedient. He recognised that he must have been a difficult underling, possibly even arrogant on occasion.

As a consequence, once Edgar left the Service he resolved to be as pleasant as possible to Porter, a man who seemed to bear no grudges and was keen to meet for lunch on a regular basis. These lunches were also Edgar's way of staying in touch with the Service.

They took place every three or four months and had an alternating pattern to them: one month in the House of Commons, the next time at Porter's club, the Oxford and Cambridge in Pall Mall. The two men had been meeting like that for years, and more often than not Porter would bring a file with him for Edgar to have a look at. 'Do you remember this chap? Ever come across this outfit? Does this place ring a bell? Read through this and see what you think... Have a good look at this and tell me if we're on the right track... Could do with a fresh pair of eyes on this...'

But the meeting in 1969 – he seemed to recollect it was in November – was different. Porter had telephoned him at home, on a Sunday. 'I've taken the liberty of booking a table at Wiltons in Jermyn Street,' he said. 'On Tuesday. I hope you're free then. In that private area at the back – table's booked in the name of Mason.'

Over lunch the talk was about their mutual impending retirements, punctuated by long periods of silence. Edgar noticed Porter did not appear to have his usual enthusiastic appetite: he pushed the oysters around on his plate and waved away the carving trolley but drank most of a bottle of Côte de Beaune. He paid the bill before Edgar had a chance even to look at the desert menu, let alone order coffee, and insisted they go for a walk. They headed south down Duke Street, towards St James's Park. There was a light drizzle and both men turned their collars up against the chill.

'There's a report I want you to have a look at,' Porter said eventually.

'There usually is, isn't there, Christopher?'

'This one's a bit different, I'm not sure...' They had stopped by the large window of an art dealer and both men were peering at a bronze sculpture which appeared to be of a woman with multiple breasts, only one of which was even approximately in an anatomically correct position. 'Is this what they call modern art, Edgar?'

'I'm really not sure: you're younger than me, you ought to know!'

Both men laughed. 'Only by a year or two, Edgar. Anyway, I always imagined you were a bit more "with it" than me, eh?'

They carried on walking. 'This report you wanted to tell me about?'

Porter glanced around before he replied. 'A few weeks ago, end of September to be a bit more precise, a Catholic priest turned up at our embassy in Bonn. He had a parcel with him, and insisted on personally handing it over to someone who worked in intelligence. All a bit tricky really – the chap was a priest after all.' They were in St James's Park now, heading towards the lake. 'I mean, it's hardly as if we advertise the fact that we have intelligence people in the Embassy, let alone call them down when someone asks to see them. It's not a bank, is it? Eventually they got one of the chaps in the military attaché's office down and the priest was persuaded to hand over the parcel to him. The priest told him the parcel had been given to him by a dying man. I ought to mention, by the way, that the priest was indeed who he said he was: a Roman Catholic chaplain at the University Hospital in Frankfurt. Shall we see if this is dry enough for us to sit on, eh?'

They'd paused by a bench and Porter ran his hands over it. 'Should be all right, sit down, Edgar – it's only a bit of water. Now, this is where there was something of a breach of protocol. The military attaché opened the parcel and found that it contained a rather large document. Of course he should have passed it straight on to the MI6 station there in Bonn; they are after all in the same bloody building. But most of our chaps there were away from Bonn dealing with some operation that had gone wrong. So, for whatever reason, rather than taking it down the corridor they popped it in the diplomatic bag and it ended up with us. Oh Christ, that's Milne from the FCO, wait until he's passed.'

A squat man wearing a long black overcoat and a bowler hat walked slowly by and nodded at Porter, eyeing him suspiciously.

'Miserable chap – Milne,' said Porter once the other man was out of earshot. 'Terribly well thought of when he joined the FCO: fluent in Arabic, first class mind – you know the type. Then he rather disgraced himself in Tunis and now he's permanently gated. Stuck in a basement at the FCO, writing papers no one reads. Now then: that report. It ended up with us, and young Lassiter on the German desk was the recipient. He's typical of the new breed, Edgar, you'd absolutely detest him. Disagreeable type.

Talent spotted at Balliol before he'd even finished his second year, and has a very high opinion of himself, one which is, I'm afraid, shared by some of the fools he reports to. Wears aftershave and ties with flowers on them and, would you believe it, brown shoes with a dark suit!'

Edgar joined Porter in shaking his head in utter disbelief.

'The thing about Lassiter though is he's lazy and when he heard the report was the result of a walk-in from a priest he asked me to look at it instead, which is what tends to happen these days.' He paused while a brace of ducks waddled past them. 'Fair enough really, chap like me approaching retirement, kept away from the more sensitive stuff. No doubt they wish I'd gone years ago. Now then, Edgar, let me pause a moment and tell you how I work these days. I no longer get up before dawn to travel into London, work ten to twelve hours and go home after the rush hour. Not like it used to be. I take things much easier now. I put in a couple of long days and stay at my club for a night or two during the week, but I tend not to come in Fridays and don't arrive until lunchtime on Mondays. And these days I do take some work home with me. Nothing too sensitive, but anyway they seem to be keeping the more sensitive stuff away from me, so I'm not doing much harm. I can tell you, I'm not the only one doing it. We have one of these new-fangled copier machines in the office and if a report is quite long and doesn't have Level One, Two or Three classification I tend to copy it, leave the original in London and take the copy home to read over my long weekend. It works fine and, as I say, there seems to be some tacit understanding that this goes on.

'I was given the document in question on the Tuesday or Wednesday. Even though he hadn't read it, Lassiter had given it a Level Four classification, which as you know means "not very secret but don't go and pin it up on a bus shelter and do let us have something back within a week or so if that's not putting you out too much." I copied it, put the copy in the drawer where I keep the papers I'm taking home, and locked the original away. I took the copy home that weekend, read it, and left the copy at home when I returned to London. My procedure, for want of a better word, is to keep the copy in case I have to do any more with it and, if not, burn it after a while. So I returned the original to Lassiter on the Monday afternoon, with a note summarising what it was about – no more than a few lines really – my conclusion being the source was too unreliable and that the information had no impact on current operations and plans – you know the score, Edgar. Marked it "not for action", which as you're aware is a Service euphemism for "file and forget".'

Porter edged closer to Edgar on the damp bench. 'The next day, young Lassiter comes bursting into my office Edgar – barely knocking on the door, if you please – demanding to know if I had a copy. Well I'm no fool, Edgar, I wasn't going to admit to him there was a copy in my desk drawer at home. So I said no, don't be ridiculous, how dare he et cetera, et cetera and he was getting quite agitated, refusing to take "no" for an answer. He demanded to look in my filing cabinet, would you believe. More than forty years in the Service, Edgar, getting on for three times his age and he thinks he can address me like that, as if I'm an office junior! I unlocked the filing cabinet and let him root through it. He stormed out when he didn't find anything, and told me to forget about the report. I'll tell you, Edgar, had Lassiter been more relaxed and less offensive about the whole business I would indeed have forgotten about that damn report, but after the way he behaved I decided it merited a bit more interest.'

'And…?'

'That's the thing Edgar. I'm not sure there is an "and". I couldn't see what Lassiter was getting so het up about. The way he was acting I assumed there was something in the report he didn't want me to see, but for the life of me I couldn't spot it. Lots of Nazi fantasy stuff and some vague allegations about someone who may or may not be a West German spook having been a Nazi, which is hardly a surprise eh, aren't they all… and that's it really.'

'So you want me…'

'To read it. Yes please, Edgar – if only to put my mind at ease, reassure me I'm not going doolally. Marjorie says I'm forgetting too many things these days, didn't manage to complete *The Times* crossword last Wednesday. You have a sharp mind still, you're naturally more...'

'Devious?'

Both men laughed.

'You were always more cut out for espionage than me, Edgar. I'm just a bureaucrat. If you'd stayed on in the Service you could have been running it by now.'

Porter paused while a group of schoolchildren silently filed past them. A flock of ducks landed noisily on the lake and swam towards the bridge. Porter leaned down, undid the top of his briefcase and patted a large manila envelope.

'There you are Edgar: the report's in this envelope. Take it out when the coast is clear and let me know what you think – tell me if I've missed the blindingly obvious.'

–

By the time Edgar finished reading the report that weekend, he found himself agreeing with Porter. In his time he had come across many Nazi conspiracies and allegations about former Nazis in senior positions in both West and East Germany. It was all hard to prove and, even if it were true, the establishment's reaction would be: 'So what?'

But now, as he waited for his train, fleeting memories of the report came back to him, small details which seemed to tie in with what Viktor had told him. He'd have to read the report again. But he'd returned it to Porter, seven years before.

–

Christopher Porter lived just outside Cambridge, in a modern house on the ring road near the village of Trumpington. The house was at the end of a long drive, its interior bathed in light from large windows that reflected off pale wood-panelled walls. Edgar was let in by Porter's wife, Marjorie, to the aroma of baking, and had his ankles nipped by two dirtywhite terriers. Porter, it seemed, was now a disgruntled and confused old man who only wanted to talk about his pension. Edgar sat patiently for an hour listening to Porter's complicated calculations which he claimed showed he was not receiving enough money. Edgar was sure he was wrong, but didn't have the heart to tell him.

'Well, as I say... Type all that up and send it to them. I'm sure they'll have a proper look at it.' Only then did he feel able to broach the crucial subject: the report.

'Do I keep any reports from the Service? Of course not, Edgar! We weren't allowed to remove them from the office. You should know that!'

'I seem to remember,' said Edgar patiently, nervously eying the open door, 'you telling me you sometimes took copies of reports, Level Four and Five ones. Apparently it was becoming common practice.'

Porter nodded slowly as if he was only now remembering. He looked confused, and not for the first time that morning Edgar was beginning to wonder whether Porter was in the early stages of something.

'Well, perhaps, yes... but only the occasional report, very low-level.'

'Of course. And you asked me to look at one that came from the Bonn Embassy in 1969... about Nazis.'

Porter's eyes lit up at the mention of Nazis. 'I vaguely remember, but there were so many bloody reports. Didn't you agree there was nothing in it?'

'Indeed. I was just wondering... Christopher,' Edgar still felt awkward addressing his former boss by his first name, 'whether you still had the report – you asked me to return it to you.'

'Why would you want to see it now?'

Edgar moved along the settee so he was closer to Porter's armchair. He drew a deep breath, and decided to confide in his old colleague. He dropped his voice and leaned further towards Porter.

'Strictly between you and me, Christopher, I was in Berlin last week…'

'East or West?'

'Both,' said Edgar. Porter's eyebrows shot up, and he no longer looked confused. Now he was interested, which was why Edgar had taken the risk of confiding in him.

'I received a message to meet up with an old contact from back in 1945.' He said nothing more, allowing the words to sink in. It took a moment or two for Porter to realise.

'Friend or foe?'

'Both.'

Porter nodded. 'Viktor Krasotkin, eh? What did he want – to defect?'

Edgar shook his head. 'No, but it's a long story. He told me something which I think corroborates what was in that report and, if it's true, well… I need to check it out. Is there any chance you'd still have it?'

'It's possible, I don't know… My memory's so shot these days. Marjorie! Marjorie, do we still have those boxes, dear? The ones—'

'The ones you were supposed to get rid of all those years ago? Yes, you know full well we do. They're still in the outhouse.'

'Well Edgar needs to have a look through them. I think—'

'Edgar can only have a look at them on the strict condition that he takes the whole bloody lot away with him. You've been promising to sort them for years!'

–

In all, there were nine large, dusty boxes which Edgar packed into his car and drove to Dorset. It was late when he arrived home, so he unloaded the boxes and locked them in his study overnight. The following morning he went through them. They contained little more than a mundane testimony to a long career: letters from personnel, old newspaper cuttings, inconsequential correspondence, civil service staff magazines, even the menus from a few

Christmas parties. There were just a dozen reports, dating from 1968 and 1969, all wrapped in plastic carrier bags and sealed with yellowing tape. They were Level 4 or Level 5 briefings, reports from various stations abroad rather than anything that could be considered secret. He soon found the report he was looking for: fifty or so pages, carefully typed, the paper thick and yellowing – almost like parchment – and the pages held together by two pieces of frayed string which appeared through two holes crudely made on the edge of the paper.

A man of habit, Edgar slipped the latch on his study door and drew the curtains against the morning sun. He settled into his leather club chair by the fire and turned on his reading lamp. The first page was blank. The writing began on the second page.

'*The Testimony of Bernhard Krause.*'

Chapter 11

Frankfurt, May 1969

My name is Bernhard Krause. I am forty-two years of age and have resided in Frankfurt since 1945. I have led a most eventful life but have always avoided writing or even talking about it. When you read my story perhaps you will understand why, it is that kind of story.

A year or so ago I began to feel unwell. I avoided seeking medical treatment for a while but my condition deteriorated, and now I am being treated at the University Hospital here in Frankfurt. Soon I will be admitted as an inpatient and I doubt I will live beyond the end of the year. Accordingly, I have finally written my story.

I am not especially distressed at the prospect of dying; although of course I hope it is neither too painful nor distressing. At one point I assumed I wouldn't live to the age of twenty, so the extra years are something of a bonus, although they certainly haven't felt like that.

Bernhard Krause is not my real name, even though it is the only one I have had since 1945. The name I was born with, and used until February 1945, was Otto Schröder. I was born in Berlin where my father was a lecturer at Humboldt University. In 1930, we moved to Rostock, because my father was appointed as a professor at the university there. My two sisters, Birgit and Heike, were born in Rostock and we had a happy childhood. My father was aware that as a professor of English he could come under suspicion, so in 1937 he joined the Nazi Party. He soon became a committed Nazi, and went from being a calm, reasonable and cultured man who had translated Chaucer into German into what I would describe as a fanatic. He seemed to believe all the Nazi Party propaganda.

At dinner every night, my parents tried to outdo each other, as if they were competing to see who could say more terrible things about the Jews and Communists. We had to listen to the speeches on the radio, my parents went to rallies and my sisters and I joined all the different Nazi organisations for children. I was an obedient child and it didn't occur to me to argue with my parents or take a contrary view to theirs. However, there was very little I could have done, even if I had wanted to. After all, I could hardly have denounced my parents to the authorities for being Nazis.

In 1939 I joined the Hitler Youth, and in early 1944 I was drafted into a Hitler Youth Division of the SS based at a camp in Schwerin. In April 1944 I was transferred to a Waffen SS division which was based much further south, near Freiburg, prior to being sent to the front.

I remember going home to tell my parents about my move and I think they feared they would never see me again – things were going so badly in the war. The night before I left I overheard them arguing. My mother was weeping and saying she was going to lose her son and it was my father's fault, and he was telling her not to be so stupid and it was not his fault, it was the Nazis'. I will never forget what she said next: 'Well, what do you think we are?' There was a long silence and eventually my father said in a quiet voice, almost as if he was pleading with her, 'But what could I do?'

The next day very few words were spoken by any of us. Everyone was very brave. We all acted as if I was just going to be away for a few pleasant weeks, and we made no fuss as we said goodbye at the station. From the moment I left my family at the ticket barrier, I never once looked back: not as I walked down the long platform, not as I got on the train and not from the door or window of the train.

I would never see my family again.

–

I did well at Freiburg. I passed all my exams and, by the May, I was waiting to be sent on active service, but in the middle of that month I was ordered to meet three men from Berlin who had come to our camp. One of those men was a *Brigadeführer*. It was odd that an SS general should be meeting with mere recruits. They questioned me for a long time: why I was a Nazi, what I understood by loyalty – that kind of thing. One of the men remained silent throughout the interview. That evening myself and one other recruit were taken to our own hut in the officer's section of the barracks and told not to talk to anyone else at the camp. The next morning we had a very thorough medical examination, and quite a gruelling fitness test, and then we met the men from Berlin again.

The *Brigadeführer* had gone. This was to be my first encounter with The Englishman. I remember our first conversation very well. I am now referring to extensive notes I made in 1947, just three years after it took place. My memory was obviously better then, but even now I can recall what happened very clearly.

'Now then, Schröder, I understand that you speak very good English. Here is your opportunity to impress me.'

I would go as far to say that my English at that stage of my life was excellent. My father, of course, was an academic who taught English and when I was young he used to speak it in the house and he made me read books in English. He recognised I shared his aptitude for the language, and he did all he could to encourage me.

I was confused when The Englishman spoke because it was evident to me he was English. By now I was very apprehensive. The man himself was rather odd. He was around forty and very pale, with a bald head on which the few remaining strands of hair were plastered down with some kind of grease. He had watery, pale blue eyes and a large moustache that appeared to grow horizontally across his cheeks, tapering to a very fine point. His head was at a strange angle, as if pulled down by the weight of the moustache. He spoke in a very precise way, licking his lips as he did so.

The Englishman asked me about my family, and to describe my experiences in the Hitler Youth and how I had come to join the SS. Once the interview had finished I was sent back to the officers' section of the barracks and told to wait. Later that evening, at around nine o'clock, I was escorted to the office of *Obersturmbannführer* Frank, the camp commandant. The men from Berlin were in there with him. *Obersturmbannführer* Frank explained that I and another recruit, Horst Weber, had been selected for a special mission. But we would remain at the camp for a while and would be supervised on a daily basis by *Obersturm-führer* Koch who, we were told, also spoke very good English. We were to talk with him in English as much as possible. With that, we were dismissed.

Horst and I were already good friends. We had Berlin in common, and we both supported Hertha Berlin. His parents had been killed in an air raid in Berlin the previous year. That night, we had our first conversation in English, which felt as if we were doing something illegal. I explained that I spoke such good English because of my father. Horst said he was good at the subject at school before the war.

We remained at the camp for nearly four months, much longer than we expected. Every month, the Englishman came to visit. On his first regular visit, he told us his name was Captain Canterbury. He would arrive in the afternoon and stay until the following day. During that time, we spoke nothing but English. He was concerned about our accents: he wanted to ensure that we spoke with good English accents.

You must understand how close Horst and I became over this period. Although we knew better than to speculate about our mission, we realised it was something very important and quite probably dangerous. I really admired Horst. He was taller than me, he was quicker to pick things up, very charismatic and very striking in his looks. He had piercing dark eyes and his fair hair was quite wavy, even what you would call curly. He was the kind of person people would notice when he came into a room, whereas I tended to blend into the background, which has probably come to serve me well.

One Monday morning in September, *Obersturmführer* Koch woke us early and we packed our bags into a beautiful Daimler driven by *Obersturmbannführer* Frank's own driver.

We headed north, but the journey was difficult. Many of the roads were closed because of bombing and we arrived in Leipzig late in the afternoon. We stayed at the SS barracks there overnight and then set off the next morning in the direction of Magdeburg, sticking mainly to small country lanes. In the early afternoon we turned off a small single country road onto a narrow lane, which opened into a large courtyard covered in camouflage netting. A couple of other SS staff cars were already parked there.

–

Those first few hours in the country house near Magdeburg were the worst of my life. It was the first time I experienced true brutality and violence first hand, and I realised my life had changed forever. I realised I would never see my family again. We were escorted into a gloomy dining room just off the main entrance hall. The room was dominated by a long table, and one end was laden with food. There were breads, cold meats, cheese, potatoes and fruit, along with jugs of water and a large tureen of soup. Two other SS *junkers* were sat at the other end of the table, already eating.

Over the next few hours, we were joined by other *junkers* and, like Horst and I, they were all young, nervous and silent. There were a few nods between us, but no smiles, and certainly no conversation. At five thirty we were joined by another *junker*. He was the same age as the rest of us, but he didn't seem to be nervous at all. He marched into the room with a confident swagger and at first I thought he was one of the officers coming to check on us. He was not tall, but well built, and with thick dark hair and noticeably jet-black eyes. He stood to attention at the end of the table, by the food, and after looking at us clicked his heels and gave the Hitler salute, without the '*Sieg Heil*'. Soon after that we were summoned into a room on the other side of the hall, and formed into two rows. I was in the front row, next to Horst.

SS *Brigadeführer* Reinher, who Horst and I had met at the camp in Freiberg, entered the room. He said our mission meant we would certainly never see our families again. He understood this was not a matter to be taken lightly, so he was going to give us a chance now to pull out, and there would be no hard feelings. He would give us a moment or two to think about it.

I was utterly confused. In the SS you did as you were told. It was not a voluntary organisation, where you opted in and out of activities as you wished. I feared this was a trap. No one around me moved or said a word. An oppressive silence prevailed over the room, the soft crackling of the fire behind us the only sound. Then there was a voice from the row behind me. He said that his name was Axel Werner and he explained while he had no wish to pull out, his father had been killed in the East and his mother in an air raid in Hamburg, and he was all his little sister had left in the world. It was a moving story, if not an unfamiliar one, but I wanted to turn round and shout at him to be quiet, not to be such a fool.

But to my surprise, the *Brigadeführer* sounded quite sympathetic. He quite understood, he told Werner. No hard feelings, he could leave now.

Werner left the room, followed by the *Obersturmführer* who must have been his escort. Moments later we could see them through the front window as they emerged into the courtyard. Then there was a shot, and the boy crumpled to the ground. He appeared to have been hit on the back of his thigh. It was horrendous, but what followed was worse. We were summoned to the window. As he lay on the ground, the *Obersturmführer* stood above him. He rolled him over with his boot and looked ready to finish him off but, as he was about to do so, the *Brigadeführer* turned to the group of us and asked if there was a volunteer. I remember thinking that in the circumstances I wouldn't be able to hold a pistol, let alone fire it. But one of our group quickly volunteered. It was the last boy who had come into the dining room, the one who had given the salute. His name was Wilhelm Richter, he told the *Brigadeführer*. He took the pistol and left the room with a spring in his step.

I heard the sound of Richter's footsteps in the courtyard and then heard Werner cry, 'No, please, no.' There was a delay and then Richter called out 'Traitor,' and then another long pause, during which time Werner was still moaning and I think I heard the *Obersturmführer* mutter something to Richter. Only then did he fire the shot and there was an explosion of sound: not just the echo of the bullet around the courtyard, but also birds and dogs and other animals that had been disturbed by the terrible noise. The temperature in the room appeared to drop by a few degrees.

Richter returned to the room along with a small man wearing thick spectacles whom the *Brigadeführer* introduced as Herr Erich Schäfer. Herr Schäfer was a civilian and wore a suit that seemed to be too big for him, although from what I could tell it was a very good quality material, like the kind my father would wear on special occasions.

The briefing was carried out by *Brigadeführer* Reinher and Herr Schäfer. I will try to summarise it as well as I can. I have also checked out some of the historical facts alluded to in the briefing to ensure its accuracy.

The previous week, they said, a small detachment of American troops had crossed the Belgian border into Germany. This meant the final phase of the war was underway. They explained that, until then, the policy of the High Command had been to contain the Allied advances by retreating to more defensible lines. The plan being to hold those lines then regroup and, once we had re-armed and brought in new weapons, we would be able to counter attack and the tide of war would once again turn our way.

But the presence of Allied troops on German soil changed that. We had to accept that military defeat was no longer just a possibility, but a probability. And so measures were being taken to plan for the consequences of defeat. This was being done in the utmost secrecy, naturally. It was imperative, we were told, that the ideals of the Third Reich were not lost as a result of a military defeat. With careful planning, the defeat would only be temporary.

Herr Schäfer said that this was not as fanciful an idea as it might sound. German Intelligence believed that if the Allies won the war they would soon fall out with each other, due to significant tensions between the British and the Americans on the one hand and the Soviet Union on the other. They would argue over how Europe should be divided – there was a fundamental difference in their ideologies which could never be reconciled. Germany predicted that chaos would ensue in post-war Europe.

Brigadeführer Reinher said that during this time he expected the 'western Allies,' as he called them, to realise the truth of what many in Germany had been saying all along: their real enemy was the Soviet Union. Out of the chaos and tension, a Fourth Reich would emerge.

'Fifteen years is a long time. It is almost as long as you have been alive. In fifteen years, you will all be thirty-three. That is still young. But I am forty-eight, so that far into the future, I will be sixty-three – and I'm one of the youngest SS generals. Our *Führer* will be seventy. And that is assuming this process only takes fifteen years. What if it takes twenty years, or longer? The Fourth Reich cannot be led by old men. It will require a new generation of leaders: and that is where you come in.'

Herr Schäfer took over the briefing at this point. 'You need to know there is a sophisticated organisation behind you. Although you may feel alone, you will be part of something big. You must be wondering why I am telling you this. After all, you are not even officers. You do not require explanations, just orders. And what we are telling you – talking about defeat – is the kind of talk that gets people arrested by the Gestapo. But we are telling you because you cannot be expected to undertake a mission like this if you have no idea of its context.'

Herr Schäfer told us a number of groups of young people were being prepared to help lead the Fourth Reich. He would not say how many, but he did say that 'when the time comes' there would need to be 'many thousands' of committed and proven Nazis in place, who could lead Germany back to its destiny.

Our group had been chosen for a very specific mission, he said. 'As well as being young and in the SS, you are all highly proficient in the English language. The mission you will undertake in the service of the Reich requires you to be captured by the British.'

I well remember the atmosphere in the room as Herr Schäfer said this: disbelief, along with a fear this could be another test – like the one Werner had failed. What point could there possibly be in a mission requiring us to be captured by the enemy?

Brigadeführer Reinher took over. 'You will remain here for a few more weeks for the first phase of your training. Much of this will involve Captain Canterbury, who I know you have met already. You will then move on to another location for your final phase of training. Within a few months you will each to be attached to frontline Waffen SS units. Your unit commander will have instructions that rather than fight to the death, he should surrender his unit to the Allies at the earliest opportunity. This will ensure that you are taken as prisoners of war. Herr Schäfer, please.'

The small man began to speak again. His voice was quiet, and he stared down at the floor as he talked. 'All Waffen SS soldiers captured by the British, Americans and Canadians are taken to prisoner of war camps in Britain. The situation with the Wehrmacht is more complicated. Our understanding is that as the number of German prisoners of war increases, most Wehrmacht prisoners will not be transported back to Britain. But we can be certain that all SS prisoners will go to Britain. As far as the British are concerned, you are all Nazis, and dangerous. We know quite a bit about the prisoner of war camps in Britain. There are over one hundred of them. Some are in remote, rural locations, others in towns and cities. Prisoners are treated reasonably well. The important point though, is that security is not too stringent. The British think it unlikely German prisoners will escape, because they have nowhere to go to. The British population is overwhelmingly hostile although, as you will see, there are a few exceptions. And of course, Britain is an island. It is not as if you can try and reach the border to escape to a sympathetic country and so make your way home, as Allied prisoners of war can do. So, escape is not only possible, it is quite feasible. It just does not happen very often. Prisoners who escape are recaptured very quickly. They do not have the right papers and, of course, they are foreign. The British can smell out a foreigner from a long way off, let me assure you.

'You will be different. By the time you are in a position to escape, you will be able to pass yourselves off as Englishmen. You will have good identity papers. And more importantly, you will have somewhere to head to in Britain.'

The *Brigadeführer* then said that it had been a long day, and we had many more ahead of us. The briefing would continue tomorrow. 'Remember, boys. You are soldiers. You are only being told to do what soldiers do. You are being sent into battle.'

I slept very little that night: I doubt if many of the *junkers* did, apart from Richter, of course. He was in the bed opposite me and not once did I detect that he was anything other than fast asleep. Whenever I glanced over at him he was lying quite still, as if to attention. His dark hair was still immaculate and his face seemed set into a smile, as if in his dreams he was replaying the days' events with some satisfaction.

–

At breakfast the next morning, Richter was the only one in a talkative mood. His bed was very comfortable, he told us. It was just a shame that there wasn't a beautiful woman to share it with him – though if that had been the case he would not have got as much sleep, he assured us. And then he talked about Werner:

the maggots would have started to eat him by now, he told us, laughing as he did so. No one said a word, although I noticed a couple of the others smiling nervously. Werner deserved to die. He was a traitor. Did we not all agree? Around the table, we all nodded our heads, some more enthusiastically than others. Horst was the only one to reply to Richter.

'Of course. You were very brave.'

After breakfast, we were called into the main room where *Brigadeführer* Reinher addressed us. 'We realise that it is strange for you to see an English officer so closely involved in your mission. The English are, after all, our enemy. But I wanted to take this opportunity to explain how important Captain Canterbury's role is. I require you to take him every bit as seriously as you would an SS officer or Herr Schäfer here. As you will find out tomorrow, without Captain Canterbury the chances this mission being a success would be very limited indeed. In fact, it would be near impossible. His role is not limited to the briefings he is giving you here. When you are in Britain, he will assume an even more important purpose. Nor must you see him as the enemy. He is a very committed follower of our cause, and he is not alone among Allied officers. A number of Allied prisoners have realised that the British are fighting the wrong enemy. They realise that Germany and Britain have much in common, and the real enemy is the Soviet Union. A number of Captain Canterbury's comrades have joined the SS and a number are also working in Berlin, some in the Foreign Ministry and some with our English language radio services. Captain Canterbury himself worked in the latter for a while. He is an intelligent and resourceful man.'

The next day, Captain Canterbury was on his own with us in the main room, smoking a pipe as usual. On the wall behind him was a large map of the British Isles. Attached to it were dozens of green stickers, dotted all over the map. They represented prisoner of war camps, he said. As SS prisoners we would be taken to one of seven camps, which he pointed to.

'Now you already know that your mission is to escape. But what are you to do then? Where will you escape to? Birmingham.

Oxford. Bristol. London.' He was pointing at four blue stickers on the map.

'I think *Brigadeführer* Reinher may have dropped a hint the other day with regards what I am going to reveal to you now. You will appreciate the need for complete secrecy. Although the British population is overwhelmingly hostile to us, there are exceptions – a very small number of people, perhaps no more than a few hundred. They are dedicated people who, like me, were sympathetic to the Nazi cause long before Churchill so misguidedly took Britain into a pointless war against Germany. He should have known that the real enemies are the Jews and the Communists who, in truth, are one and the same.'

That afternoon Herr Schäfer joined Captain Canterbury for the next stage of our briefing. They explained that we would join our Waffen SS units using our real names, but would be given British identity papers, along with some money and maps. Herr Schäfer said these documents would be expertly sewn into our uniforms, so it would be almost impossible to find them. He explained that the reason for using our real names was in case the British checked out our identities – it was important we were seen as genuine.

'Once you've escaped you'll lie low in your safe house for a few weeks. When it is all right to do so, we will move you on to other safe houses. In these houses you will assume new British identities, that should last you for the rest of your lives. You will remain at these houses until the war is over and then you will be sent away. We will identify locations where we think you should live. You will then be expected to establish your new lives. You will find jobs, have families and become normal Englishmen. We will maintain contact with you. This will be very discreet, although you should understand that we will always know where you are and what you are up to. You will never, ever again have contact with your families here in Germany. You must be very clear about that. You will get on with your lives and wait for us to contact you. As we have said, that may take many years. You will be patient. You will wait, but be assured that we will contact you.'

Following Captain Canterbury's briefing, the pattern for the next seven weeks began to emerge: physical training sessions in the morning, mapreading exercises, weapons training, and a series of briefing sessions with either Captain Canterbury or Herr Schäfer.

In the evenings, we would be immersed in British culture. We were shown British films, most of them at least ten years old, and given British magazines and newspapers to read. Surprisingly, some of these were not that old, maybe only a year or two, so they were all about the war. Captain Canterbury explained that we should realise that the Jews owned the press in Britain, and therefore everything we read was Jewish or Communist propaganda. Nonetheless, it was important that we understood it: it was good for us to get a proper sense of British life and the popular subjects that people spoke about.

In the last week of November, our time in the house outside Magdeburg came to a sudden end. We had been on a map-reading exercise in the country and when we returned to the house, *Brigadeführer* Reinher was waiting for us. We had performed better than he had expected: he'd imagined at least two or three of us would not complete this level of training, but with the help of Herr Schäfer and Captain Canterbury and the *Obersturmführers* we had exceeded expectations. We had served the SS well, and he was optimistic that our mission would be a success. With young men like us, he said, the ideals of the Reich would live on.

I remember feeling quite emotional at this stage. After the death of Werner on our first night at the house, it felt like the same fate would befall any of the rest of us if we put a foot wrong. That was a terrible burden to have carried around with us, and now I could feel it being lifted. We had a good meal that night, a wonderful pork stew and cold beer. Afterwards, we had a cake which tasted so wonderful I think they must have used eggs and real cream.

I think I need to add something here – the names of the recruits. Of course Axel Werner was dead, and I have already mentioned Wilhelm Richter. So apart from myself and Horst the remaining six were: Konrad Hartmann, Christian Schäfer, Arnold Bauer, Lothar Meier, Mathias Hahn and Carsten Möller.

The next morning, we left the house near Magdeburg for the very last time.

–

We were driven to Dortmund where we stayed in a large Wehrmacht barracks, all of us sharing one large room, but it was warm and the beds were comfortable. We were able to relax for a couple of hours, and there was a real sense of camaraderie: we had, we sensed, reached the end of our journey together. We had somehow survived – or so we thought.

The following afternoon we were taken to the police station in Hörde, in the south of the city. When we arrived *Brigadeführer* Reinher briefed us. He seemed rather nervous. 'You have already shown that you are very well qualified for this mission. You have the right backgrounds, you all speak English well and you are the right age. In addition, the training at Magdeburg showed that you possess the right skills. However, this mission is so important that we also need to be absolutely certain you possess other essential qualities we are looking for: unquestioning obedience, an ice-cold nerve, decisiveness and, finally, the ability to undertake even the most unpleasant task in an efficient manner. We will now test all of those qualities.'

He went on to tell us that this police station was also the Gestapo headquarters for the area and they had brought together a number of enemies of the state, the kind of people for whom they no longer had any need.

We were then taken into the basement and to my dying day I will never forget the sight that greeted us. It was a very large room, brightly lit, and arranged against the far wall was a group of ten people, each of whom was naked and strapped to a post with a number hanging round their neck. There must have been at least another fifteen people in the room as we entered it. Half a dozen were in civilian clothes, and I took them to be Gestapo officers.

The rest were guards, apart from two men operating a large movie camera on a slightly raised platform opposite the prisoners.

It was hard not to stare at the prisoners – they were such a shocking sight. They all looked so frightened and pathetic. I have to be frank and say that this was the first time I had seen a naked woman in real life, although I know that this sounds like a most inappropriate observation.

Brigadeführer Reinher went to stand by a small table to the side of the row of prisoners. On the table was a small wooden box. A tall man in his early thirties, wearing a light grey suit, joined him. He spoke without introducing himself. He addressed the ten of us directly.

'The vermin here are all enemies of the state. We have finished questioning them and we have no further purpose for them. In normal circumstances we would have disposed of them by now – but we giving you that honour.' One of the other civilians addressed the prisoners in French. I have no knowledge of French, but I assume he was translating.

The man in the suit continued, 'Some of these people are members of the so-called resistance, some are Jews, some are black marketeers, others have engaged in defeatist behaviour.'

There was a pause while the Gestapo officer and Reinher conferred with each other. I noticed that the cameraman on the small stage was filming us and then panning across the row of prisoners. It was *Brigadeführer* Reinher who spoke next, this time directly to us.

'Now we have come to the time when we can give these criminals what they deserve. You will be the ones carrying out that task. In this box there are numbers corresponding to the prisoners. Each of you will come up here as I call your name, pick a number and then go over to the prisoner and dispose of them. Remember what I told you upstairs: we are looking for obedience, an ice-cold nerve and the ability to carry out a task such as this in an efficient and decisive manner.'

It is impossible to describe exactly how I felt at this point. I had assumed the test would be to watch these people being executed.

To be expected to kill them ourselves was unimaginable. I experienced a mixture of fear and disbelief, but also a very strange sense of understanding quite clearly what I had to do. I knew full well that if I did not do it I would certainly be killed too.

The *Brigadeführer* picked up a piece of paper and called out Arnold Bauer's name. He marched swiftly to the table, gave a smart '*Heil Hitler*' salute and took a piece of paper from the box. Seven: a woman whose crime had been to tell her neighbours she thought the war was lost. Arnold was handed a small knife and walked towards the woman, who only now fully understood what was going to happen to her. She started to wail, a sound that was more of sadness than fear. Without hesitating, Bauer grabbed the woman by the hair, pushed back her head and slit her throat. However, the blade was clearly too small and blunt to do the job cleanly. Blood was gushing everywhere and the woman was now screaming. She sounded as if she was drowning.

Bauer turned round, a look of panic on his face. He turned back to the woman and stabbed her repeatedly and violently about the torso – maybe a dozen times – before her body slumped, lifeless. Bauer walked back to the group, his face and uniform splattered with blood, and we all slapped him on the back. The prisoners were now all screaming and crying.

I do not propose describing each execution, if that is the right word, in detail. It is too horrific and has been the stuff of my nightmares for these past twenty-five or so years. The other five who came after Bauer and before me all killed their victims with much the same degree of violence that Bauer had used. All of the deaths were slow and brutal.

Wilhelm Richter came immediately before me. Without going into detail, let me tell you he set about his prisoner – I think it was a German Communist – with more enthusiasm than the rest of us. He spent so long torturing his prisoner that *Brigadeführer* Reinher eventually told him to hurry up. I selected number six, a black marketeer. I decided to use the knife, as I remembered from somewhere in my training that even a blunt knife could be lethal if used in the right way, and I was confident I remembered the method. I had to look right into the man's face. His eyes were frozen, staring into the distance. I did my best to avoid staring at his naked body as I thrust the knife into his midriff and then pulled it sharply upwards. I could see his lips moving as I did so, but then they froze, as if in mid-sentence. His skin swiftly turned pale as life poured out of his body.

You do not need me to tell you how those moments have haunted me ever since, even though at the time I still believed I was doing my duty. What has compounded my feelings is that I am certain I know what he was mouthing at me as he died: 'So young.' Those were his last words, I am sure of it. I have lost count of the number of times I have seen those words being mouthed at me in my sleep, and sometimes even when I am awake. Each time it happens, I am as horrified as on the afternoon itself. And it is getting worse. I see those lips moving in front of me every day now. I am certain that they will be the last thing I see as I slip away from this earth. I was young – only eighteen – but from that moment on, I felt like an old man. I had been cursed.

Horst's victim was a Jewish woman. He walked behind her and strangled her very fast, pushing his knee against the post to give him extra leverage. She seemed to lose consciousness very quickly. I would say that she died more quickly than any of the other prisoners. Horst had his head down as he walked back to stand next to me. I caught a glimpse of his face and I promise you, I saw that his eyes were moist, as if he was about to cry. He blinked a couple of times and a moment later he looked up, by which time he was composed again.

I am concerned I may be giving you the wrong impression. I am writing this many, many years after the event, and perhaps seem a little detached about it. At the time, although I found the events in Hörde police station shocking and difficult, I felt I was doing my duty. Life was simple then, we were given orders and we obeyed them. I hope you will have realised that I am now utterly horrified at what we did. Let me be honest and clear: we committed war crimes. The fact that we had been ordered to do so was, as we now know, no defence. It was such a clever move:

we committed war crimes and they filmed it, giving them a hold over us.

–

We were woken at six the following morning. The *Brigadeführer* explained this would be our final test. 'Forty eight hours from now you could be with your units,' he told us.

Our final test was to make our own way from the barracks in Dortmund to the police station in Essen. We would travel individually, leaving the barracks at fifteen minute intervals, starting at nine that morning. We should arrive at the police station in Essen by four the following afternoon. Essen was around thirty kilometres away.

I do not propose to go into detail here about the journey. It was not without its dangers, not least from the many air raids I encountered. Suffice to say that I made it to the police station on Jager Strasse by three thirty. By four, eight of us were there. Just Horst had yet to arrive.

Over the next hour, the *Obersturmführers* kept coming in and out of the room, increasingly flustered. They asked us if anyone had seen Horst. No one had. At six o'clock the *Brigadeführer* came in, along with the three *Obersturmführers* and what I took to be two Gestapo officers. If any of us had seen Horst and out of an understandable but mistaken sense of comradeship had decided to say nothing, we should say so now. Still, none of us had seen him.

They must have gone into a room nearby because we could hear everything. I think the correct phrase is that all hell broke loose. The *Brigadeführer*'s rage at the disappearance of Horst was directed at the Gestapo who, it appeared, had been responsible for following us from Dortmund to Essen.

We were taken to a barracks in the south of Essen that night. The next morning we were joined by *Brigadeführer* Reinher who wished us luck, and reminded us that the future of Germany lay in our hands and those of other brave young men like us. If our mission succeeded, which he had no doubt it would, we would see Captain Canterbury again in Britain.

He finished by saying that in a few moments we would each be taken to separate parts of the barracks to meet the commanders from our new units. They had been here all day themselves to be briefed. They understood their orders: to protect us and surrender to the Allies at the earliest possible opportunity. They would be the only people who knew anything about our mission.

And then with a suddenness that came as quite a shock – that was that. In the corridor outside the room we had a few seconds to say 'good-bye' and 'good luck' to each other, but it was all very rushed. The eight of us were taken off in different directions. In a matter of moments I was being hurried across the parade ground to an office behind the Armoury, where I found myself in the company of SS *Sturmbannführer* Rottgen. He told me I was now a *Sturmmann*, or Storm Trooper, in the 17th SS Panzergrenadier Division which was currently fighting in France, where we would now go.

There is no point in me telling you here about my career as a *Panzergrenadier*. For a start, *Sturmbannführer* Rottgen had clearly been given quite strict instructions about me so, as far as possible, I avoided front line duties. He told me he intended to wait until it was safe for me to be captured, if that makes sense, and only then would he send me to the front line.

Early in January 1945, I was transferred to a small front line unit which was involved in an attack on American forces around the French village of Rimling, in Moselle. One Sunday morning my unit and some others, all under the command of *Sturmbannführer* Rottgen, moved towards Rimling. We made good progress at first, and just before seven had crossed a main road and were about to enter a wooded area when they hit us from every side.

At first it was artillery, followed by assaults from the air, and finally what seemed like hundreds of American troops attacking us. I was terrified: this was my first experience of being attacked or even of fighting. I had no idea what to do. Despite the chaos, *Sturmbannführer* Rottgen had managed to find me. He shouted in my ear: I should get into a ditch and surrender when the Americans came, which would be any moment now. He would stay by me, he said. No sooner had he said that than a shell exploded near us. It was not just the noise that was deafening, but the light was unbearable too. I was quite disorientated and wondered if I had been hit. When I came to my senses, I saw *Sturmbannführer* Rottgen next to me on the ground, smiling at me as if he had no cares in the world. The rest of his body was some way behind us. Realising that I was not hurt, I scrambled across the road and the last thing I remember is colliding with something and then the world going black and very quiet.

I have no idea how long I was unconscious for, but when I came round I was on a stretcher out in the open, in a field alongside the woods. I could see a few American troops nearby and dozens of German soldiers lying on the ground. My ankle was agony, but apart from that and a terrible headache, I was all right. I lay there, realising I had, after all, been captured.

The Americans gave us water, medicine and food, and even cigarettes. A *Panzergrenadier* from my unit told me that he had seen me being run over by an American jeep. At around noon we were taken to a field hospital. Of course, I could understand what everyone was saying to one another, but decided not to let on. I heard a doctor telling an orderly that the tent I was being put in contained ten men, the ones they did not need to worry about. They were either like me, not badly hurt and about to be moved to a prison camp, or so badly wounded that there was no hope for them.

The two other walking wounded were taken off to the prison camp in the early afternoon, but I pretended to be asleep and moaned a bit, so I heard an orderly telling someone that I would need to stay there overnight. Of the seven mortally wounded men in the tent, three died within an hour of being brought in. As night fell, there was just me and four dying men.

Two of them were SS *Panzergrenadiers* like me, but the other two were Wehrmacht. One of them was on a stretcher next to me. From what I could tell, which was not easy, he was a similar age, height and build. He lay still and breathed slowly and heavily, moaning occasionally. His head was swathed in thick bandages, with blood seeping through in more than one place.

It was then that an idea began to develop: I would escape. I realised my situation may not, after all, be that hopeless. The one person who knew the purpose of my mission – *Sturmbann-führer* Rottgen – was dead. So I opened the jacket pocket of the Wehrmacht soldier next to me. I found his identity card, some letters, a small amount of money and a photograph of a family of four, dated 1938, along with two or three photographs of a plump girl with thick glasses.

This was my opportunity, and I knew I needed to move fast. With some difficulty I removed my uniform – remember, my ankle was in a bad way – and with even more difficulty removed his. I then dressed in his uniform, which was perhaps just one size too large. Fortunately his boots, though not as good quality as mine, were large enough to take my now very swollen ankle. It was even more difficult dressing him in my SS uniform: he started to moan more loudly and began to move his arms. Unfortunately, I had to be quite rough with him. After about ten minutes the changeover was complete, and I lay back on my stretcher to look at his papers and learn my new name. I paused while an American came in to check on us, and pretended to be asleep while he went from stretcher to stretcher.

I could see my name was now Mathias Bernhard Krause. I had been born in Mainz in 1925, just two years before me, if you see what I mean. My plump girlfriend was called Ulrike. According to a note on the back of one of her photographs, not a minute of any day went past when Ulrike did not think of her Mathias. I was a *Gefreiter*, or private first class, in the 62nd Volksgrenadier Division, which I had joined in 1943. In the half light of the tent, I read through the letters I had found in Krause's pocket. Tragically for him, but most conveniently for me, his parents and elder sister had all been killed in an air raid which destroyed their house in Mainz in January 1944. A letter from a colleague of his father's assured him that they could have known nothing. Every house in the street had been destroyed. The family photograph I'd found showed a mother, father, girl and boy. I therefore felt it was safe to assume that I had no other siblings who may want to search for me. Apart from Ulrike, I was all alone in the world. I contemplated my situation: I had managed to assume the identity of a Wehrmacht soldier. If I continued to be lucky, I might get away with it.

Next to me, Mathias Bernhard Krause began to breathe more noisily, which I recognised as his final moments. I watched over him as his life slipped away.

I was concerned the same orderly might come into the tent and see that the dead man was wearing a different uniform. So, with some considerable difficulty, I got up and hobbled out of the tent. It was sheer agony, as I could not avoid putting weight on my ankle. It was a nightmare walking across the pitted field, until I found a large tent where the walking wounded and uninjured German prisoners were held and I gave them my name. No one spoke much, everyone avoided eye contact, and we just all sat quietly. My ankle was so painful now that I thought I would pass out, but I knew that I needed to get away from the field hospital and the *Panzergrenadiers* as fast as possible. Some French soldiers came round taking our names and military details. One of the soldiers took a passing kick at any SS officer, but no one said anything. An hour later, they came back in and called out a list of names. Everyone who was called up and assembled at the front of the tent was Wehrmacht. The SS prisoners remained where they were. They called out 'Mathias Krause' three times before I realised that was me. I remember thinking I had better get used to the name, and on the lorry that drove us through the night to our prison camp I kept repeating it over and over.

–

I was finally released as a prisoner of war in October 1945, and I went to live in Frankfurt am Main. Like most German cities, much of it had been destroyed and thousands of its inhabitants had been killed. Many thousands more had left the city or moved to different parts of it. I know this sounds harsh, but you will understand when I say that this suited me fine. It was very simple for me to arrive there and not stand out as a stranger. Frankfurt in 1945 was a city of strangers.

By the time I arrived there I had dropped the Mathias, so I was now Bernhard Krause.

Otto Schröder had long ago ceased to exist.

I ought to point out that by the time I sought medical treatment I had done permanent damage to my ankle, which meant I would be disabled for the rest of my life. I also had to face the prospect of never being able to see my family again, which was almost too much to bear. At first, I assumed that I would be able to contact them again, after a decent interval. But the more I contemplated my situation, the more I realised this was impossible. If I contacted them it would be as Otto Schröder – but Otto Schröder was a war criminal who'd murdered a prisoner in cold blood in the cellar of the Gestapo headquarters in Dortmund. At least twenty people had witnessed this unforgiveable act, and it had been filmed. I could not risk being linked to him, not even if that meant never contacting my family again. In any case, they would have been informed that I had died of my wounds in January 1945. I had to come to terms with this, but it was very hard. Looking back on it now, I must have gone through a grieving process for my parents and sisters, without being able to share my grief with anyone. You must remember I was still only eighteen. It was a truly terrible time.

If I was going to survive, I would need to keep a low profile. I resolved to lead my life in the half shadows, with the mundane and the unnoticed. My ambition of going to university would have to go unrealised. Getting married and having a family could not be considered. I would trust no one.

I found a room in a lodging house, and a job as a porter at a hotel near the station. But I had a policy of moving on in those early years, of not putting down roots. My rule was never to stay in a job for longer than a year, and to move place of residence every six months. So I moved from lodging house to bedsit, from one district of Frankfurt to another, from mundane job to mundane job.

It was a miserable life. I allowed myself no friends, just acquaintances. For the first few years I thought it was just a matter of time before I was tapped on the shoulder and someone would say 'Otto Schröder'. I couldn't go to bed without thinking that there was a good chance the door would be broken down during the night, and I would be arrested.

I would not say that there was a moment when I felt safe, but by 1956 I was aware that the war had been over for more than ten years and no one had ever as much as given me a knowing look, or asked me an awkward question. I found a nice apartment in the Nordend district and it suited me perfectly. I felt safe in the flat, I began to sleep better – sometimes for as many as four hours at a time – and I looked upon this place as home. I lived there for one year, then for two, then three and then I just stayed there.

My biggest regret was having no contact with my family. Although I had resolved that I could not allow myself to contact them, there were many times in my early days in Frankfurt when I found the loneliness too much. At times, I thought it would be worth risking the consequences by going to see them or making some contact. Even if just to let them know that I was alive, and to see how they were – although I didn't know if they had survived the war. However, my dilemma was solved for me by the Cold War. Rostock, of course, was in the Soviet sector and then in the DDR, which meant contact would have been extremely difficult if not impossible.

In 1958 I began working for a medium-sized law firm, called Schmidt Legal, in the main legal district in Innenstadt, as a messenger and clerk. It was a good place to work. The senior partner was Alois Schmidt, a most decent man – quiet and thoughtful, very well thought of by clients and staff, and what you would call an intellectual. An intelligent and cultured man: a gentleman. For the first time in many, many years I felt almost settled, and even content.

But that all changed after two events in 1968, last year. The first was in February. Herr Schmidt was representing a Frankfurt company that was taking legal action against Deutsche Bahn, German railways. Some other companies were also involved in similar actions against them, so Herr Schmidt organised a conference of the law firms involved, in Frankfurt, and I was set to work arranging the files and the paperwork.

Because there were so many people involved, Herr Schmidt arranged for the meeting to be held in a nearby hotel, which also meant that they could have lunch there. I took all the paperwork to the hotel in time for the meeting, and then went back to the office. At around eleven o'clock, Herr Schmidt called me. There was a specific file he needed and only I would know where it was. I should add that part of my job was to take files to and collect them from a depository we used in Grosse Gallusstrasse. I knew my way round that place like the back of my hand.

I picked up the file and then went straight to the room where the meeting was taking place. As I entered the room, there he was: directly ahead of me. We must have seen each other simultaneously because I became aware that I was staring at him, and he was staring at me. He certainly recognised me and I definitely recognised him. I had no doubt that it was Horst – Horst Weber.

Herr Schmidt must have sensed something was up because I remember him asking me if I was all right. I then had to walk down the room to pass the file to Herr Schmidt, which meant I was even closer to Horst and we could see each other very clearly – we were less than half a metre apart. By now his face was quite flushed, in the way it is when people are embarrassed or angry. I knew that it was more than twenty years since we had last seen each other, but to me he had changed very little. Maybe his face was a bit fuller, but the piercing, dark eyes were the same, the way he held his head was the same. He still had a good head of hair and it was the same as I remembered, fair and almost curly. Everything about him was the same. You must remember, Horst was no passing acquaintance. For nine months in 1944 we had been closer than brothers. We shared a room, we spent all day in each other's company. I have already told you how much I admired Horst, how much I looked up to him. Since the day he disappeared in Essen, I do not think a day had passed when I did not think of him. I had often wondered what had happened to him, whether he'd been killed in the air raid or had escaped and, if escaped, where to?

On the table in front of him was a card with his name on it: Georg Stern. By the time I had passed the file to Herr Schmidt and had taken some papers from him in return, I saw that Horst... or Stern... had opened his attaché case on the table in front of him and had his head bowed in it, as if he was looking for something.

I left the room as quickly as possible and returned to the office. I was in a terrible state – it was only a matter of time, maybe only a couple of hours, before they came for me, arrested me and I would be charged with being a war criminal. They were still arresting Nazi war criminals and putting them on trial, although it has to be said, not with much enthusiasm. The trial would be on television. In fact, I didn't go straight back to the office, but I went to a bar first, something I never, ever did during working hours. To be honest, I hardly ever drank: maybe a beer once or twice a week and only then in my apartment. I realised that if I got drunk I could end up saying things that could get me into trouble. But on this day, I had to have a beer just to calm my nerves.

When I got back to the office I expected to see the police waiting outside for me, but it was all quiet. No one said anything when I entered. There were no phone calls and even though I kept looking out of the front and rear windows of the office, there was no sign of the police. I checked up on the attendance list for the meeting and saw that Georg Stern was one of two lawyers from a Berlin law firm called Rostt Legal.

Herr Schmidt returned to the office later that afternoon, at around four o'clock. I had to go into his office to sort out the files with him and he acted perfectly normally towards me. As I was leaving, I asked him how the meeting had gone and it he said it had been good, although one of the Berlin lawyers had unexpectedly left at lunchtime. Something had cropped up in Berlin that he needed to attend to urgently, apparently.

To me, it was obvious Horst had gone to the police. I was more upset than frightened – did our friendship mean nothing to him? They would come for me that night. I was actually very calm when I returned to my flat. I was almost relieved that the years of waiting were about to come to an end.

I didn't sleep that night, but there were no knocks at the door and no unusual activity in the street. Nothing was out of the ordinary when I got to the office the next morning, but an hour later I was sitting in my little cubby-hole behind the reception desk when I overheard Anke answering a call. At first she said something like, 'No, not here.' I'm not sure what it was exactly she said as I was not really concentrating. But then her voice rose as she became quite insistent. I will never forget what she said next: 'Look sir, I keep telling you. We have no Otto Schröder working here!'

I promise you that if I had not been sitting down at this point I would have fainted. What doubt could I have now that it was Horst I had seen the previous day? I tried to sound normal as I asked Anke about the call. An out of town call, she said, a middle-aged man, insisting we had an Otto Schröder working here.

But still no one came for me. Over the weekend, I began to think about matters in a more rational way. Georg Stern could certainly report me to the authorities as a war criminal, and I would be arrested. But by reporting me, he would be incriminating himself. He was as guilty as I was: I had seen him strangle the Jewish woman at the police station in Dortmund. Of course, we all did terrible things that day. I had no idea about what had happened to him after Essen, but it was clear that he had a new identity.

I came to realise that most likely he would do nothing. In fact, maybe he was just as scared I would report him. It became clear that nothing was going to happen. But I remained curious. I checked Georg Stern's details in a directory of law firms throughout the Federal Republic. He was born in Berlin on 15th

March 1927, it said, and became a partner at Rostt Legal in 1956. But what I read next really shocked me. Georg Stern had been educated for a time at a Jewish school in Berlin and had survived the war, though it did not say how. He was now prominent in a number of Jewish charities in Berlin.

I was utterly confused. It was evident that Georg Stern was Horst's true identity: indeed, it appeared he had always been Georg Stern, but... a Jewish boy in the SS? None of this made sense. I'm sure I would have realised if Horst was Jewish. Don't forget, we were trained to spot them, weren't we? And I know this is a bit delicate, but remember that we shared a room for many months. I saw Horst naked many times and I can assure you that he was not circumcised. I toyed with the idea of going to Berlin to find Georg Stern. I wanted to know the truth and, perhaps more than anything else, I wanted to spend some time with the last friend I had.

Before I could do this, the second event occurred. I've told you about how my boss, Alois Schmidt, was a decent man with a reputation for integrity and discretion. For that reason he sometimes handled matters for clients in very sensitive positions from outside Frankfurt. He took on a number of divorce cases, in particular, where for reasons of sensitivity the client didn't want to be represented by a lawyer based near to where they lived.

In the April of last year – so two months after my encounter with Horst Weber, or Georg Stern, as he now apparently was – Herr Schmidt asked me to stay after the office closed because he had a new client from 'out of town,' as he put it. Herr Schmidt told me I should let him know when the client arrived, and I shouldn't ask the client his name.

The client arrived around seven thirty and hurried in and was very brusque: he wanted to be taken to Herr Schmidt as soon as possible. He hardly looked at me, and I would be lying if I said I recognised him immediately, but there was certainly something familiar about him. It was hard to make out his features. Despite the warm spring weather he was wearing a large overcoat with the collar turned up and a hat which covered his face, as well as spectacles. But something about him made me uneasy. Perhaps it was his bearing and his demeanour, I don't know. But I felt uncomfortable.

Herr Schmidt rang me and I said I did not need to stay, but perhaps I could bring up some coffee before I left? When I entered his office, the client was sitting at the table next to Herr Schmidt. He had removed his coat and hat and his spectacles were perched on the top of his head. I immediately had no doubt whatsoever that this was none other than Wilhelm Richter, my fellow SS recruit and the worst one of us all. He had the same build, the same thick, dark hair and most definitely the familiar jet-black eyes. But unlike Horst – Georg Stern – Richter did not look up. He was engrossed in a document which meant I had a good opportunity to observe him from different angles. It was definitely Richter.

The following day I was in the main filing room, and I tried to find a file for Richter. Unsurprisingly there was nothing there under that name, but nor could I find any file for a client last night. I had to assume Herr Schmidt kept the file in his own safe, which he did for special clients. Over the next few months I did try to locate the file. I needed to know Richter's new identity – but I failed. The case must have been current because I could not trace the file at the depository in Grosse Gallusstrasse. In my experience, it would not be moved there until the case was over, at which point it would be put in the archive section.

Around this time I began to feel ill. I am now of the view that the shock of my past seeming to catch up with me could have triggered my illness. So I did nothing. But then, as my condition worsened and I realised that my fate is inevitable, I decided Wilhelm Richter must be exposed. The safest way I felt I could bring this about was to get my story to the British: they should be able to find out Richter's new identity.

So here it is. And you have Georg Stern as a witness, should you need corroboration. And maybe, if you can, think of me once in a while.

Chapter 12

England, April 1976

Edgar took the best part of an hour and a half to read through Bernhard Krause's testimony, pausing every so often to make a note. He locked the document in his safe and sat silently through lunch. His wife recognised a familiar look about him: the one he had when he'd spotted his prey in the distance and was focussing solely on it. When she caught his eye he smiled pleasantly, but she knew he'd retreated once more into the world he was most comfortable in and had always regretted leaving – in as much as he'd ever really left.

After lunch he went through Porter's boxes once more and, having established that there was nothing else of any interest, carried them all out to the secluded patch at the back of the garden which he used for bonfires. For a while he stood close to the fire, gazing into it as tiny flecks of greyed paper and bits of ash swirled around him. Once he was satisfied everything was well ablaze, he returned to his study and retrieved the document from the safe. He read the testimony through once more and then moved from his club chair to the desk, placing two large sheets of blank paper on it. The desk was by the window overlooking the garden, at the end of which wisps of smoke from the bonfire were still visible.

He thought about what Viktor had told him in the flat in East Berlin, and started to make notes on one of the sheets.

Former Nazi intelligence officer (Schäfer)… works at the Soviet Embassy in East Berlin… runs an agent in West

Germany, codename 'Goalkeeper'... 'very high-grade intelligence'... probably works for the BfV (proof???)... (possible) real name of 'Goalkeeper': Wilhelm Richter (born Dresden 1926)??... war crimes allegations Jan '45... Gdansk June '46, Sturmbannführer Krüger... September '49, Carsten Möller (Soviet PoW camp)...

And then he flicked through the notes he had made on Krause's story, and re-read the last few pages of the testimony. He wrote on the other sheet of paper.

Bernhard Krause... young SS recruits, secret mission... Richter possibly (probably?) alive April '68, seen by Krause at his office. NOT from Frankfurt 'out of town'... cannot find out his new identity... WHAT IS REAL NAME/IDENTITY? At BfV??

Any connection between Reinhard Schäfer (KGB) and Erich Schäfer (Nazi)??...

Goalkeeper's real identity - ???

Georg Stern (Horst Weber) – lawyer, West Berlin... Others: Axel Werner (dead) Konrad Hartmann, Christian Schäfer, Arnold Bauer, Lothar Meier, Mathias Hahn and Carsten Möller (dead, see above).

Edgar could quite see how in 1969 both he and Porter had dismissed the Krause testimony as being fanciful and, even if it was to be believed, of precious little consequence. But reading it now was utterly frustrating: there was no reason to doubt Krause when he said he had encountered Richter in 1968, but there was no clue as to his identity or a link to the German security service. For Viktor's theory to stand up, they needed a name. Krause's testimony was tantalising but got them little further.

Edgar gathered up the folder containing Krause's testimony, along with his notes, and returned them to the safe. He thought of Viktor's parting words when he'd asked if Viktor wanted him to return to East Berlin.

'No! It would be too risky to come here a second time. These days it is easier for me to travel, and as long as it is to another Warsaw Pact country then I won't arouse suspicion. I'll tell you what, here's where we'll meet…'

–

'Edgar… its Ronnie – Ronnie Castle!'

It was a week after Edgar had returned from Cambridge, and just days away from his visit to Viktor. The telephone had rung as he'd walked through the front door after his morning walk with the dog. Ronnie Castle, a dreadful bore who'd joined the Service a few months before Edgar had left it. In candid conversations with those he could trust, Edgar would confide that the recruitment of people like Castle was one of the reasons he'd left. No subtlety, no manners, no brains; but he was an alumnus of the same Oxford college as the Director.

'I just happened to be in your area, Edgar, and wondered if I could pop in?'

'Well fancy that, eh Ronnie?' Edgar did not fancy that at all. It was what he meant by Castle's lack of subtlety: it was quite obvious that Castle had not 'just happened to be' in his area. Likewise the phone ringing as soon as he walked through the door was a giveaway. They'd have been watching him. Knowing the way these things happen, Edgar realised he must have been watched from at least the day before, otherwise Castle would not have travelled down to Dorset. He ought to have spotted them, and that was not good. He must be losing his touch.

'Mind if I pop round? Could be with you in five minutes.'

No subtlety.

When Ronnie Castle arrived he was not alone. His companion was an awkward-looking type, perhaps in his early thirties, who seemed to blink a lot and was wearing a gold watch and carrying an attaché case that appeared to be made from expensive leather. Castle introduced him as 'Lassiter'. Edgar recalled what Porter had told him about Lassiter seven years previously, shortly before his retirement.

'Typical of the new breed Edgar, you'd absolutely detest him. Disagreeable type. Talent spotted at Balliol before he'd even finished his second year… very high opinion of himself… shared by some of the fools he reports to… wears aftershave and ties with flowers on them and, would you believe it, brown shoes with a dark suit!'

Today Lassiter was wearing a brown suit with black shoes, which in Edgar's opinion was even worse, and a shirt with thick blue stripes and a white collar which was at least one size too tight, contributing to the younger man's altogether uncomfortable appearance. Even before they began talking Lassiter had removed a large notebook from the attaché case. Edgar glared at it and even Castle spotted the faux pas. 'Won't be necessary,' he whispered to Lassiter.

Edgar had taken them to the lounge at the back of the house, overlooking the garden and caught in the shade of its trees. Even in April, without any heating the room was somewhat chilly. Edgar intended it to remain so.

'I'll be frank with you, Edgar,' said Castle, in the manner of a man who was unfamiliar with being frank with anyone, 'we need to ask you some questions.'

'Is there a problem, Ronnie?'

'Good heavens no, Edgar! Nothing of the sort, purely routine – you know the score. Imagine you've done it yourself countless times. I'll tell you what it is…' Castle leaned forward to pick up his cup of tea from the low table that lay between him and Edgar. Lassiter did likewise. 'Porter… poor old Porter, eh?'

'What about him?'

'Not sure if you know, but Sheridan spends most weekends in Cambridge. His wife's something terribly important in some kind of physics there. He makes a point of popping in to see Porter once a month or so, went to see him last weekend. I say, Edgar, is it me or is it a bit chilly in here?'

'Must be you, Ronnie, but I suppose I could put the fire on if you're really cold.'

Castle held up his hand in a reluctant don't bother gesture and pulled his jacket tight around him. 'Sheridan tells me Porter told him you had been up to see him a few days previously. Apparently it was your first visit for quite a while. You probably noticed the poor chap is not what he was…'

'A bit doddery, Ronnie, certainly. Happens to us all I suppose…'

'Early stages of dementia in Porter's case, I'm told. He is not the man he was, but some of the time he is surprisingly clear. He told Sheridan you rather pushed him on a certain subject.'

'Really?' Edgar leaned forward, intrigued as to what this certain subject could possibly be. 'And what was that?'

'Apparently you asked him about a case from seven years ago.' Lassiter spoke in an assured drawl as he slouched on the settee next to Castle. Edgar noticed his socks were pale yellow with what appeared to be a flower motif on them. Lassiter paused, waiting for Edgar to assist him with an answer. Edgar remained silent, allowing a hint of a frown to form. 'Does the name Krause help?'

'Good heavens, that? Really now… it was something Porter worked on just before he retired. It was all to do with the Second World War and Nazis, my bag really. He asked me for my opinion at the time, that's all. All above board in case you're worried, Lassiter. I had full clearance then, still do now, not that I'm consulted much these days. I mentioned it to Porter as I thought it might be something he'd remember. It was a passing comment, no more than that – an attempt to fill the silence, to be honest. I just asked him if anything ever came of it. It was a bit of a mystery at the time.'

'What did you know about the case?'

'Porter asked me about it back in '69, I think it was. Ran some names past me, that kind of thing. Unfortunately I wasn't able to help.'

'Ever see the file?'

'Of course not.'

'Do you know if Porter had a copy of the file?'

'Why would he have that? Indeed, how…?'

'According to Sheridan,' said Castle, in a less aggressive tone, 'you took some boxes of papers away with you.'

'For Christ's sake Ronnie, you're confusing matters. I chatted with Porter about all manner of things: his garden, my garden, cricket, dear old Harold Wilson, the Common Market and this bloody case, which accounted for perhaps five minutes of our conversation – if that. Then Marjorie came in and had a moan about all the boxes stored in an outhouse and had a bit of a go at Porter about it, so I said I'd take them away.'

'And what did you do with them?'

'Really, Lassiter, you're beginning to make this sound as if it's an interrogation. I brought the boxes here and looked through them, checking there was nothing important, which of course there wasn't. Porter is not the type to have done anything naughty, is he? The boxes were full of rubbish, all kinds of inconsequential stuff he'd kept over the years. None of it classified before you ask, not even Level 5.'

'And what happened to everything?'

'I burnt it, Lassiter: on a bonfire. I can show you the ashes if you care, though most of them are now helping my roses. I'm hardly going to keep the boxes here for my own wife to complain about, am I?'

Lassiter shifted uncomfortably and looked at Castle, as if seeking help. Castle remained silent. 'So you've… not… seen the – erm… file?'

'Which file, Lassiter?'

'The Krause file?'

'No. Never did, either in '69 or the other week. In any case, the file would be in the registry, wouldn't it?'

'For some reason it's not,' said Castle. 'Which is why we were wondering if Porter may have taken a copy…'

'You've asked that already. Of course he didn't. In any case, that would have been against the rules,' said Edgar.

'The rules were being bent then, especially by some of the old timers. People started to take home copies of stuff with a lower security classification. That's all stopped now, of course,' said Castle.

'Why are you so interested in this case anyway?' Edgar already sensed victory.

'It's not so much that we are interested – more we thought you were.'

'Well I'm not, and I'm sorry I can't help.' Edgar stood up. His visitors were approaching the end of their welcome.

'Just one other thing,' said Lassiter, half standing, half sitting. 'Have you been abroad recently?'

'Depends what you mean by recently. We were in Madeira in January, that's the last time we were abroad.'

'You sure?'

'Of course I'm bloody sure, Lassiter. Do you want me to show you my passport?' Edgar turned to the senior man. 'Look what is this, Castle, have you brought him along as part of a training course?'

Chapter 13

'Next week!'

'Yes, dear, next week.'

'Vienna, you say?'

'Yes dear, I told you… for our anniversary.' Edgar shuffled awkwardly in his chair as his wife stared at him in disbelief.

'Other than our first, I cannot recall you remembering one wedding anniversary, certainly not before the event. And yet now, you suddenly… and in any case, our anniversary isn't for another month!'

'I know but I thought it would be a nice surprise. We'll be staying at the Sacher and I've booked tickets for the opera.'

'To see what?'

'Something by Mozart… *Cosi* something or other. I thought you liked opera?'

'I adore it, but just what precisely is this all about?'

Edgar felt like a child who'd been caught lying. He leaned across the dining table and placed his hand on his wife's. He was rarely disconcerted, other than on occasions such as this. 'You complain we never go anywhere or do anything, yet now I have booked something and you seem unhappy.'

His wife said nothing but studied him carefully. Edgar could tell she was suspicious. 'Of course I'm not unhappy, but… is this connected in any way with work?'

'I'm retired, dear.'

'Come on now,' she said, pulling her hand away from his. 'It's to do with the Service, isn't it? I insist you tell me the truth, otherwise I shall simply refuse to go.'

Edgar placed his cutlery across the plate and folded his hands, almost in prayer. He trusted his wife, though he rarely confided in her. In the forty or so years since he had first worked for the Service he had only told her something about his missions on three or four occasions, and even then in only the briefest of detail. So now he told her his plans. She listened carefully. He was surprised how calmly she took it.

–

Edgar not only managed to remain awake throughout the opera but had even made a perfectly plausible effort at appearing to enjoy it. He'd then allowed a whole day to be devoted to more culture: the Hofburg Palace in the morning and the Kunsthistorisches Museum in the afternoon. On their first day in Vienna they had gone to the office of a company that organised day trips, and left their passports with them. They returned the following morning, just before their visit to the Hofburg. All was in order. Their visas had been issued and they paid for their tickets. The following day, their third in Vienna, they arrived at Wien Westbahnhof at half seven in the morning. The Vienna–Budapest Express left on time, half an hour later. At nine thirty it cleared the Hungarian border, at Hegyeshalom, and after a brief stop at Gyor they arrived at Budapest Keleti at the scheduled time of twelve twenty. As they pulled in to the station, Edgar recalled what Viktor had told him when they met in March in Berlin.

'Hungary is the most relaxed of our Warsaw Pact countries at the moment – maybe they never quite managed to shake off the effect of '56, maybe it's because their economy is surprisingly strong, I don't know… but it's easier for Westerners to get in and out of than anywhere else in Eastern Europe. One week before you go, send a postcard to this address in Paris. Give birthday greetings to Otard for the date you will be in Budapest. I'll make sure I'm there on that date.'

At Keleti station, on the Pest side of the city, they were met by a tourist guide and shepherded onto a coach which drove around for an hour, pausing outside various sights while their guide spoke in a quick monotone – German first, then English, followed by a few words in French. She extolled the progress Hungary had made since the defeat of fascism, and made one or two obligatory references to the fraternal aid and friendship of the Soviet Union, but by and large she stuck to the safe territory of the city's buildings and its architecture, of which there was plenty. Ottoman this, Byzantine that... Baroque... Classical... Art Nouveau and, of course, Bauhaus. They were not allowed to take photographs, other than at designated spots where they were permitted to leave the coach for a few heavily-supervised minutes.

At half past one the coach pulled up in Dohány Street outside an enormous synagogue – the largest in Europe, the guide told them in her monotone. They were permitted to go in briefly to take some photographs before being ushered out and informed that they were now going to lunch. They should not leave the restaurant, they were told. The coach would leave at two thirty promptly for their tour of Buda, on the other side of the Danube.

'*The restaurant they use is a five minute walk from the Dohány synagogue, on Károly. It's very large, has two floors and a large internal courtyard, which is typical of Pest – not unlike Paris. Once you're inside the restaurant they won't worry about you because you won't be able to leave. Ask for a table on the first floor. The manager on duty there is called Bartos – he'll come and introduce himself to you. He'll ask you where you're from. Tell him you're from England, and then he will ask you which football team you support...*'

'Tottenham Hotspur,' replied Edgar, as instructed by Viktor.

'Ah! The English team I love is Manchester United,' said Bartos, pulling a chair up so he could talk more intimately with his new friends.

'I've been to Old Trafford,' replied Edgar, showing an interest in football his wife was unaware of. 'Tell me Bartos, which Hungarian team do you support?'

'Honvéd,' answered Bartos, looking very slightly offended that Edgar even needed to ask the question. 'The team of Puskás: you've heard of Puskás?'

They had established that the other was who each expected him to be. Lunch was served, but Edgar waited until a quarter to two, forty-five minutes before they had to leave the restaurant. He called Bartos over. Would he be so kind as to show him to the bathroom?

The Hungarian led Edgar to the back of the restaurant and through a door, which opened onto a small landing. He unlocked another door and bolted it as soon as they had entered. They went three floors up a winding staircase and there, in a room opening from a small landing, was Viktor, sitting behind a table with a plate of steaming goulash.

His mouth was full as he gestured with his fork for Edgar to sit opposite him. Drops of gravy fell onto the table. Through his food he muttered something to Bartos in Russian.

'He'll come back in half an hour, Edgar. That will have to be enough time. Do you like Budapest?' He heaped another large forkful of goulash into his mouth as he spoke. Edgar nodded.

'I like it too. It is, in my opinion, the most handsome city in all of Europe,' said Viktor, wiping bits of goulash from his mouth with an enormous serviette. 'Not the prettiest, like Paris or Prague. But it's a dramatic city, eh? The Danube, the hills, the buildings…'

Viktor stopped speaking as he concentrated on emptying his plate. When he had, he wiped his mouth. 'So tell me, Edgar, have you got me a name for Herr Richter?' He was still chewing as he spoke, flecks of meat spraying towards the Englishman.

'In 1969,' said Edgar, 'I was asked to read a document relating to allegations about war crimes committed at the end of the Second World War. At the time I attached little significance to it and it was soon forgotten. However, after we met in Berlin I recalled this report and managed to have a look at it once more. In light of what you told me in Berlin I now realise the person who wrote the document – it's his testimony – was another of the young Nazis recruited with Wilhelm Richter. He says he witnessed Richter carry out war crimes, and admits he did too. It backs up what you were told by Carsten Möller and the SS prisoner in Gdansk. At the end of the war the person who wrote this testimony managed to escape and change his identity.'

Edgar paused, expecting some reaction from the Russian. Viktor looked impassive and said nothing, but waved his fork: carry on.

'He is convinced he saw Richter in 1968.' Edgar paused to allow Viktor to take in what he had just revealed. 'Apparently Richter didn't recognise him.'

Viktor at last showed some interest and held up his fork to indicate that Edgar should pause. He removed a brown leather notebook from his pocket, and sharpened a pencil with a knife.

'What name was Richter using?'

'He never got that, Viktor—'

The Russian struck the table hard with his knife. 'Come on, Edgar. You tell me you have something, we go to all this effort – for you to tell me… what? That a man you won't name thinks he saw Richter somewhere – you don't say where – in 1968, but didn't find out his name?'

'Let me finish, Viktor, be patient. This man worked at a lawyer's office in Frankfurt. He was asked to stay late one night – this would be April 1968 – to let in a new client for his boss. Apparently he handled many sensitive matrimonial cases: clients from out of town liked to consult him, usually because they were in sensitive positions. This is how he saw Richter, he was one of those clients.'

'This was in 1968, you say?' Viktor wiped the plate with a forefinger and licked the gravy off it.

'Yes, the April. And there's something else I picked up from this report…'

'Go on,' said Viktor, glancing at his watch. 'You'd better get a move on.'

'The German intelligence officer at your embassy in East Berlin, the one running Goalkeeper…'

'You mean Reinhard Schäfer?'

Edgar nodded. 'Describe him… his physical appearance.'

The Russian shrugged as if he couldn't quite see the point of the question. 'I don't know… short, always wears suits too large for him, and his glasses are very thick, so much so that it's hard to make out his eyes. Does that help?'

'You said he was a police officer in Berlin during the war?'

'Yes, criminal police – a detective with the Kripo apparently. It seems that Schäfer was a Communist in the early thirties: he held a KPD card until '31 or '32. Tell me why you're asking, Edgar – and you need to get a move on, you'll be leaving soon.'

'My source describes one of the men behind the recruitment of himself, Richter and the others. His description matches that of Schäfer.'

Viktor snorted, unimpressed. 'You mean short?'

'If it was just a physical description, Viktor, I'd be sceptical too. But his name then was Erich Schäfer.'

'Schäfer is a common name.'

'I know, but surely this is more than a coincidence?'

'You say this man is in Frankfurt?'

'Was – he died soon after writing his testimony.'

Viktor looked concerned. 'There must be a way of finding out Richter's identity. You say this was in April 1968… do you have the name of the law firm?'

Edgar nodded.

'Well, that's something I suppose. I presume you have brought a copy of the document with you?'

Edgar took an envelope out of his jacket packet and hesitated for a moment before passing it to the Russian, as if he was having second thoughts. 'I thought long and hard about giving this to you, Viktor. I don't have to tell you what a risk I'm taking, do I?'

'And you think I'm taking no risks? Remember, we're in this together, Edgar.'

'Just promise me you'll be careful when you act on what you read and don't do anything that would provide a link to me. If we can find out Richter's name now and if he has any connection with the BfV or any of the security services of the Federal Republic, we'll pass it on – usual channels, they'll soon sort him out. Meanwhile, you let your people know that rather than being a secret Communist during the war, Reinhard Schäfer could actually be Erich Schäfer and involved in some crazy Nazi plot. I'm sure they'll be able to verify it. We just need to get our timing right, make sure they're both investigated at the same time and—'

'No, Edgar, no!' Viktor had banged his fork hard on the table. 'I told you in Berlin, trust no one. I've survived over the years by trusting my side no more than I trust the other side. And as I tried to suggest to you in Berlin, you have very good reason not to trust your own side.'

'What do you mean?'

'I believe Schäfer has a mole in MI6.'

'Who?'

'I don't know. Maybe I should have told you before, but I wanted you to concentrate on Richter. Clearly one of the reasons Schäfer is so well regarded at Unter den Linden is that he has such a good network of agents. I know he has at least one in MI6, possibly more. I have no more details, just tiny clues I have picked up. The agent in MI6 is called "Winger". Irma thinks he has another person who is connected to "Winger" but is not inside any of your agencies. He is called "Defender". It would seem they're part of the same network, controlled by Schäfer. Tell me Edgar, is anyone in Six aware of your enquiries? You need to tell me. Our lives could depend on this. And there's one other thing...'

Viktor hesitated, unsure whether to tell the Englishman one more thing after all. 'You also need to be careful if you go anywhere near Bonn, which you may well have to. In the last couple of years your embassy there has been the source of very high-grade intelligence.'

'How highgrade?'

'High enough for the source to quite possibly be MI6. I can't be sure, but it is someone there who has links to Goalkeeper. I shouldn't really be telling you this because it's not connected directly with Schäfer, the source is handled out of our Paris station and we get intel through them. But I need you to be very careful, that's why I'm telling you.'

Edgar said nothing. Viktor could tell he was worried, and was unsure what to do.

'Edgar, my friend… we are in the same boat. This may feel like treason, telling the enemy something. I feel the same too, but we're not really enemies, are we? For me, I realise we are dealing with Nazis, and that justifies anything. Over the years I have experienced so many ideologies. You and the Americans and the rest of them in Western Europe – you believe in democracy and you'll fight for it. In the Soviet Union and elsewhere… well, many of the people I have worked with have been committed Communists. They believe in Marxism-Leninism and will fight for it. But I have never, ever encountered such blind fanaticism as I did with the Nazis. You have experienced it too. This is what we're up against.'

'Two men came to see me,' said Edgar after a while. 'From MI6, a few weeks ago. They knew I had been to see my source and knew I had been asking about the report from 1969, the one written by the man who knew Richter. They wanted to know who, why, what, when… the usual. They had nothing other than the rather incoherent recollections of my source.'

'Did you know these men?'

'One of them I did: he joined the service shortly before I left it. The other I know of: looks after the Germany desk, not sure which one. They came away empty-handed and I doubt they suspect me.'

'Before you go, write down the names of the two men you've just told me about.' Viktor pushed his notebook towards Edgar.

'You haven't been followed in Vienna, if that's any consolation,' said Viktor. 'Nor here, as far as we can tell.'

'What should we do now?'

'Give me some time, a couple of weeks possibly. I need to see if I can find out more about Schäfer's agents. We need to know who "Winger" and "Defender" are.'

'And Richter?'

'I have a plan… write down the name of the law firm in Frankfurt, which will help.' Edgar was already through the doorway when Viktor called him back.

'There is something you can do in the meantime actually, Edgar. If these people are asking questions of you, there's a chance there may be something else going on. Say some of these SS recruits really did make it to England? Unlikely, I know, but I'm sure you have some contacts you could ask questions of. You never know.'

—

The coach left the restaurant on Károly at two thirty. Edgar had reappeared at his table five minutes before that, not saying a word to his wife and acting for the entire world as if he'd been detained in the bathroom for a minute or two longer than he'd planned.

The coach crossed the Danube on the Chain Bridge and drove around the hills of Buda for a couple of hours before depositing its passengers at Keleti station at four thirty. Only once they'd crossed the border did Edgar feel it was safe to acknowledge the situation with his wife.

'That was a very successful day. Thank you for your help.'

His wife smiled and told him it was no problem. In fact, she said, she had rather enjoyed it. It's been quite exciting! But then the look in his eyes told her to be quiet. She had said enough.

Chapter 14

The two men met in the Princess Louise on High Holborn, just south of Bloomsbury where the West End of London gets close to City. It had been raining heavily all day: puddles of water rising to the kerb, the pavements slippery. Most of the customers had come in drenched, resulting in an unpleasant fug about the place.

Lassiter and his elderly companion were sitting at the back of the pub in a carefully chosen alcove which allowed some privacy along with a view of the entrance. Just in case anyone tried to be sociable, they'd spread briefcases and coats on the seats either side of them. The man sitting next to Lassiter was perhaps in his mid-seventies, his almost unhealthily pale face clean shaven, and his watery eyes firmly fixed on the younger man next to him. Had anyone looked closely at them they would have observed that both men seemed particularly distracted and bothered. Had they sat close enough they may have noticed Lassiter's hands trembling as he lifted the pint glass towards his mouth, and they'd have seen and possibly even smelt the sweat gathering on the older man's bald head, settling on the few strands of hair stretched across it. Both men spoke so quietly that each had to lean close to hear what the other was saying.

'You sounded terrified on the telephone, Lassiter. This had better be important, you know I worry about the possibility of people listening in… and bringing me to London – meeting up like this, you know it's for real emergencies only.'

'This is a real emergency,' said Lassiter as he allowed himself a sip of his drink, a thin foam of beer forming a brief moustache.

'You know of Chris Porter, don't you? Big cheese in Six during the war, retired a few years ago… Edgar's boss.'

The older man nodded and leaned closer to Lassiter.

'Porter lives in Cambridge now, seems his mind is not what it was. Paul Sheridan – used to be station chief in Nairobi and now oversees the whole of Africa – is up in Cambridge most weekends, his wife works there, and once a month or so Sheridan pops in to see Porter. Last time he did so Porter was in a bit of a flap: seems Edgar had turned up unannounced a week or so before and was pushing him about the Krause case. Edgar took some papers of Porter's away.'

The older man leaned even closer and gripped Lassiter's forearm. 'You were meant to have dealt with this business seven years ago: you promised me!'

'I did deal with it, that's the thing. I told you so at the time, didn't I? Porter read the report and passed it to me marked "not for action." When I actually got round to reading the bloody report a day or so later I was worried sick, as you can imagine, not least in case Porter had a copy of the damn thing. But it seemed he'd forgotten about it. We agreed, did we not, it had been a lucky escape…'

'And the report, remind me?'

'As far as the Service is concerned, it doesn't exist. There's certainly nothing in registry. I managed to remove all trace of it.'

'And now Edgar…? How the hell did Edgar even know about it?'

Lassiter exhaled deeply and lifted his beer glass to his lips, spilling some onto the table. 'I've no idea. However, Sheridan mentioned it to Castle and Castle told me because the report had come from Bonn. I managed to persuade Castle that I couldn't recall the case but we nevertheless ought to find out what Edgar knew in case it had implications for current operations. I assured him I'd sort it all out.'

'And?'

'I'm afraid Castle rather overreacted. He's never much liked Edgar. They overlapped a bit at the start of Castle's career and

Castle always resented Edgar having never really gone away. He thought if we confronted Edgar then he could get Edgar into some kind of trouble, and be shot of him once and for all. I went along with it because I thought… well, you know, I thought it would be a way of finding out what on earth Edgar knows and is up to. It wouldn't surprise me in the slightest if Porter had consulted Edgar about the Krause file all those years ago. But even if so, why on earth would he be interested in it now, after all these years? Castle decided that he and I would just turn up at Edgar's place in Dorset, which we did.'

'How did Edgar react?'

'Like he had no idea what we were on about. Rather made Castle look like a fool – and me too by the same token. Admitted Krause had briefly come up in conversation with Porter but said it was more in passing than anything else – more for the sake of having something to talk about. He admitted he'd removed some boxes of papers but said it was nothing to do with Krause, just a favour to Porter, all inconsequential stuff… told us he'd burnt it on a bonfire in his garden.'

'And did you believe him?'

'Well, he offered to show us the ashes—'

'No, you fool. Do you believe him about why he asked Porter about the Krause report?'

'He was certainly very plausible. But then why would he have brought up Krause, of all things, when he met with Porter? He said Porter had mentioned Krause back in '68 or '69 – he couldn't remember – to see if the name rang a bell. He insisted he never saw any documents. Can't believe he'd have mentioned it after all these years just to help the conversation along, especially as he told us it was all so inconsequential at the time.'

The older man removed a folded handkerchief from somewhere deep inside his jacket and dabbed his head nervously, pausing every so often to inspect the handkerchief. 'After all these years, I really thought we had nothing to worry about… but it appears we may do. You'll have to tell him. He'll be fucking furious. If you'd done your job properly in 1969 and read the report before passing it on to Porter, then no one other than you would have seen that Krause file. And now... now it's come back to bite us. Why are you bothering me with this Lassiter? You're meant to be in charge, you should be dealing with this.'

'I wanted your advice.'

'Really? Didn't realise you trusted me that much. Does he know yet?'

'No. I was wondering if there was any way of avoiding telling him. You know... perhaps just waiting to see what happens.'

The older man shook his head. 'No. You'll have to tell him. You'd better get over there and tell him in person, hadn't you?'

–

They met a week later in a safe house on Stauffenberg Strasse just south of the Tiergarten in West Berlin: it was less risky for Reinhard Schäfer to travel to the west than Lassiter to the east.

'I have two hours, three at the most.' That was how Reinhard Schäfer greeted him. No greeting, no niceties, not even a smile. It was a Sunday, and the German had slipped through with a set of papers showing that he was visiting a sister in West Berlin: a five-hour visa. 'You'd better tell me what's up.'

'Are you keeping well?'

The German shrugged. He had sat down when he came in but now stood up again and started carefully folding his coat, as if he was about to try and pack it into a small suitcase. 'I was until I got your message. You are only meant to contact me directly in the most extreme case of emergency, otherwise it's through London. You don't look too well yourself.'

'You remember the document we got our hands on in '69 about Otto Schröder?'

Schäfer nodded.

'He'd become Bernhard Krause and was living in Frankfurt, where he died. That report was—'

'Yes, yes – I remember… He thought he'd come across Richter in '68, you don't need to remind me.'

'Well, you'll remember then that nothing came of it at the time, I managed to make the report disappear.' Lassiter paused, unsure how to continue. When he did start talking again he looked at the floor and then at the ceiling – anywhere but at the man in front of him. 'The one problem we had in 1969, which I may or may not have mentioned to you at the time, was that I very foolishly allowed an experienced officer called Christopher Porter to read the report first.'

'You most certainly never mentioned that to me!'

'In which case it was an oversight, for which I apologise. My only excuse is I was overwhelmed with work. It's one of the consequences of working for two sides. It's like having two jobs.'

Schäfer had stood up and walked angrily over to the window, and then paced up and down the room. 'That is more than an oversight, Lassiter, it's negligence. But this was what… six, seven years ago? Why do you feel so urgently that you have to admit to it now?'

Lassiter coughed for longer than seemed necessary, and hesitated. 'At the time I obviously was unaware of what the report was about, which is why I asked Porter to read it first. Fortunately, Porter attached no importance to it and his recommendation was to forget it. It was only then that I read it: I sent a copy to you and removed all trace of the original from registry, and all has been well for the past seven years. However, to cut a rather long story short, it seems a former colleague of Porter's, called Edgar, turned up at Porter's house recently and asked him about the Krause case.'

Schäfer abruptly stopped pacing the room. 'When was this?'

'A few weeks ago. Porter is retired and lives in Cambridge. His memory appears to be going but he told another former colleague that Edgar had turned up and asked him about Krause, and had even taken a few boxes of papers away with him. Ronnie Castle told me about it and he decided that the two of us should go and see Edgar. Edgar was rather plausible, I have to say. Told us Krause's name had come up as a very short part of a longer conversation. He said he'd never seen any file and the papers he took away were just odds and ends which he removed as a favour, and burned in his garden.'

Schäfer stood up and paced the room for a while, deep in thought. 'This is not a good situation.' He had returned to his seat, moved it to directly opposite Lassiter, and was staring at him as he spoke. 'In fact, it is an intolerable situation. You have exposed us all. I was even named in that report!'

'It's is hardly my fault, Reinhard, if anyone is to—'

'Your job, Lassiter is — and always has been — to make sure none of this gets out, that no one compromises our plans or our safety. It's not much, but you can't even manage that. We must assume that this Edgar has the file and may contact the authorities. Remind me who's still alive?'

'You mean the ones I have responsibility for? Just the four of them. Konrad Hartmann lives in Kent, where he is called Martin Page. Lothar Meier is in Nottingham, his name is Christopher Vale. Christian Schäfer is in a place called Huddersfield, near Leeds. His name is Tom Hartley. Arnold Bauer lives in Chel- tenham, not terribly far from me as it happens: he goes by the name of Tony Norton. They all lead what you would describe as very ordinary lives.'

'Plus Captain Canterbury.'

'Of course.'

'You know what you need to do, don't you Lassiter?'

The Englishman nodded, a blank expression on his face. The German leaned closer and spoke in a menacing tone. 'If this Edgar is interested in what Krause said, then he will no doubt investigate. If he does that there is a good chance he'll get close to your four men. And if that happens, we're all in trouble, aren't we?'

Lassiter nodded slowly, a look of fear now slowly replacing the blank expression.

'So you have to ensure they're silenced before Edgar gets to any them. You do understand what I am saying, don't you?'

'And Canterbury?'

'Especially Canterbury.'

Chapter 15

It was all well and good Viktor imploring him to find these recruits, but Edgar knew it was a task which, on the face of it, would make finding a needle in a haystack appear straightforward. Even assuming any of the SS recruits had made it to Britain, tracking them down after more than thirty years seemed almost impossible.

But there was one thing which gave Edgar hope. In his testimony, Krause had mentioned how the recruits would have to use their original names until they escaped. The more Edgar thought about it, the more he realised perhaps there was something to go on after all.

–

'All I can say sir is that this is most irregular, and if it wasn't for the fact there are so few of us still around from the old days, I wouldn't be going along with this. As it is, I'm really not sure…'

Edgar was in a corridor below Century House, the headquarters of MI6. He knew that the basement extended like tentacles under the building, but he had never had cause to reach quite so far into them. He'd managed to persuade Walker – one of the old-school MI6 clerks – to help him on a Sunday, and not tell anyone about it.

'You see sir – I'm sure you recall – when MI9 wound up whenever it was, '45, '46, it more or less withered on the vine so to speak, didn't it? Do mind your head please sir, the ceiling dips a bit here. MI6 inherited its work, didn't we? Naturally, all British prisoners of war were safely accounted for by then. There were still a few Germans around, but not many. So there was no longer really a role for MI9 was there? That is why all their files came here. I was a junior clerk in registry at the time, sir, as you know. Oh dear, sir, I did warn you about the ceiling – the floor's a bit uneven here too, careful now. Now then, just let me unlock this door and then we're more or less there.'

The door Walker had unlocked was to a cage-like room, with serried ranks of shelves laden with files, enormous ledgers and boxes. The smell and the dust suggested no one had been in the area for months, if not longer.

'This room sir contains files and documents relating to Nazi prisoners of war held in this country. That is what you were after, wasn't it?'

Edgar nodded.

'The files for the Nazis who were held prisoner on the continent and elsewhere but not brought over here, they're in another room. You won't be wanting those, will you?'

'This will be fine, Walker. I'm most grateful. Explain how they're organised?'

'MI9 were quite meticulous sir. They're arranged by the year the prisoners were brought over to this country, and then alphabetically within those years if you see what I mean. There's a desk over there and a lamp on it that may even work. How about I leave you down here for a while and I go and get a cup of tea, eh?'

–

Just an hour later, Edgar was muttering prayers of gratitude to whichever idiot it was in German intelligence who thought they didn't need to change the German identities of the young SS recruits that were going to be captured by the Allies. Of course he could see some logic in their thinking: the recruits had enough to think about without having to worry about assuming and memorising another identity. There was always a danger that, under interrogation, a false identity could be picked apart, which in turn could cause their whole crazy plan to unravel. Even so, it broke so many rules of intelligence: using real names meant the recruits were traceable.

With Werner, Schröder and Möller all dead, Richter apparently living somewhere in West Germany and Weber in Berlin, Edgar knew he was looking for no more than five of the original ten recruits.

The large, leather-bound and slightly mouldy ledgers displayed the name, rank, and serial number of all German prisoners of war who had been brought to the United Kingdom in 1945. Further columns showed, in careful copperplate writing, the prisoners' regiments, where they had been captured, the camps they had been held in, and when they had been released. It took Edgar less than half an hour to discover that Arnold Bauer, Konrad Hartmann, Lothar Meier and Christian Schäfer had all been captured as members of the SS and brought to prison camps in the United Kingdom in 1945. There was no reference to a Mathias Hahn.

But what Edgar discovered sent a frisson of fear shooting through him. In the feeble light thrown up by the lamp on the desk he read three words in the final column alongside each of the names.

Escaped, not recaptured.

Edgar carefully copied out the details alongside each of the four names into his notebook. By the time Walker returned the desk was covered in ledgers, with a pile of files next to it on the floor. Edgar affected an exasperated air.

'Any luck, sir?'

'Afraid not, Walker. It was always going to be a long shot, but I didn't have enough decent information to begin with. Still, nothing ventured, nothing gained...'

–

'And this is all above board, Edgar? You absolutely promise me that?'

Edgar nodded. He was feeling uncomfortable. Detective Superintendent Paget had insisted they meet in a police pub in Victoria, not a venue Edgar would have chosen. He disliked their unfriendliness and their Masonic handshakes and he didn't trust the police in general, Special Branch less so and Detective Superintendent Paget in particular, but he needed an enormous favour and Paget was his only option.

'It's just that you've got me into trouble before, Edgar, doing favours for you.'

'This isn't a favour, as you put it, Martin.'

'So what is it then?'

Edgar leaned closer to Paget over the wobbly damp table between them. A trickle of spilt beer edged towards him and he caught it with his sleeve. He composed himself as he tried very hard not to come across as patronising. Maybe calling Paget 'Martin' hadn't been a good idea.

'Well, if anything it is me doing you a favour. Your responsibilities at the Branch include the far right, isn't that correct?'

Paget nodded, beginning to look interested. 'Amongst many other things, yes.'

'And that includes Nazis?'

Paget's eyes widened. Edgar was sure one or two men standing near them had turned round. 'Yes, not that I've come across any for many years, if you don't include the poor beggars who get sectioned because they think they're Adolf Hitler.'

'If there's anything in this, Martin then the case will be yours, and I can promise you it would be quite a feather in your cap. You can say it came from a contact: I won't want any credit.'

'Not that I believe you, Edgar, but carry on.'

'I'm going to give you an envelope: inside it are the names of four German prisoners of war who escaped from captivity in this country in 1945. None of them have been heard of since – as far as I can ascertain, they're the only German POWs who escaped in this country and were never recaptured. I'm certain none of them have used their German name since the day they escaped, but you never know… Somewhere on a file one of these names may exist. It's worth a try. I know your systems are very sophisticated these days.'

'I wouldn't hold out too much hope, Edgar.'

'Nor would I, but if there is anything it will open up a very big case, I can promise you. If you get anything, contact me the usual way.'

Edgar and Paget got up at the same time. They were outside and had already begun to part when Paget hurried after Edgar. 'You were going to give me an envelope, Edgar?'

'It's in your jacket pocket, Paget!'

–

Edgar had not held out a lot of hope, but Paget was nothing if not very thorough. If he couldn't find anything, then it wasn't there. Edgar was nevertheless shocked when, just a week later, the telephone rang at eight in the evening at his home in Dorset.

'No,' he answered, sounding characteristically annoyed, 'we most certainly are not a taxi company.' Soon after he took the dog for a walk, and dialled a Surrey number from a call box outside the pub. He let the phone ring three times, terminated the call, waited one minute and rang again.

'That was quick,' said Paget.

'Sounds like you may have been too?'

'I think you may want to meet up, as soon as possible.'

–

They met the following morning in St James's Park. Edgar watched from the bridge spanning the lake as Paget entered the park through the Mall, as instructed, walking round the north-east side of the lake and then along its southern edge as Edgar checked whether the policeman had been followed. Once Edgar was satisfied, he joined Paget as he walked along a path parallel with Birdcage Walk, heading in the direction of Buckingham Palace.

'You have something, Paget?'

They stopped at a bench. When they sat down Paget took a while to settle and light a cigarette, smoking his way through half of it before speaking. Edgar noticed that Paget had wedged a scruffy briefcase between his body and the armrest of the bench.

'Last month a man called Christopher Vale was killed in a road traffic accident in Nottingham. A few years ago – in 1970 to be precise – Mr Vale had given his solicitor a sealed letter with very strict instructions that it was to be kept, and only opened in the event of his death. There was a cover note to the effect that unless Mr Vale had died of natural causes the solicitor was to pass the sealed letter to the police. As his client did not die of natural causes, the solicitor did just that, as per his instructions. The letter contained allegations of a political nature, so it was passed on to the local Special Branch. As is standard procedure, they sent the original to us and retained a copy. I have the letter for you here, Edgar,' Paget tapped the briefcase next to him. 'I'm giving you the original, just in case any of your boffins want to check the typewriter or the paper. I've kept a copy. I'll no doubt get in trouble for that, but hey ho.'

Edgar waited patiently for Paget to continue.

'Go on, Paget, tell me what's in the letter.'

'The details were entered into our system which, as you acknowledged the other day, is now quite sophisticated. So when I started looking into the names you gave me, guess what flagged up?'

'You said: Christopher Vale?'

'Well, that's the thing, Edgar. I didn't know about a Christopher Vale, did I? Turns out, Christopher Vale claims his real name is Lothar Meier.'

Chapter 16

Lothar Meier's Letter

To Whom It May Concern
Nottingham, January 1970

*This letter is written in some haste because recently I have
had good cause to fear for my life. If the circumstances of
my death mean you are now reading this letter, I beg you
not to dismiss what I have to say as anything other than
the truth, as unlikely as it may seem.*

Edgar struggled to read those two sentences. They had been
scrawled, evidently in some haste, in pencil on a single sheet of
paper and he had to hold the page up to the light to see them.
When he turned the page he was relieved to see that the rest of
the document was typed.

*Although my name now is Christopher Vale, I was in
fact born Lothar Meier in November 1926 in Bremen in
northern Germany. My father was a clerk at a finance
company and my mother was a housewife. I had a brother,
Konrad, who was three years older than me. I do not intend
that this should become an autobiography so I will not talk
too much about my early childhood. I would say that it
was perhaps an average one: I was good at school but not
exceptional. My family were not political but my father did
join the Nazi Party a year or two before the war began. I
joined the Hitler Youth sometime in 1940, as most boys of*

*my age did. My mother died in 1942. I remember that she
had been unwell for a few months, but I was not aware she
was so seriously ill. Her death came as a terrible shock, but
this was wartime and death was much more of a feature of
everyday life. My brother had been in the army since 1940.
He did not come home when my mother died. I think the
last time I must have seen him was when he was home on
leave in 1941.*

*So it was just my father and me at home. I would say
that ours was a formal rather than close relationship. By
1943 most of my time out of school was spent with the
Hitler Youth. At the end of 1943 my father was conscripted
into the Wehrmacht and sent to fight in the east. At the
same time, I was recruited into the SS. After training at
some local camps, I was sent to a large SS training camp at
Klagenfurt in Austria, or at least what had been Austria.*

*I did well at the camp and was highly regarded and was
told I was officer material. On exercises I was very level
headed and showed good judgement. By the early spring of
1944 I thought I was about to be transferred to a front line
unit, but that was not to be the case.*

Edgar had kept the envelope that Paget handed to him in the park
unopened until he returned home to Dorset that evening. After
supper with his wife and a hurried walk with the dog, he retired
to his study and retrieved the envelope from the safe. The main
part of the document was neatly typed over fifteen pages, with
the text on one side of the page. Edgar settled into his club chair
and began to read.

The story was almost identical to and corroborated those of
Bernhard Krause and Carsten Möller. Meier explained how he
had always excelled at English at school, and was given intense
tuition in the language while at Klagenfurt, before being transferred to the house at Magdeburg. From Essen he had joined
the second Panzer Division of the SS, otherwise known as Das
Reich. He told of how his unit fought in the Battle of the Bulge,

a desperate and ultimately failed rearguard action by the Nazis. On New Year's Eve in 1944 they were trapped near Dinant in Belgium, trying to cross the River Meuse. The following day he and the *Sturmbannführer* who was looking after him surrendered to the Americans.

Meier went on to explain how he had been brought over to England, as all SS prisoners were. By late February he was moved to a prison camp in Cheshire, but he escaped and made his way to one of the safe houses they'd been told about. The one he went to was in Shepherd's Bush, in West London. Meier would have been eighteen at the time.

> *I was relieved to have found my destination though I was very aware that my journey had now reached its most dangerous point. I followed the protocol and walked past the house. As far as I could tell, all was in order: no red vase in the upstairs window to warn me not to approach the house.*
>
> *I used the large brass knocker, as instructed: two loud knocks, a pause of two seconds, and two more knocks. It was a good minute before I heard any sound inside the house, someone moving from a room at the back and then into the hallway, before undoing bolts at the top and bottom of the front door. Once the bolts were undone I heard a woman's voice from behind the still-closed door.*
>
> *'Who is it please?'*
>
> *'A friend of your niece – she said I would be able to stay the night if I needed to.'*
>
> *There was a pause before she replied, 'And which niece is that?'*
>
> *'Catherine,' I replied. Another pause before the door half-opened and I was ushered in.*
>
> *We stood together in the hallway, which was now dimly-lit from the kitchen at the back. She seemed elderly to me then, though I now realise that she would have been in her mid-fifties. She was thin, with metal-grey hair which*

reached down to her shoulders, and dressed in a thick brown cardigan that flowed over a black skirt. The overwhelming first impression I had of the house was the smell. It is hard to describe, but it was a mixture of gas, coal fire, fried food and body odour. As I would find out, hygiene was not a priority in the house.

I followed her into a dark room at the back, next to the kitchen and overlooking a small garden. A tall man was standing in the shadows at the back of the room next to the window and, as soon as I entered, he pulled down the blackout material and then drew the curtains. The woman gestured towards an armchair and I sat down. She turned on a small lamp, which threw some kind of a little light across the room, before silently going into the kitchen and returning with a cup of tea and some bread and jam, placing them on a small table next to where I was sitting. She sat on a sofa opposite me.

The man stood with his back to the window and addressed me in appalling German: it was an honour to meet me; they had been hoping and praying that one of us would turn up; I should not doubt their commitment to the Reich. His eyes were almost closed but as he spoke they slowly opened, so much so that by the time he had finished they were wide open, unblinking.

His wife cut him short. She called him Ken and reminded him somewhat sharply that German was not to be spoken. It was too dangerous. The woman clasped one of my hands with both of hers, her bony fingers holding me tight. There were tears in her eyes. Her name was Linda, she told me, their surname was Frost. This was such an honour, they had dreamed of meeting someone like me. I could have no idea of what life was like in this country: the Jews controlled everything and we would end up being part of the Soviet Empire. People like me gave them hope. They had no doubt that Germany would triumph. Did I not agree?

I was not sure how to respond. I was assuming now that this was not a trap. This was my safe house and these were my hosts but, even though I was a good member of the SS, I knew that the war was lost.

Although I was committed to my mission, deep down I must have been aware of the futility of it or, at the very least, that its chances of success were limited. Yet these people seemed to be so... strange. I was in a dimly-lit and foul-smelling sitting room in west London, with apparently English Nazis who were quite convinced of Germany's triumph, and whose sanity seemed to be in doubt. The whole thing felt utterly incongruous. Looking back now it does seem to be almost comical, but I recall feeling deeply uncomfortable at the time.

The woman explained that I would remain in the house for a 'few weeks'. Under no circumstances was I ever to leave it during those weeks. There were two bedrooms upstairs and I would have the small one at the back. I was to stay in there as much as possible. If I had to come down during the day I was not to enter the front room or go near the front door. I was never to answer the front door or the telephone. There was a trapdoor in the ceiling of the upstairs landing that led into the attic. They would show me how to get in there. If anyone came to the house I was to go into the attic before they were let in.

She explained they lived alone and rarely had visitors, and would especially avoid having any as long as I was there. Linda said to me that as soon as it was safe to do so, they would contact 'their people' – which was how she always referred to them – to let them know where I was. They, in turn, would move me on when the time was right.

By this stage I was exhausted. All I wanted to do was sleep. But it was quite evident that Linda and Ken were so excited at being in the presence of a member of the SS that they were going to take full advantage of it.

Linda was sure that I wanted to know all about them. I would have been more than happy to wait until the next day, but she was having none of it. Both she and Ken had joined the British Union of Fascists — Oswald Mosley's party — in December 1932, soon after it had been formed. But they soon felt it was not hard line enough for them. 'Too soft on the Jews,' she said. They had voiced these concerns at meetings and began to feel somewhat on the fringe of the organisation. Sometime in late 1935 or 1936 they had been approached by a man, not long after leaving a party meeting. He completely understood their point of view, he told them. Many people held similar views, but they should understand that the party had to be careful about its public image. He said that if they were prepared to do what he was going to ask them to do then they could help 'the cause' — which is how Linda said he described it — in a most effective way. Linda said that they agreed to meet the man at a pub behind Haymarket the following week. Both she and Ken suspected that the man might have some links with Germany. The man explained that he would like them to quietly leave the Fascists and undertake no political activity whatsoever. They were to lead ordinary lives. He would keep in occasional contact with them and at an appropriate point he would approach them and ask for their help. They would meet with him from time to time, perhaps every six months or so. These visits continued even when the war started. They would always meet at a Central London pub, but the 'confidential' parts of their discussions took place in the street.

According to Linda, about four months previously the man had unexpectedly turned up at their house. Until then, he had never been there and they had no idea that he knew where they lived. He explained that 'his people', as Linda said he put it, may be expecting some 'visitors' and he was looking for trustworthy and loyal people who could look after them, maybe for a few days, or perhaps even a few months. It was not without risk, but it would be doing the cause a great service.

Ken then spoke. Up until this point he had sat there silently, nodding occasionally but always staring at me with an unbroken gaze, as if he could not believe what he was seeing. He said that they had begun to suspect the man was working for the Germans, but now they were certain, and they were also certain they wanted to do all they could to help.

Long ago, he said, they had realised that Britain's real enemies were Jews and Communism, and the war against Germany was a 'mistake'. He was certain the British people would soon come to regret fighting on the 'wrong side,' as he put it. They had told the man they'd be honoured to help and he explained what they had to do, how to ensure that the house was safe, all the precautions they needed to take, the signals they needed to show.

By then it must have been obvious how tired I was, and they showed me upstairs. My bedroom was small and somewhat stark, but comfortable enough. There was a single bed, a cupboard, a bedside table and a shelf with some books on it. The bathroom was next door, a room which needed a thorough clean and had a distinct smell of damp, which must have been due in large part to a permanently sealed window. It clearly reflected their standards of hygiene: the bar of soap on the sink was filthy and the one on the side of the stained bath just as bad, with hairs embedded in it.

I quickly fell into a routine. I would go downstairs at seven in the morning and have breakfast with them. They both had clerical jobs at nearby Hammersmith Hospital, and when they left for work at around seven thirty I would go back to my room. The front room was always locked – in my time in that house I never once went into it – and their bedroom, another room that I never once went into, was locked during the day.

I was able to go downstairs while they were out, but only to the kitchen and even then I had to be as quiet as possible. I could not go into the sitting room at the back during the day because the curtains were not drawn, so as not to arouse suspicion. So I stayed in my bedroom, reading any book I could find and lying on the bed thinking and daydreaming.

Naturally, I had far too much time to think. I felt safe enough in the house: no one ever visited and despite being in a busy part of London, it felt quite isolated. But I did begin to develop a real concern about how safe I was overall in England, and during my stay I never relaxed.

I hardly slept at night, alert to every sound. During the day I would doze but I never felt rested. When Ken and Linda were in the house, the atmosphere was strained. They were such a strange and secretive couple, with their odd habits. Although they were quite evidently thrilled a member of the SS was staying in their house, they could be very short with me. They did not like being asked questions and if I did something of which they did not approve they would go into a sulk that could last for days.

I should mention the events of 20th April, a few weeks after I arrived. It was a Friday, which I was to learn was the one evening of the week when the Frosts came anywhere close to relaxing. On his way home from work Mr Frost would collect fish and chips and we would sit in the back room, eating them out of newspaper, accompanied by a glass of warm ginger beer. I also ought to add that on Friday nights, after they had gone to bed, the unmistakable sounds of them having sex could be heard through the walls. The noise would either last a very short time or a very long one. Mrs Frost could be heard making sounds either of encouragement or admonishment. They never sounded as if they were enjoying themselves.

On this particular Friday, after the fish and chips were cleared away – I recall Mr Frost wiping his greasy hands down the side of the grey trousers he always wore – they returned to the back room, checked that the blackout and curtains were secure, closed the door and then poured three glasses of sherry. Was I aware what day it was, they asked? I wasn't, to their dismay. It was the Führer's birthday – what SS soldier would be unaware of that! Mr Frost then gave a long toast to Hitler in his appalling German, which was so bad that I could not really make out what he was saying, other than something about an everlasting Reich. He then gave an enthusiastic 'Sieg Heil' with the Nazi salute. His wife did likewise, as did I. We then toasted the Führer, drinking the small glass of sweet sherry before shaking hands. As this bizarre ceremony ended, I noticed both of them had tears in their eyes.

On other evenings we would eat a meal that Mrs Frost prepared as soon as she came in from work. The meal would be predictable, plain and the best that could usually be said about it was that it was hot. The three of us would eat sitting in silence around the small dining table in the back room. After supper we would sit on the easy chairs in the same room, listening to the radio, which was a large contraption with poor reception. The highlight of the evening would be the news. Throughout the news, any references to the war were accompanied by remarks from both of them. Bad news was always dismissed as 'Jewish lies.' I ought to point out here that by 'bad news,' I mean bad news from a German perspective – and there was plenty of that. At the beginning of May there was a news report on the liberation of Dachau, accompanied by much head shaking and comments of 'lies'. News of Hitler's suicide was treated with incredulity, as was the capture of Berlin by the Red Army a day or so later. The next week we heard about the German surrender and not just on the radio – we could hear people coming out onto the street and the sounds of a spontaneous street party. Mrs Frost left the room in tears and went straight to bed. Mr Frost sat still on the sofa, his unblinking eyes staring at the wall, his fists tightly clenched.

I remained at the house in Shepherd's Bush for four months, by which stage I was reaching the limits of my endurance: I did not know how much longer I could manage locked in that miserable, smelly house. Just a few days after we heard the news about the Hiroshima bomb, in the first week of August, there was a knock at the door while Mr Frost was clearing away the plates. I quickly went upstairs and into the attic, from where I could just make out the sound of the door opening and much talking going on. Five minutes later there was a tap on the trapdoor. Please could I come down?

In the back room Mr and Mrs Frost were standing together facing a tall man with his back to the window. As I entered the room he moved towards me with a limp, shaking my hand warmly. 'I am very pleased to meet you, Lothar.'

He had brought with him a small suitcase containing clothes and toiletries and a new set of identity papers. I was to familiarise myself with my new identity and then leave the house at nine o'clock through a small side gate in the garden. Just along the road that backed onto the house I would see a dark green Morris 8 van, on the opposite side of the road. A driver would be in the van, and if there was a newspaper rolled up on the dashboard then I would know all was safe. I should walk past the van and if no one was watching I was to climb in through the back doors. There would be some blankets on the floor and I was to lay on them and cover myself. The journey could take as long as three hours. This man was leaving now, but would meet with me 'in a day or two' at my next destination.

While I studied my new identity, Mrs Frost brought me a cup of tea and a cheese sandwich, and the three of us sat in silence in the back room, the lights out but the blackout and curtains open so that we could watch it getting dark.

The radio was on but just for music now: since the bomb on Hiroshima the Frosts seemed to have given up and had stopped shouting at the radio and accusing the BBC of telling lies. Since the German surrender they had slipped into a state of mourning.

At nine o'clock Mr Frost went into the kitchen and quietly unlocked the door that led into the garden. I watched him walk gingerly over to the garden gate, unbolt it, and push the door just far enough to see into the street to the side of the house. Apparently satisfied, he returned to the house. It was all clear, he told me. The Morris 8 van was parked where they said it would be. I should leave now.

I walked into the kitchen and the Frosts followed. There was an awkward silence as I wondered what to do next. Should I thank them profusely or just slip away? I turned round and they were both standing right behind me, as if blocking my return into the house. I shook hands with Mr Frost who solemnly kept shaking mine. I then shook Mrs Frost's hand. She seemed relieved to see me go, to be honest.

I assumed that they were pleased to look after me orig-inally because of their Nazi sympathies, but as time went on I think the enormity of what they were doing, which carried the death penalty after all, became too much of a strain. Four months was a long time, perhaps longer than they had bargained for.

Edgar put the letter aside and strolled around his study, checking the door was locked before turning on a reading lamp and returning to Meier's document. It went into some detail about what happened next: how his new identity didn't last long and a series of new identities followed, moving around the country until finally settling in Nottingham as Christopher Vale. He found work as an engineer but never married. He'd decided the secrets he carried would be an unfair burden on anyone else.

Soon after moving to Nottingham, in 1956, Captain Canter-bury had appeared at his digs. The Englishman explained how he'd been imprisoned for a while after his return to England, but he now had a new identity. His job was to keep in touch with Lothar Meier 'and the others.' Canterbury would telephone him: weekly at first but then monthly, and they'd actually meet once or twice a year. For a few years there'd been some halfhearted pretence that their mission still existed, with conversations about how the situation in Europe was turning in their favour, how the Fourth Reich was regrouping in South America. But Meier had his doubts, and by the mid-1960s it was clear that Captain Canterbury's job was restricted to keeping an eye on him, ensuring he kept out of trouble and kept his mouth shut.

However in the weeks before Meier wrote his letter, Captain Canterbury's approach had been more menacing, making all kinds of threats about not saying a word to anyone. This, he wrote, was his reason for writing everything down. He was worried, and felt his life was in danger. After this, the letter appeared to come to an abrupt end but, as Edgar held the final sheet up, the light picked up something on its reverse. It was dense pencil writing, similar to that on the first sheet but so faint that he had to take it over to his desk and play the light of his powerful angle-poise lamp across the page.

March 1970

The reason for Canterbury's recent threatening tone became apparent today. I am writing these notes late at night just after my return to Nottingham, and I intend to drop this letter off with my solicitor in the morning as a matter of urgency. I don't even have time to type this as my typewriter is being serviced and I cannot risk waiting any longer. Yesterday – which was a Saturday – I received a telephone call from Captain Canterbury. I was to travel today to Birmingham and meet him at a hotel near the station, where he had reserved a small meeting room on the ground floor.

When I arrived I was shocked to discover I was not alone. Three of my fellow recruits were also present. It was the first time we had seen each other since late 1944. Because so long had elapsed, Captain Canterbury introduced us all, and not just by our original names – the German ones by which we had known each other – but also by the English names which we now used. To me this was surprising, but no more so than much to do with this mission. Here are the names of the other three. I hope their English names are correct, I had to memorise them.

Konrad Hartmann (Martin Page)
Christian Schäfer (Tom Hartley)
Arnold Bauer (Tony Norton)

The Captain explained that we four were the only ones of our group in England. He said nothing about any of the others. Recently, he said, there had been a security lapse. He didn't go into details about it but said it was very serious and could have exposed all of us but, he assured us, it 'had been dealt with'.

Then he told us someone else would soon be coming into the room. Under no circumstances were we to turn round. We were to say nothing and keep looking ahead. Soon after that, Captain Canterbury left the room. When he returned he was not alone. He stood at the front while the other person remained at the back of the room, us with our backs to him. When he spoke it was in English, in what I would term an upper class accent. He sounded quite young, though I'd be hard pushed to give a much better description than that.

The man said he wanted to see what we looked like in person, so he had observed us as we'd entered the hotel. He wanted us to be in no doubt that we were being watched all the time – he repeated that – and 'not just for your safety.' That was how he phrased it, in a very menacing tone. If any of us had thoughts about escaping, moving away or turning ourselves in – anything like that – then we should remember that we had committed war crimes *and we should be in no doubt that evidence of those crimes would soon appear if we did anything foolish.*

Once Edgar had finished reading the letter he sat at his desk making notes and gazing out of the window as he pondered what to do next. For a man who had been on clandestine missions in Nazi Germany, fear was a rare companion in Dorset. But that night, as he locked the letter and his notes in the safe and quietly went around the house to make sure all the windows and doors were locked, Edgar felt fear rising behind his eyes and deep in all his senses.

He would need to involve Paget. How much could he tell him? And how much could he trust him?

And he urgently needed to see Viktor.

Chapter 17

'Is this really the best place for us to meet?'

'Don't you like boats?'

'You know full well what I mean, Viktor. Vienna… is it really safe?'

The large Russian shrugged and pulled his coat tight around him. Despite it being summer he was dressed more for winter, though perhaps not a Russian one. Edgar was dressed more casually: a jacket and shirt, but no tie.

'Nowhere is safe, Edgar. Given the nature of what we're dealing with, anywhere in the DDR or the Federal Republic is far, far too risky. It's the same with your country – and with mine, too dangerous for you to enter a Warsaw Pact country so soon after your last visit to one.'

'But not dangerous for you to leave one?'

'Hah! You have a point there. It's a similar situation to the last time we were together in Vienna, eh Edgar? Thirty-one years ago. Who'd have thought the world would be almost as dangerous?'

'And the last time you were here you sent me on a trip down the Danube.'

'Actually it was up the Danube and, anyway, these are different circumstances.' The Russian waved his hand, as if to dismiss those circumstances.

They were on a pleasure cruise, and Edgar's instructions had been to be on the first trip of the day – one which would be less crowded. Viktor had been very specific about the boat, the time and place of departure, and what to do once on the boat. 'Sit on the outside, at the back – away from other people,' Viktor had instructed him. 'I'll join you once the coast is clear, so to speak.' So Edgar had boarded the boat at Schwedenplatz, as instructed. He sat on the port side, which was alongside the quay and gave him a good view of those boarding. He had been one of the first on board, but saw no sign of Viktor.

They headed up the Danube Canal, passing under the Nord Brücke before joining the Danube river itself, continuing slowly upstream to the accompaniment of a recorded commentary in German, English and French interspersed with a speeded up version of *The Blue Danube*. There was still no sign of Viktor. After an hour or so they pulled in to the town of Klosterneuburg, where half of the boat's passengers disembarked to begin a coach tour of the Vienna Woods. Only three or four people joined the boat, and again Viktor was not one of them.

The boat turned round and headed downstream, staying on the river itself, passing the entrance to the canal. As it emerged from the shadow of Floridsdorfer Brücke, Edgar felt a tap on his shoulder.

'May I join you?'

And now Viktor, who naturally had provided no explanation as to where he'd been or why he'd taken so long, was explaining why he'd chosen Vienna for their meeting.

'It's odd you know, Edgar.' The Russian had shuffled closer towards Edgar, enabling him to speak more quietly, despite the noise of the engine. 'All the trouble before – in '45 – was over whether this city should be neutral after the war. That was the plan, wasn't it? Then we took control and eventually it became part of the west. Well, now it appears it fancies itself as a neutral city after all. Look over there...' Viktor was pointing to their left, where cranes towered over an enormous building site. 'They're building a United Nations headquarters here. The Austrians are very keen to collect international organisations and provide a home for them in Vienna. It makes them feel important and they hope people will forget what they were up to in the war. For us, it's been very easy to operate here in recent years. Vienna is becoming the centre of European espionage. We're expanding our operation at the Embassy and Yevgeny is the new head of the KGB station here. You remember I told you about him? I trained him in Moscow and he asked me to help out when he was appointed deputy head of station in Berlin. So it wasn't too difficult for me to find a pretext to come down – he appreciates my help.'

Viktor leaned back, looking very satisfied with his explanation. The Reichsbrücke loomed ahead of them: Vienna's most famous bridge.

'That document I gave you, Viktor, Krause's testimony. I trust you're being careful with it?'

The Russian nodded, looking slightly aggrieved that Edgar had even thought to ask.

'And what are you doing with it?'

'Don't worry, I have plans and of course I'm being careful. Look, we have perhaps an hour to talk Edgar. Now, tell me – you said you had important information?'

Edgar leaned forward, his arms resting on his thighs. Viktor joined him in the same position. 'I managed to get access to the old MI9 files, which detail all the prisoners of war held by the British. According to these files, four of our five missing SS men were held in the United Kingdom as SS prisoners of war. The only one who I could find nothing on was Mathias Hahn. Against each of those four names was the same phase: "escaped, not recaptured".'

Edgar paused while the boat's commentary battled with the wind to point something out on the starboard side. 'The fact that they escaped is not in itself so unusual, because a number of German prisoners of war did escape from camps in Britain. But virtually all of them were recaptured: they found it impossible to get the right documentation, to find places to hide and to get anywhere near the ports. So for these four to have evaded capture was very significant – unique, as far as I'm aware.'

'And did the files indicate anything further about them?'

'Nothing: my assumption was that all of them would have had false British identities and somewhere to go once they'd escaped. They would have disappeared and become untraceable. But I had a hunch, a feeling, that maybe somewhere at some time over the past thirty-one years one of those names might have cropped up somehow. It was a long shot, but it was worth a try. The British police have a department called Special Branch which looks after political matters, among other things. As you can imagine Viktor, they have close links with the intelligence services and I have a very good contact there, a senior officer who looks at matters involving far right groups. I gave him the list of four names to see if he could find anything on any of them.'

The boat was now turning round an island and beginning its journey upstream, back to the centre of Vienna. Edgar paused as this manoeuvre took place, allowing Viktor to absorb the information.

'My contact told me he had checked all the names on their system. In June this year a man was killed in a car accident in a city called Nottingham. In 1970 – six years ago – this man had given his lawyer a letter which was to be passed on to the police in the event of his dying of anything other than natural causes.

'The lawyer did indeed pass on the letter and, because it contained allegations of a political nature and concerned Nazis, it ended up in Special Branch files in London. This was how my contact found it.'

'Which one was he?'

'Lothar Meier, Viktor. The letter substantially corroborates what we already know. Meier went into some detail about his recruitment, Magdeburg and what happened after that. He explained how he was captured and brought over to this country, how he escaped, found a safe house in London, how he had been moved on after the war, where he'd eventually settled. Captain Canterbury kept in touch with him over the years, but as for their mission – well, as we always knew would be the case, nothing ever came of it. It's a very long account Viktor. I have a copy of it here for you. I can understand how a busy policeman reading this would dismiss him as a crank. At the end of the letter Meier explains how he was summoned to meet Captain Canterbury in Birmingham in March 1970. There, Canterbury announced there'd recently been a security lapse, but it had been dealt with.'

Viktor nodded, as if he was beginning to understand something complicated. 'That would be soon after the Krause Report emerged. I imagine someone became aware of it? This is very interesting, Edgar...'

'But not nearly as interesting as what I am about to reveal. Lothar Meier was not alone when he met Canterbury in Birmingham. Three of the others were present: Arnold Bauer, Konrad Hartmann and Christian Schäfer.'

Viktor looked at Edgar in astonishment. 'All four of them — they must have been mad!'

'Not only that, Viktor, but Meier — whose English name was Christopher Vale — had written down the English names of the others...'

The Russian shook his head in disbelief. 'But that is... extraordinary. That's the only word I can think of. What an extraordinary breach of security, what could they have been thinking of?'

'There's more. Before the meeting ended, Canterbury brought another person into the room. This person stood at the back and Canterbury instructed the recruits not to look at him. This man was very menacing. He told them they were all being watched, and if they ever had any thoughts about escaping or anything like that, the evidence of the war crimes they'd committed would be released.'

'We don't know who this man is?'

'No. Vale — Meier — said he was English, well-spoken and sounded youngish.'

'And the other three — were you were able to track them down?'

The quay at Schwedenplatz was in sight now. The boat slowed down and sounded its horn. Edgar spoke quickly, as if to ensure he would finish before it docked. 'I read the police report on Christopher Vale's accident. It was what we call a "hit and run". Witnesses describe how the car which hit him appeared to accelerate as Vale crossed the road, and then sped away after the collision. The car has never been traced. Christian Schäfer – known as Tom Hartley – was a painter and decorator in a town called Huddersfield, in the north of England. One week after Meier's death he was found dead at a building site where he was working: he had fallen from a ladder. It was not terribly high up, but his neck was broken. He would have died instantly, according to the police report. Arnold Bauer – Tony Norton – went missing from his home in Cheltenham at around the same time as Schäfer died. His body was found by the side of the M5 motorway, not far from where he lived, a week after he disappeared. According to the police report he died from multiple injuries.'

Edgar stopped for a moment. The boat's engines had gone into a noisy reverse thrust as it edged towards the quay.

'And the fourth one?'

'Konrad Hartmann, otherwise known as Martin Page: he lived alone in Kent. His wife had died some years previously, and their daughter died when she was quite young. Konrad Hartmann was found dead in his house the day after Meier was run over. Neighbours telephoned the police to say they'd heard a gunshot during the night. Hartmann was found dead on his bed, a revolver in his hand. It is being treated as a case of suicide.'

'Was there a note or anything?'

'Not as far as I know.'

'This all sounds very professional: textbook, I would say. No one suspects anything about any of them?'

'Not as far as I can tell from the police reports. Suicide is always unsatisfactory, and the hit and run is still subject to investigation. But from a police point of view none of these deaths seem very much out of the ordinary. Of course if looked at together and with a connection established between all four men – yes, absolutely, very suspicious indeed. But as isolated cases? No.'

'And your contact in the police, surely he is now aware? What are you going to do about him?'

People were beginning to queue to leave the boat now, and a crew member pushed in front of them to tie a rope to its mooring. Edgar leaned closer to Viktor.

'Lothar Meier had typed his report in January 1970 and was clearly waiting to send it to his lawyer. After the meeting in Birmingham that March he wrote in pencil on the reverse of the final sheet of the letter. Special Branch filed the letter as "Christopher Vale/Lothar Meier/Nazis". I suspect my contact did not read that, or didn't have the time or the inclination to attach much importance to the whole letter. He saw the name Lothar Meir, which he'd been looking for, and contacted me. He probably skimmed through the whole document but, knowing him, I suspect he'd have dismissed whatever he read as the words of a crank. He certainly didn't seem to be terribly exercised about the whole business when we met. Don't get me wrong, Viktor, he was pleased to have found it, but he has more important things to worry about. He is glad he's done me a favour because I now owe him one. You know how it is.'

The boat had now docked at Schwedenplatz and the two men disembarked together, walking silently for a while through the 1st District.

'What do we do now?'

Viktor did not reply at first, deep in thought and appearing not to have heard Edgar. When he began to speak he held Edgar by the elbow for a while. 'Unlike so many of our colleagues, we saw what the Nazis were like at first hand, didn't we? We both operated behind enemy lines during the war. And it was the same enemy. How many people who are still alive can say that? The Cold War between us… that has not been without its tensions and its dangers but, compared to what we know and we what saw, it has not been the same. I thought we would never encounter such evil again.'

Viktor gave such emphasis to the word 'evil' that he almost shouted it out, causing a couple passing them by to turn round.

'And my job in the Soviet Union, all those years interrogating Nazis – well, I felt I was confronting evil then. But as the years went on I came to believe that within a few years there'd be no Nazis left, certainly not those still committed to their cause. And now, here we are. We need to expose the ones remaining, Edgar. We need to think what to do.'

They entered St Stephen's Cathedral and slowly walked round the church, eventually settling in an unoccupied pew close to the pulpit.

'Are you religious, Edgar?'

The Englishman vigorously shook his head, shocked the Russian could suspect him of being so. Viktor gestured toward the ornately decorated pulpit.

'Just before I was summoned back to Moscow in May '45, I visited this place a few times with Irma. I know it's not quite the kind of place a senior NKVD officer should be seen in, but it was somewhere we could get away from the tension in the city. And although Irma's a good Communist, she is nonetheless interested in religious buildings.'

Viktor stopped, folded his arms and gazed up at the pulpit. 'You see those animals carved into the pulpit – around the handrail, apparently crawling up it? They're lizards and toads. They're meant to symbolise evil, climbing up the pulpit to attack the preacher. And there at the top, can you see? It's a dog fighting them off, protecting the preacher. The dog represents good.'

Viktor continued to stare at the pulpit. 'Was life as simple in medieval England as it is on this pulpit, Edgar? It certainly was in Russia. A man stood in a church and told people what was good and what was bad: they did not question what they were told, and lived their lives accordingly. I often wonder what life would be like if we still lived like that today.'

Chapter 18

Düsseldorf, West Germany, August 1976

She was questioned by two men. At first, she'd found it hard to distinguish between them, especially in the over-lit, windowless room and with so little sleep and her nerves stretched to breaking point. Both looked to be in their forties, though possibly younger. Both were tall and skinny and wore glasses, and both had fair hair cut, in a severe military fashion. They didn't play the 'bad cop, good cop' game either, which she'd been told to expect.

But after a while she found she could tell the difference. The one who called himself Franz seemed to have a cold and spoke so quietly that at times she had to lean across the table to catch what he was saying. The other one, Konrad, had a hint of a Bavarian accent and seemed bored, as if he had more important people to interrogate. But whenever she tossed back her head and ran her fingers through her long blonde hair and smiled, looking directly at them, Konrad was the one who responded, looking her up and down, sometimes even smiling in return – though not in a pleasant way.

They were in the basement of a police station in Düsseldorf where she'd been taken after being arrested three days previously. Franz and Konrad had turned up the day after her arrest and, as far as she could gather, they weren't police. Her guess was that they were the security service, the BfV, which she didn't need telling was ominous.

'Sabine, you were observed entering an apartment in Ratinger Strasse in the Altstadt district on no less than eighteen occasions over the past two months: that is almost once every three days. From that apartment last Thursday, two men and one woman were observed leaving at six thirty in the morning and departing on motorbikes. Two hours later, the industrialist Heinrich Albrecht was shot dead as he left his car after arriving at his office in Wuppertal. The gunmen escaped on motorbikes. The registration plate on at least one of those bikes corresponds to the plate on one of the bikes that had sped away from Ratinger Strasse two hours earlier.'

Silence. Silence for quite a long while. Franz and Konrad seemed to like silence.

'I have told you already: I was nowhere near Altstadt last Thursday, nor Wuppertal for that matter. You know I have an alibi. I had an appointment at the University Hospital on Moorenstrasse at eight forty-five that morning, minutes after Albrecht was shot. You can't get from Wuppertal to Düsseldorf in fifteen minutes.'

'You may well smirk, but I can tell you that this is no joke for you. Tell me, Sabine, what do you think of the shooting of Heinrich Albrecht?'

'I don't have an opinion.'

'Really?' It was Franz speaking, and she had to lean close to hear him. 'A prominent and respectable industrialist, a family man, a stalwart of his local church—'

'And a Nazi.'

'He served as a soldier in the war. There was conscription, Sabine.'

'He helped run the ghetto in Lublin, and is rumoured to have been involved in the nearby Nazi death camp at Majdanek. Maybe one of the few people who survived it was seeking revenge—'

'How do you know this?'

'Pardon?'

'I said, how do you know this – about Lublin? You seem to know a lot about Herr Albrecht.'

'I read it in the newspapers. There was a lot about him after he was shot. But if my alibi stands up, why are you holding me?'

'What were you doing in the flat?'

'It was the kind of place where lots of people come and go. Altstadt is like that, you should visit it sometime. Very Bohemian, I'm sure you'd fit in nicely. There was a guy there whom I was seeing, it was very informal.'

'What does "seeing" mean?'

'We slept together. Do you want me to explain that?'

'His name?'

'Christian.'

'Christian what?'

'I don't know, I never asked.'

'You mean,' said Franz, sounding genuinely perplexed, 'you slept with this person and never asked his surname?'

'I didn't need to. Surnames don't turn me on.'

'How old is Christian?'

'Nineteen, maybe twenty...'

'And you're how old?'

'Twenty six. Why do you look so shocked?'

'We will finish playing games now perhaps. We accept your alibi: we know you were indeed at the University Hospital at the time you said last Thursday morning. But that doesn't mean that matters aren't serious. We know for instance that your name is not really Sabine Falkenberg. That is a false identity you have been using for at least the last six years, which is a serious criminal offence. We know that your real name is Ute von Morsbach and you are from Augsburg, where your family still live, not that you have much to do with them.'

Franz took over, his voice a bit louder now. 'I see you're no longer smiling. We know that Ute von Morsbach was a student at the Free University in West Berlin from 1967, and was active in the early days of the Red Army Faction, as a supporter at the very least. Sometime in 1970 Ute von Morsbach disappeared, but our sources indicate that you remained active in the Red Army Faction. It is likely that since the arrest of Baader and the rest of that criminal gang in 1972 you have been less active, who knows. But once we spotted you as such a frequent visitor to the apartment in Ratinger Strasse, we investigated you. We discovered that Sabine Falkenberg had been living in Aachen since 1970, but moved to Düsseldorf a year ago. We even managed to get your fingerprints, which of course showed us that Sabine Falkenberg and Ute von Morsbach are one and the same person.'

'So,' said Konrad, standing up and beginning to pace the room, a lawyer addressing a court, 'Ute von Morsbach was a member of the Red Army Faction. Sabine Falkenberg is Ute von Morsbach. Sabine Falkenberg was a very frequent visitor to the apartment where the gang that murdered Heinrich Albrecht was based. Therefore we have ample grounds to charge you with being part of the conspiracy to murder Herr Albrecht.'

'And with using a false identity,' added Franz.

'Both very serious offences.' Both Franz and Konrad were standing now and gathering their papers.

'We'll leave you to think about your situation,' said Konrad. 'But if you are found guilty of these offences, I would be surprised if you served less than ten years in prison.'

From the doorway Franz turned round to address her, speaking as if something had just occurred to him. 'Of course, if you were to co-operate then we'd just charge you with the false identity offence. I'm sure if you were to plead guilty to that, the state prosecutor would recommend a suspended sentence. Think about it, eh?'

–

They gave her the weekend to think about it. By sometime on the Saturday Sabine's bravado had been severely dented. In fact, by the Saturday evening – she assumed it was the evening, she couldn't be sure – she stopped thinking of herself as Sabine Falkenberg and began to think of herself as Ute von Morsbach again. She even found she missed her family and when she thought of them she began to cry. She cried the whole of the following day, and asked to speak to the men who'd been questioning her, but the police just told her they'd be back 'after the weekend' and she thought of Franz and Konrad being with their families and that made her miss hers even more.

Franz and Konrad had hardly sat down on the Monday morning when Ute – as she now insisted they call her – began to speak. Ute didn't stop speaking for the rest of the morning, other than to listen to the occasional question.

She had indeed been involved with the Red Army Faction, she told them. But she wanted to make one thing clear: other than one incident back in 1972 – in which no one was killed, thankfully – she had not taken part in any 'actions', as she described them.

They pressed her about the 'incident.' Could they assure her, she asked, that she wouldn't be charged in connection with it, if she told them?

Almost certainly, replied Konrad.

So she told them: the bombing of the British army base at Rheindahlen in Mönchengladbach in the May of 1972. She'd made sure no one was killed by it. But she had an accomplice and she wanted to tell them all about the accomplice. She thought they'd be very interested in this accomplice.

She told them how the Red Army Faction had found out about a Werner Pohl – no, she didn't know how. She was just told what she needed to know.

They had found out that he was a very wealthy businessman who might be sympathetic to the Red Army Faction. Very little was known about him, other than that he had an apartment in Aachen and spent a few days there each month. She was instructed to move to Aachen as soon as she could and to befriend him, which happened in April 1970. His apartment was in Jesuiten-strasse, near the cathedral, and when she'd checked it out she discovered it had been rented by him for a couple of years, so she believed he was who he said he was.

Werner Pohl turned out indeed to be very wealthy, and very well disposed to the Red Army Faction. He was certainly well read on Marx and Lenin, often quoting them. She found some of his political views odd though.

What did she mean by that?

Well, he didn't seem to like Jews very much, but then he was from an older generation she supposed.

How old?

Forties, she replied. She never found out exactly how old, just as she never found out many things about him. Anyway, Werner Pohl gave the Red Army Faction hundreds of thousands of Deutschmarks, though none of it came through her. He also made suggestions about targets for the Red Army Faction and urged her to pass these ideas on. And he got hold of detonators for them. But all of this came at a price, she said, pausing for a while as she sobbed. He was a cruel man. As broadminded as she was about sex, and as much as she realised that what she was doing helped the revolutionary struggle against fascism, and so was justified, sometimes she found his cruelty too much.

What kind of cruelty, Franz and Konrad both wanted to know?

Sexual cruelty: he was a sadist. He got pleasure from inflicting pain on her. In fact, unless he was able to hurt her he didn't seem to be able to become aroused or satisfy himself.

Please be more specific, said Konrad.

Ute, as they were now calling her, was reluctant to elaborate, but Konrad insisted. He hit her, sometimes very hard she told them – in fact, usually very hard. And he'd tie her up, very tightly. Sometimes he'd put his hands around her neck while they were having sex and occasionally she'd black out. He liked to drip hot wax on her body. And, towards the end of their relationship, he brought along a strange instrument, like a very long fork, and he'd used it to scratch her body and it was agonising.

The Red Army Faction had wanted to find out more about Werner Pohl: where he went when he wasn't in Aachen, whether Werner Pohl was his real name, where his money came from... but he was elusive. She never managed to get any of this information from him and the Red Army Faction never managed to follow him from Aachen to wherever he went, though they tried on a number of occasions. In the end they decided not to push it, as long as he was coming up with the money. They'd told her to be very circumspect about what she told Werner about the organisation but, looking back on it, she probably told him more than she should have done.

Then he disappeared. June 1972. There had been a spate of bombings in the May, including the one she carried out in Mönchengladbach – he'd driven her to and from the place, by the way. Come to think of it, he'd even suggested the British army base as a target. Then in the first two weeks of June Baader, Raspe, Meins, Ensslin, Meinhoff and Müller had all been arrested, and she thinks that frightened him. It certainly frightened her. She didn't see him again after that: he disappeared, and she stayed in Aachen. The Red Army Faction was in turmoil and her contact with them was quite limited, but the instructions she had were to stay there in case he got in touch.

He never did. She completed her Masters and had occasional contact with her family, enough for them to keep her in funds and to believe she wanted to be alone so she could find herself, which was very much in vogue at the time.

In 1975 she decided to move to Düsseldorf. Some comrades from the Red Army Faction were in Altstadt and she made contact with them. She was not very active, more of a messenger than anything else. In truth, she was having second thoughts about the whole business and doubted that imperialism was about to be overthrown, but she stayed involved because she thought she may as well... and then there was the trial going on at Stammheim, and Ulrike Meinhof's so-called suicide in May and...

They pushed her about the apartment in Ratinger Strasse: did she know what they were planning? No, she said. She knew they were planning something, but she didn't know what. She mainly went to the apartment because of Christian: he was a wonderful lover, the best she'd ever had, so gentle, he was able to... was Christian involved in the shooting of Heinrich Albrecht? Franz had asked that question. Konrad looked annoyed that Franz had interrupted her.

Yes, Christian was probably involved, she admitted. But he was very easily led.

And the others?

Hard to say, there were so many people in and out of the apartment, but the woman would probably have been Ulrike – she didn't know her surname, but obviously not to be confused with Meinhof. And as for the man, well that must have been Horst. Horst was always playing with guns – and motorbikes.

'What type of guns?'

'Sub-machine guns. Horst had two Heckler & Kochs: MP5s.'

'Horst's surname?'

'Don't know.'

'Jesus Christ, Ute, do you know how many fucking Horsts there are…?'

'Thousands I imagine, I—'

'It was a rhetorical question. Same goes for Christians and Ulrikes.'

Then they calmed down. Konrad left the room to see what they could find out about Werner Pohl. Later that morning Konrad went out again, and when he returned he said there were a few Werner Pohls in the Federal Republic but, as far as they could tell, none of them matched her Werner. There were certainly none who had that kind of wealth. They'd keep checking but the most likely explanation was that 'Werner Pohl' was a false name. He was untraceable.

There was another of Franz and Konrad's long silences, broken by Ute. 'There is something perhaps I should have told you earlier, about Werner…'

'What?' they replied, apparently in unison.

'I saw him, recently. I was in Cologne, collecting a package for Horst. I took a bus back to the station and at a stop on a busy road I saw him crossing over. I had a very good view: I have no doubt whatsoever it was Werner.'

'Do you happen to know the name of the road?'

'I do actually: it was Innere Kanalstrasse. I heard the bus driver call the name of the stop. It was about six in the evening; it looked like he was leaving work. He was wearing a suit and carrying a small briefcase.'

Both men shot worried looks at each other.

'Innere Kanalstrasse, you say?'

She nodded.

'Ute, when was this?'

'Maybe a month ago – in July certainly.'

Chapter 19

Before parting in Vienna, Viktor told Edgar he'd had an idea thought. 'I think I know a way of finding out Richter's real identity. Give me a few days, but I need to contact someone first. You may have to go to West Germany to follow this up, Edgar.'

Viktor remained in St Stephen's Cathedral for at least fifteen minutes after Edgar's departure. When he left he headed south east, crossing Schubert Ring into the 3rd District and then walking a short distance to Reisnerstrasse. When he arrived at the Soviet Embassy he went straight to the security floor. Yevgeny did not appear to be a happy man.

'Viktor, Viktor, Viktor… you're an old man. You've lived your life. I'm half your age and I have a wife, three children and a career. Because of you I may lose all that!'

Viktor stared at the younger man, unsure of how serious he was being. Yevgeny held the stare for a while and then winked, a half grin appearing on his face – but one which made it clear he was only half joking. 'Look, of course I trust you, and I know it is thanks to everything you did for me in Berlin that I became head of station here so early in my career. But, Viktor, it's tricky enough for me to bring you down to Vienna and give you the run of the city – and now you want to go from here to West Berlin?' Yevgeny pronounced 'West Berlin' as if it were a place wracked by plague, where only the bravest or most foolhardy dared venture.

'It makes sense, Yevgeny.'

'So, I'm a travel agent now?'

'I travelled here from the DDR through Budapest with diplomatic cover, Yevgeny – I'm most grateful for that. But I can't travel into the Federal Republic with diplomatic cover, can I? I'd have to go back to the DDR and then slip in and out again, and that's risky. If I can go direct from here to West Berlin and back it would be so much easier.'

'And you want me to organise all that for you…'

'Just get me decent cover Yevgeny, I can do the rest. Austrian documents will be ideal. I only need two days in West Berlin.'

'And you're not going to tell me what this is all about?'

'I've told you, Yevgeny: I have a source from many years ago… this could be a big intelligence coup for us. If it works out then it's all yours. First, I have to see someone in West Berlin.'

But before Viktor went to see someone in West Berlin he needed to see someone else. A person he hadn't seen since 1945.

Peter had worked for Viktor in the 1930s: a young German Communist who helped him train and run Comintern agents in Germany and Switzerland. He'd been brave and clever but in 1939 decided to return to Frankfurt. His parents were elderly, and Viktor agreed that he should go home. Peter, he realised, was burnt out, exhausted – and in any case, it would be useful to have someone in the city. Peter had operated under assumed names while working for Viktor, so no one in Frankfurt was any the wiser about his politics.

The next Viktor heard of Peter was when the war ended: Viktor provided him with papers to show he'd helped the Allies and as far as he was concerned, Peter owed him a favour. Now, thirty years later, he was calling it in.

Viktor telephoned Peter from his hotel room. The man who answered the phone was unmistakably his old colleague. The voice had aged, from years of cigarettes no doubt, but it was recognisably him.

'*Synok!* Good afternoon: after all these years we get to speak again!'

Silence on the other end. Viktor knew full well that Peter was still there, and knew he would need a moment or two to compose himself. He would be understandably shocked. *Synok* was an affectionate Russian word Viktor used for his younger agents. It meant 'son'.

'Where are you?'

'That's how you greet me?'

'It's been more than thirty years, Viktor. I stopped working for you almost forty years ago. What the hell is all this about?'

'I need to see you, *synok*.'

'Do I have any choice?'

'You know the answer to that, my friend. In any case, surely you'd want to see me after all this time? Where is easier for you to get to from Frankfurt: Vienna or West Berlin?'

'Neither.'

'Peter, you know that's not an option—'

'When would you want to see me?'

'Tomorrow, *synok*.'

Viktor heard what sounded like swearing down the line. 'Vienna I guess: there are more flights and my brother-in-law lives there so I suppose I can say I'm visiting him if anyone asks.'

–

Early on an already hot Tuesday morning late in August, Viktor emerged from Uhlandstrasse subway station in West Berlin. He wore a shabby, slightly stained jacket and ill-fitting trousers. A two-day beard was in keeping with his attire, without making him appear too disreputable. He shuffled along with the aid of a stick, crossing Kurfürstendamm before walking slowly down Fasanenstrasse, the heart of West Berlin's legal district. Just before the junction with Lietzenburger Strasse, he found the offices of Rostt Legal. The lady behind the reception desk was unable to disguise her disdain as she looked him up and down.

Yes, Herr Stern is in this morning but he has a full schedule. Do you have an appointment with him?

Viktor replied that he didn't, but he had heard Herr Stern was a very good lawyer. Perhaps you could ask if I could see him?

The receptionist reluctantly rang through to Herr Stern. As I said, he has a full day. Perhaps you can make an appointment with one of our junior lawyers?

Viktor took a leather notebook and pencil from his jacket pocket, tore out one of the pages, wrote briefly on it before folding it into quarters and handed it to the receptionist. 'Please give Herr Stern this piece of paper.'

Less than a minute later the flustered-looking woman hurried out of Herr Stern's office. 'He'll see you now. He's told me to cancel all his appointments for today.'

–

The man behind the large desk appeared remarkably calm in the circumstances. He gestured for Viktor to sit in one of the two smart chairs in front of him. He looked much as Krause had described him after their encounter in Frankfurt eight years previously: perhaps slightly younger than his late forties, a full head of wavy fair hair with some grey flecks at the sides and, most notably of all, piercing dark eyes that studied Viktor with an intensity he found unnerving. In his hand was the piece of paper Viktor had written on. He waved it in the direction of the man opposite him.

'You're Horst Weber?'

'No. You are.'

The lawyer brushed his forehead with the back of his hand, looking slightly flushed now. He folded and unfolded the piece of paper, adjusted the knot on his tie, looked down at his desk, across at the window and then once more at Viktor, noisily clearing his throat.

'There is a misunderstanding. My name is Georg Stern. I am a senior partner here at Rostt Legal. You need to tell me who you are.'

There was no hint of the anger Viktor would have expected had this all indeed been a misunderstanding.

'I know that you are Georg Stern. You were born Georg Stern, and that is your legal identity. But there was a period during the war when you were Horst Weber, which is why I am here.'

During the ensuing silence Viktor could hear doors opening and closing along the corridor and the ticking of a carriage clock. A steady breeze caused the half-open window to rattle in its frame, and he could hear the lawyer breathing more heavily as he tried to work out how to respond.

'And who are you?' The lawyer looked genuinely curious.

'Who I am is immaterial,' he replied, 'but you do need to listen carefully to what I have to say. I have a testimony from a Bernhard Krause in which he claims his real name was Otto Schröder, and that he was recruited into the SS in 1944. He was part of a small group of young recruits who were taken to an isolated house near Magdeburg, where they were trained for a special mission. During this training some terrible things took place, which he admits he played a part in and which amount to war crimes. As part of his mission, Herr Krause was meant to allow himself to be captured by the Allies and taken to Britain as a prisoner of war. However, Herr Krause managed to escape just after he was captured in France, and assumed a new identity. He ended up in Frankfurt, where he died in 1969. In his testimony Herr Krause gave the names of the other recruits. There were ten in total, though one was murdered very soon after arriving at Magdeburg. Schröder – or Krause – says he was very friendly with a recruit from Berlin called Horst Weber. The last time he saw Weber was in or near Dortmund in December 1944, when all the recruits were asked to make their own way to Essen. Apparently Herr Weber never arrived in Essen, the assumption was that he escaped...'

'I keep telling you, this has nothing to do with me! I am a very busy man, I—'

'But not busy to cancel all your appointments as soon as you saw a piece of paper with the words "Horst Weber" on them? Herr Krause claims in his testimony that in February 1968 he was working for a law firm in Frankfurt when he encountered Horst Weber. He claims that Weber was, in fact, you – Georg Stern, from Rostt Legal in Berlin. That, Herr Stern, is why I am here.'

Georg Stern stood up and walked over to the window and then to a more comfortable chair on one side of a coffee table, and gestured for Viktor to join him on a facing chair. Viktor had interrogated so many people in his career that he was familiar with changing patterns of behaviour during an interrogation. Stern was behaving exactly as someone would when they became aware that the other person had a strong case against them. He was buying time while he thought. It was the Russian who spoke first.

'Herr Stern, it is significant that you have singularly failed to address the very serious allegation I've made, namely that you were a member of the SS. You are a respectable man now. I understand that you are Jewish...'

Stern held up his hand in a 'stop' gesture. 'They are barely allegations: as a lawyer I would say they amount to little more than hearsay. You come into my office and make these wild claims with no proof – and expect me to do what?'

'I had expected you to deny more convincingly that you lived for some time as Horst Weber.'

Stern leant back in his chair, crossed his legs, and held his hands in front of his face, fingertips touching. It was as if he was forcing himself to be calm. 'In the war, people adopted all kinds of identities in order to survive, especially people who were persecuted. This man, whoever he is, he died what – seven years ago? What has he to do with me?'

From an inside pocket of his jacket Viktor produced a bulky envelope. 'I thought I'd just explained that, Herr Stern. Here is a copy of Herr Krause's testimony. I'm giving you the whole testimony up until and including the meeting with you in the '60s. I would like you to read it.'

Stern reached out for the envelope. 'I need to have some idea about who you are – I'm not even sure if you're German. Are you here in an official capacity? Are you a war crimes investigator? How do I know you're not a Nazi!'

'I am not a West German official of any kind. Nor am I East German, and I am most certainly not a Nazi. I am someone that you would do well to co-operate with.'

'So what do you want from me?'

'I told you, Herr Stern. I would like you to read this testimony. Then I will have a very specific request for you. You will not be reported to anyone, your story will be kept from the authorities here. Your secret will remain just that.'

Stern studied the envelope in his hands, clearly intrigued by its contents. 'Come back and see me this time tomorrow. And tell me this: Herr Krause – what was his cause of death?'

–

The Austrian identity Yevgeny Mironov had provided meant Viktor didn't need to stay in any of the KGB safe houses in West Berlin, which was just as well – he wouldn't want anyone in the KGB office on the Unter den Linden to know he was there. He found a pleasant hotel on Budapester Strasse, overlooking the Landwehr Canal. From there he rang Peter again.

Viktor was surprised how little his former comrade from Comintern had changed when he'd turned up in Vienna three days previously, the day after Viktor had summoned him. He was now in his sixties, but he looked considerably younger. He also looked suspicious.

'Let me tell you one thing first, Viktor,' he'd said as they found a table in the darkened rear of a coffee shop, no one within earshot. He sounded emotional as he spoke. 'I regret nothing I did when I worked for you. In fact I'm proud of it. And when I returned to Frankfurt in '39, and for the rest of the war,

I did nothing to be ashamed of. I became a teacher, I taught mathematics. I never joined the Nazi Party and I even managed to help a few Jews, although only in a minor way. Because of my poor eyesight – which of course I was able to exaggerate – I was exempt from military service. I am now retired. What possible use can I be to you now?'

Viktor nodded, slightly impatiently, waiting for Peter to get whatever it was off his chest. 'Very well, now listen, *synok*. There is a law firm in Frankfurt called Schmidt Legal. Its office is on Hochstrasse, the principal is an Alois Schmidt. On 17th April 1968 – which was a Wednesday – Herr Schmidt saw a new client, a man who was quite possibly from outside Frankfurt. It was about a divorce.'

'Viktor, in 1968 I was a teacher, I—'

'This has nothing to do with what you were up to in 1968, Peter. It is to do with what I need from you now. Please concentrate.'

But when Viktor called Peter from the pleasant hotel on Budapester Strasse, he recognised an altogether much more upbeat tone in the other man's voice. A good agent rarely loses the excitement of being in the field, even after a gap of some forty years.

'Tell me, *synok* – tell me.'

And Peter told him. He told him how the day after his return to Frankfurt he had turned up at the offices of Schmidt Legal on Hochstrasse and explained to the receptionist that, although he didn't have an appointment, he needed to see a lawyer about an urgent and sensitive matter.

A few minutes later he was ushered into the small office of one of the lawyers, a young woman who insisted he call her Trude. Peter recounted a most distressing tale to Trude: how he and his wife had been leading separate lives for some time, but in the past month he had been diagnosed with a most serious illness and he needed as a matter of some urgency – he was sure Trude would understand – to put his affairs in order… and his wife now wanted a divorce. Well, at this point, Peter told Viktor, he broke down. 'It was so convincing, Viktor. I felt genuinely upset: I actually cried. You'd have been proud of me: it was how you taught me, to live the part.'

'And what happened then, *synok*?'

'Trude looked uncomfortable and asked if she could get me anything and I told her a coffee with no sugar and a dash of milk would help, and maybe if I was allowed a minute or two to compose myself. No one wants to spend too much time alone with a sobbing man, so Trude left me alone for a good five minutes, which was ample time. I found Schmidt Legal headed paper and an official stamp, with which I stamped one of the sheets. When Trude returned I was more composed, to her obvious relief. I asked what the fees were and when she told me I was suitably shocked and explained that as it was considerably more expensive than I'd envisaged, I'd need to visit my bank manager first. Would she mind if I did so and returned the following week? I think she was pleased to see the back of me, to be honest.

'Her office was on the third floor so I walked down to the second floor, and at the end of a corridor I saw a trolley laden with files. I waited until no one was watching, slipped half a dozen files into my briefcase, and headed for the exit. I ought to add that while I was waiting in reception when I first arrived I'd picked up a brochure about the firm. Most helpfully it contained a note of introduction from Alois Schmidt, with his signature at the bottom of it.'

'The name, *synok*, I need to know whether you got the name of this client.'

'I'm coming to that, Viktor. You always told me that information needed to be presented in its correct context, didn't you? From the Schmidt Legal office I went home: I reckoned I had perhaps two hours before someone spotted the files were missing, so I typed the letter on the paper I'd taken from the office. The letter said that I was a new messenger, authorised to have access to the Schmidt Legal files at the depository on Grosse Gallusstrasse, the place you told me about. I used the name of my late father-in-law: he died three years ago and we've kept his *personalausweis*. I copied Alois Schmidt's signature from the brochure I'd found in reception.

'I then went to the depository. It was very busy – it seemed that just about every law firm in Frankfurt was using it – so the clerk who checked my papers was in a hurry and just glanced at the letter and the identity card. I think once he saw I had files with me he thought there was no problem, I'd obviously brought them from the office on Hochstrasse. He gave me a badge and told me where to go, which was down a corridor in an enormous basement. When I found the Schmidt Legal section I left the files in the "in" area and then went to look for the archive section. I was quite enjoying myself to be honest, Viktor: that sense of danger, of trying to stay one step ahead of whoever may be following you, I'd forgotten quite how exciting that is. Over the past couple of days I've actually found myself regretting the fact that I retired from your game.'

'You didn't retire, *synok*. Carry on.'

'I found the section for 1968. The files were arranged under the names of the different lawyers and then by the month in which a case was started. Under the Alois Schmidt files for April were four relating to new matrimonial cases. The first one was a woman, called—'

'I'm only interested in the male clients, *synok*.'

'Very well then: the first male client he saw in April 1968 on a matrimonial matter was… hang on, here we are, a Franz Sommer.'

'From?'

'Offenbach, which is, to all intents and purposes, part of Frankfurt.'

'And do you have any details about his occupation – and age?'

'I do have that, yes. An architect. Herr Sommer was an archi-tect, a sixty-year-old architect.'

'No, next one please, *synok*.'

'A Günter Schulte, apparently his wife was having an affair. You said you thought the client did not live in Frankfurt? Well

Herr Schulte fits the bill: his address is in Mainz. He was thirty-eight and a television executive. I know ZDF is based in Mainz so maybe…'

'Unlikely, *synok*. What about the third client?'

'Here we are. Christ, Viktor – this one lived even further away. This could be your man!'

Chapter 20

Georg Stern's Story

When Viktor returned to see Georg Stern the following morning he was still shocked at what Peter had revealed about Richter's identity.

He was clearly expected at the offices of Rostt Legal on Fasanenstrasse. 'Herr Stern asked for you to go straight through. Coffee, perhaps…? Sugar?'

'I read the testimony of Herr Krause,' said Stern in a matter of fact manner as he tapped the document on his desk. It was as if he was referring to a routine property transaction. 'I decided the best way to present my story would be verbally, by recording it.' He pushed a cassette player on the desk towards Viktor. 'It is very simple to use. Just press this button here to play and the one next to it – yes, that one – to pause. Come, follow me.'

Georg Stern opened a door in the panelled wall behind him and led Viktor into a narrow, windowless room with a long table and chairs taking up most of the space. Prints of hunting scenes were hung on the walls.

'This room is where the partners meet, it's very private – you won't be disturbed. It would be best if you listen straight through and then come back into my office. You can ask me any questions then. I will say one thing though: there are sections of the story – for instance when I describe events at the house near Magdeburg – where I have been brief. That is because I don't dispute what Otto said in his account, but see no point in repeating it. I'll leave you alone now.

Viktor settled into a chair and waited for Georg Stern to leave before pressing 'play'. Stern's voice was quiet, as if he hadn't wanted to be overheard, and Viktor turned up the volume.

I was born in Berlin on 15th March 1926. My parents were Arno and Eva Stern. We were Jewish but not at all religious: we were what you would call a secular family, so much so that I wasn't even circumcised. My father was thirty-nine when I was born, my mother ten years younger.

Father was an optician with premises in König Strasse and was most successful until the Nuremberg Laws, one of which prohibited Jews from owning businesses. In 1935 my father was required to sell his practice for next to nothing to a man who ran a much less successful opticians nearby. The man who took over the business failed to do a proper stock take so my father brought home a good deal of spectacles, lenses and equipment, meaning he was able to scrape together some kind of living by supplying spectacles on a private basis. My mother was a dressmaker.

We lived on the second floor of a small apartment block in the northern part of Charlottenburg, on Mindener Strasse, just south of Osnabrücker Strasse. After Kristallnacht in November 1938 things really got bad, especially after we had to wear those dreadful yellow stars.

You may well wonder why my parents did not leave Germany while it was still possible. In the early 1930s there were 160,000 Jews in Berlin. By the time Jewish emigration was banned in 1941, 90,000 had emigrated. My mother had relatives in London and had even lived there for a few years before she married my father. She spoke excellent English and, from a young age, she spoke English with me. From the moment my father lost his business my mother wanted to leave Germany. It was still possible then. But my father would not go. Despite what had happened, he thought things could not get any worse. He felt more German than Jewish and said: why should he leave his country because of a few thugs who would not be around for very long? After all, he would argue, he had fought in the German Army in the Great War and even the Nazis, he would say, are not going to arrest an army veteran. My parents had terrible arguments. By 1941 when even my father accepted we should leave, it was too late. We felt doomed.

The event that changed the course of my life began on the afternoon of Tuesday 23rd September, 1941. There was a knock at the door and we were terrified: we assumed it was the Gestapo coming to arrest us. My mother went to the door and then called my father and me into the lounge and there she was with Herr Weber and his son, Horst. The Webers were non-Jewish family friends: Heike Weber had been a colleague of my mother's when she was a dressmaker. They had become very friendly, especially as her son and I were the same age. My mother used to describe Frau Weber as a truly good person, always helping other people without making a fuss about it. Herr Weber – Manfred – was a civil servant and somewhat shy, like my father. Horst and I had less in common. He was rather studious and wore glasses and was also asthmatic, whereas I was more interested in sport. So our families were friends right up until the war started, when it became too dangerous for the Webers to be openly friendly with a Jewish family, and my mother felt we shouldn't put them in danger by socialising with them.

Herr Weber explained that because of his work at the Transport ministry he had discovered that the arrest of Jews in our area was going to take place the coming Thursday – and he and his wife had come up with a plan. They had recently moved to a new house in Treskow Strasse, in Wedding, and in the basement had discovered a small hidden cellar which would be a perfect hiding place for me.

I remember my parents and Herr Weber then went into the kitchen alone to discuss it. When they came back I could see they had been crying and my mother was holding my father's hand, which was most unusual. They said they could see it was a good idea and my father explained how I could travel safely to the Weber's house. Horst was the same age as me and a similar height. We also both had light brown hair. With one or two "adjustments", as he put it, I could pass for Horst. The plan was this: I would take Horst's coat, which obviously did not have a yellow star on it, and his papers and travel with Herr Weber back to Treskow Strasse. Horst would stay that night in the apartment with my parents. I would be hidden in the cellar and the next day, after work, Herr Weber would come back to the apartment, with Horst's papers and coat, to bring him home. He would also be able to bring back a small case for me.

My mother packed a few things for me, not much, enough to go into a school bag. While she did that, my father went into his study and prepared a pair of spectacles, just like Horst's but with clear lenses as my eyesight was perfect. Our departure was hurried: my mother hugged me and I could tell that she was very close to tears.

Frau Weber was most welcoming and explained they'd just moved to this area. Horst should have started a new school a week previously, but because of his asthma had yet to attend. I clearly recall her saying that having me around the house would help his confidence. Then they took me to the cellar. The basement was reached down a steep flight of stairs and had been converted into Frau Weber's workshop. On the floor against the far wall was a large trunk. Herr Weber pulled it aside to reveal a trapdoor with a ladder, leading down into the cellar. They had put a strip of carpet on the floor with a mattress, some boxes and a chair. There was a small table near the trapdoor, which had a bowl and a jug of water on it, with a towel hanging on a hook on the wall. On the wall was a small light, with a cord to turn it on and off. Herr Weber explained that the lamp was wired to the mains, so there was no problem about keeping it on. I would be allowed into the house once or twice a day to use the bathroom, but they felt that for the time being, at least, it would be best to stay in the cellar. And with that, they left me. I slept very little. I thought about my parents and became somewhat tearful: the fact that I might never see them again was beginning to dawn on me. I do remember feeling terribly grateful to the Webers and wondering how I would ever repay them.

My overwhelming memory of the next day – the Wednesday – was the utter silence in my cellar, so much so that I could hear every sound my body made. It was quite unnerving. If I had not kept the wall lamp on for much of the time I think I would have begun to go mad. But as the day went on, I did see the silence in a different way. I realised that unless someone informed on me, it would be impossible to detect me. Don't forget, at home we'd spent every waking moment waiting for the Gestapo to come.

Herr Weber had said he'd be back with Horst at around six, but seven o'clock passed and nothing – then seven thirty, and by eight o'clock I was beginning to get concerned. And then I heard the noise. It sounded as if an animal was dying a most painful and horrendous death. It did not last long, perhaps two or three seconds, and then it stopped, suddenly, as if it had been stifled. For the next hour, nothing: silence. As you can probably imagine, by now I was very worried. Just after nine the trapdoor unbolted and Herr Weber was there pointing a torch at me. I noticed that his hand was shaking so violently that the beam bounced wildly around the cellar. He told me to hurry upstairs. I followed him out of the basement and up into the house and into a side parlour, where Frau Weber was sitting upright on a sofa. The curtains were drawn and her eyes were red and she had been crying. She looked most distressed, as did Herr Weber. He stood behind his wife and was very pale, as if he was ill. For a minute or so neither of them said a word and then she said, 'Tell him, Manfred.'

'Georg,' he said. 'I went to your parents' apartment in Mindener Strasse after work at five o'clock as arranged. As I reached the top of the stairs I noticed your door was sealed with tape and there was a sign on it. I went closer and saw that it was from the police, saying that no one was to enter without authorisation. I stood outside the door for a moment, confused and unsure whether to knock. At that moment, the door of the apartment opposite opened and an elderly lady appeared in the doorway – your neighbour Frau Braun. I have to warn you, Georg, Frau Braun told me something truly terrible. Early this morning the Gestapo came. They took away your father, your mother and Horst, except your neighbour assumed he was you. She said she heard all the commotion and looked out of her window and into the street and saw the three of them being led towards a truck. She would have seen them from above and from behind, so she would not have known that Horst was not you. She also said she had heard that all the other Jews in the neighbourhood had been taken away that morning. I don't understand it: my information was the arrests would be tomorrow. You do know what this means, don't you, Georg? It means that the authorities have arrested your parents and will be sending them out with the other Jews to the East. And they are also sending our dear Horst. They assume he is you.'

Frau Weber spoke next. 'I cannot imagine that Horst will say anything – to do so would implicate Herr Weber and me and we would be arrested.' She said it would arouse suspicion if the school and neighbours realised Horst had disappeared so there was no alternative now but for me to assume Horst's identity in all aspects of his life. It was fortunate they had only been in the house for a few weeks and so the neighbours hardly knew Horst: because of his asthma he had stayed indoors most of the time, and he hadn't been to the school yet. She said they rarely had visitors and all their family was in Stuttgart. In the event of anyone visiting, I would stay in the cellar.

So I became Horst Weber. It was surprisingly easy. I wore his clothes, slept in his bed, read his books and ate his food. I lived his life. On the rare occasions when the Webers had visitors who had known Horst, they would say he was out and I would hide in the cellar. But it was as if I were a stranger living in the house. Nothing could replace their son and they were grief-stricken, my constant presence in their lives a reminder of what they had lost. They had, in effect, sacrificed their son to save me.

School was my salvation. No one there knew me already, so I was just another new student. I was very good at sport, so I fitted in well. I had to join the Hitler Youth, which I did in April 1942, not long after my sixteenth birthday. It would have been madness not to — especially in our circumstances. I was more than competent in all their activities. I even look quite Aryan and I wasn't circumcised, so I easily passed all their requirements.

I always endeavoured to be positive and even optimistic. I had a sense that everything was going to work out fine. I hoped my parents would survive, Horst too. That may sound deluded now, but I think it was my way of coping with such an awful trauma.

My life took another dramatic turn in August 1943. I was seventeen, and still at school. My Hitler Youth group was attached to a civil defence unit. We helped with night patrols, rescuing people from bombed buildings, that kind of thing. On the night of August 14th I'd been on patrol and returned home at approximately two in the morning. There was quite a lot of activity as I came down Treskow Strasse and as I turned the bend, I saw that our house had been destroyed, along with one or two others around it. On the pavement were the corpses of the Webers. It was a terrible shock of course and people assumed I was devastated. A neighbour, Frau Schulte, took me in. I realised that the only people in Berlin who knew I wasn't really Horst Weber were dead, so in truth I was safer than I'd been before they were killed.

I stayed at school until December 1943, when I joined the SS. I transferred to Freiburg in March 1944. Otto Schröder would have come to the barracks in Freiburg in the April. I knew him as Otto, so that is the name I will use for him, rather than Bernhard Krause. I ought to add here that my English was also excellent thanks to my mother.

I have read his account very carefully and while there are some small details in it I don't remember, by and large it is very accurate, and I don't see any point in repeating what he says. It goes without saying that I am deeply ashamed of many of the events he describes, not least the murders at the police station in Dortmund. As Otto says, there is no doubt that we took part in a war crime.

When the officers explained the purpose of our mission – for us to be captured and then wait years for instructions, and all this talk about a Fourth Reich – well it was such a ridiculous and dangerous notion that from the outset I determined to escape as soon as the opportunity arose. That opportunity came in Essen. I knew I was being followed by a Gestapo officer, so I decided to go into the area around Krupp Strasse where it was quite built up. I thought I had a better chance of losing the Gestapo in the network of tight streets and apartment blocks there. But just after I entered Planck Strasse an air raid began, and I decided to run. There was an explosion and the impact threw me to the ground. When I got up there was no sign of the man who'd been following me.

Nearby was a crater in the pavement, caused by a bomb which had impacted where the building joined the pavement, and exposed a basement. I jumped into it and then scurried like a rat through a warren of rooms and basements, dropping lower, into the sewer system, when I spotted the chance to do so. Eventually I met up with a group of people who had been hiding under the city for months: a mixed group of about a dozen deserters, and resisters.

And so I began my life in the cellars and sewers of Essen. As far as they were concerned I was Horst Weber, from Berlin. My parents had been killed in an air raid. I'd been conscripted into the Wehrmacht and then deserted. I avoided politics. I wanted to come across as a young man who did not want to fight in the war, rather than as an anti-Nazi. Mostly we just hid in the cellars trying to avoid the war, venturing out occasionally to find food.

When the American Army arrived in the city on 10th April I had no problems, because they soon realised that the people who had been hiding underground were, at the very least, not Nazis. I eventually met an officer from the US 507th Parachute Infantry Regiment, which had captured Essen, and when he discovered I spoke good English I ended up working for him for three months. I never told the Americans the truth, it would have been too complicated.

My plan was to get back to Berlin and somehow make Horst Weber disappear and Georg Stern reappear – apparently from hiding. The 507th moved to France in June, which is when I decided to go back to Berlin. Berlin had not been captured until early May – by the Russians – and for a while it would have been far too dangerous for me to return to the city. However, in July the city was divided up – with the western half of the city in sectors controlled by the Americans, the British and the French, and the eastern half under the control of the Russians. Once the British and Americans had full control of their sectors, I could return. My American officer arranged my papers and I travelled to Berlin on 1st August.

From the airport I got a lift as far as Wilmersdorfer Strasse and from there walked to Mindener Strasse. The destruction was quite marked in the area, but our block was apparently undamaged.

I recall waiting outside our block for some time before going upstairs. I feared that, any minute now, someone was going to tell me that my parents were dead. And so I was terribly nervous and apprehensive. I climbed the stairs and could hear laughter and the voice of a man and a woman from inside our apartment. For one brief and extraordinary moment I actually believed that my parents were there, so I knocked on the door. There was a sudden silence from inside and a delay of a minute or so before I heard someone walk down the hallway to open the door. It was a man who came to the door, probably in his early forties, quite big and just wearing a vest and trousers. His accent was a very working class one, from the East.

He asked me what I wanted, in quite a curt manner. Behind him, a woman and two young children appeared in the hallway of our apartment. On one wall I could see a beautiful gilt mirror which had belonged to my father's family. I explained this was my parents' apartment, and they had been arrested in 1941. I didn't know what else to say, so there was a pause. At first, he looked very shocked, but then he turned angry and went red in the face. 'And what has that got to do with me?' he said. 'You can fuck off. I've been the legal tenant since September 1941.'

Finding these people here seemed to confirm all my worst fears. I politely explained that the apartment had been illegally taken from my parents and I now wanted it back — that he should move out. The man looked outraged. At the top of his voice he shouted, 'Get lost!' I shook my head. I find it hard to explain, but I felt confident. I knew I was in the right. Instead of doing as he requested, I tried to push past him into the apartment, although he was far too heavy for me to budge. His wife and children started screaming and he struggled with me. And then he screamed out, 'Dirty Jew!' Can you imagine, shouting that out in Berlin in July 1945, after everything that had happened? At that moment I heard the voice of Frau Braun, our neighbour. She was standing in the corridor between the two apartments, her thin arms folded across her chest. When I turned round, she gasped and said, 'Georg. You are alive!' I saw that there were tears in her eyes.

Frau Braun was the neighbour who'd spoken to Herr Weber when my parents and Horst were arrested by the Gestapo. She was always most kind and proper with us. She was, what you'd describe as, a refined lady. She said in quite a loud voice, 'This is his apartment and I can prove it.' From there, a terrible row developed. The fat man insisted he had papers and, even if my parents had owned the apartment, they would now be dead so there was nothing I could do about it. He added that they deserved to die. Berlin had been destroyed, Germany had been defeated and it was all the fault of the Jews. He then became very threatening: he had in his hand a broom and was jabbing it in the direction Frau Braun and myself, shouting that if we didn't leave him alone he'd kill us. I was now most concerned about Frau Braun. She was a tiny lady and just one poke from the broom would have hurt her, so I hurried her into her apartment and as I did so I heard the door of my parents' apartment slam shut, and bolts ramming home.

Frau Braun's apartment was very neat. Just about every wall appeared to be a bookcase – it was like a library. The first thing I did was ask if she had seen my parents, or heard of them, since they were taken away, but she said no. 'But you were with them?' she said. So I told her I had managed to escape and had been in hiding ever since outside of Berlin. 'You'll stay here until we can sort out your apartment,' she said. We hadn't really been talking for very long when there was a loud knock at the door. I feared that it was the fat man, possibly with friends. I was afraid, but Frau Braun called out, asking who it was and a man's voice replied – Herr Tegel, a neighbour from downstairs. He had brought help.

When I opened the door, Herr Tegel was standing there with four British soldiers. One of them spoke to us in the most appalling German. I think he was trying to ask if there was a problem, so I told him in English that there was, and they came into Frau Braun's apartment. Herr Tegel explained that he'd heard the commotion and had come up to see what was going on. He was watching from the stairwell and recognised me. He'd decided to go and get help, and had found a British patrol outside.

I told the soldiers my story, or at least a version of it: how I had escaped from the Nazis, had been in hiding and had ended up in Essen where I had joined the anti-Nazi resistance. I showed them my papers, explaining that obviously I had been hiding under an assumed name. The sergeant who was in charge was very sympathetic, but said he would need some proof that I was really Georg Stern. I realised that I couldn't prove I was Georg Stern. All the papers I had were in the name of Horst Weber, and any papers linking me with my real identity would have disappeared. I translated this into German. Then from the back of a sideboard Frau Braun produced a package wrapped in heavy brown paper, held together by string. As she unwrapped it I started to recognise the contents: some old school books of mine, my old identity card with the 'J' for Jew stamped on it, photographs of me with my parents, including one taken outside this very apartment block. There were notebooks, letters, other papers and some jewellery. Frau Braun explained that my mother had given her this parcel the night before they were taken away. I was now Georg Stern once again.

The sergeant seemed satisfied because we left Frau Braun's apartment and went over to mine – the three of us and the four soldiers. I was escorted into the lounge, the room my father called the study. The German family were standing by the sofa, looking quite terrified. I noticed on the mantelpiece a pair of silver candlesticks, which we'd *occasionally used for lighting candles on Friday nights. They were given to my parents for their wedding. I told the sergeant that he would find my parents' names engraved at the base of the candlesticks, along with '1925,' the year of their wedding. And when he picked up them up, there was the date and their names, Arno and Eva. By then, the four soldiers had been joined in the apartment by an officer, a young man who spoke very good German.*

The sergeant explained what had happened and the officer turned to the German family and spoke to them very politely. They were in the apartment illegally, he said. They had fifteen minutes to gather their possessions and get out. At that they became hysterical, that is the only word for it. The woman and the two young children, both boys, cried and the man ranted and raved. The officer kept very calm, looking at his watch the whole time. With just a minute or so before their deadline, the father said they weren't leaving. He demanded to see the authorities. Why should a soldier believe the word of a filthy Jew? With that, the officer snapped. He threw a punch right at the man's jaw, stunning him, then grabbed him by the scruff of the neck and, with the help of one of his men, frogmarched him out of the door. The man tried to push his way back into the apartment. The officer, who was much smaller than the man, pushed him back into the corridor and towards the stairwell. The man stumbled and charged back at the officer but he was ready for the attack, landing a perfectly-timed kick on the lower part of the man's chest. He went flying down the stairs, backwards. He fell onto the next landing with an almighty crash, clearly very badly hurt. The officer told his men to get the woman and children out of the flat, and said that I should point out what they could take with them.

I was more shocked than anything else — both at the violence and at the speed at which things were happening. Also, I was frightened. I had grown up in Berlin when it was the Jews who were kicked around. What would happen to me? Would this man and his friends come back for me? By now, the soldiers had bundled the family into the street, with a few of their possessions. The officer came back to check that I was all right. I explained my story to him again and showed him my Horst Weber papers. He promised to get me new papers in my proper name. He also promised that he would keep a guard on our apartment block to protect not just me, but also Frau Braun and Herr Tegel. The officer returned the following day with a full set of papers for me, and also with the offer of a job. I was to be a guide and interpreter.

I worked for the British most days and, in return, I got some money and more food than most people in Berlin. I was able to help Frau Braun and Herr Tegel out: I gave her the food and each night she cooked for us, quite delicious meals. We talked about everything but the war. We mostly talked about the future. Both of them were old socialists, who had somehow managed to slip through the Nazi's net, probably because they were old and neither of them had been members of a political party. Herr Tegel was quite romantic about the Russians. He even talked about wanting to live in the Soviet sector.

One thing you have to say about Germans is that we are marvellous record keepers. The Nazis were meticulous in recording everything, so the names of all the people arrested and the transports they were sent on, certainly from Berlin – all of that existed. I was able to establish some of what had happened to my parents quite quickly. According to the records, Arno and Eva Stern and their son Georg had been taken to Sachsenhausen after their arrest. Sachsenhausen was a concentration camp just north of Berlin; it was where most of Berlin's Jews were taken in the first instance.

My parents were on a transport of 1,529 Jews to Auschwitz on 2nd March 1943, but there was no record of a Georg Stern being on that transport. And then I couldn't find any information about what happened to them after that.

Most days I would go down to a Jewish information and refugee centre that had been set up in the old synagogue in Oranienburger Strasse, which amazingly was still standing. There you could get information on missing people, and it was where refugees registered their names. I had put my name on the list: Georg Stern, son of Arno and Eva Stern. I thought nothing of it. Who'd be looking for me? Once or twice I bumped into people I knew, more by sight than anything else, but in truth I was alone in the world.

As I say, I visited the Jewish centre most days. However, in the middle of September – I cannot remember the date other than the fact that it was a Monday – I attended the Day of Atonement service there. I was not religious, but there would be a lot of people there and I thought I might recognise someone. Don't ask me who. You must realise that I was nineteen and, apart from a couple of kindly neighbours, I had no friends or family. To have come across a distant cousin twice removed with whom I had nothing whatsoever in common would have been like a miracle. But there was no one, and I was so depressed I did not return to the centre for quite a few days. I just stayed in the apartment. It was a week before I snapped out of this gloom.

I returned to the centre on Tuesday 25th September. I went to the information desk and gave my name. That was the procedure. You gave your name and if you were already registered they would check on their lists and tell you if anyone had been asking for you. So I gave my name and the man behind the desk nodded and said, in a most routine manner, 'Yes, there has been an enquiry for you.' Naturally, I assumed this was a mistake. Who would be enquiring after me?

But he went to an office at the back and I was called through, where a nice American lady told me to sit down and then she sat down too and closed the door. 'Do you know an Eva Stern?' she asked.

'That was my mother,' I replied.

'Do you know what happened to her?' she asked. I said I knew she had been on a transport to Auschwitz in March 1943, along with my father. 'Well, she came in last Tuesday looking for you,' she said. I was so shocked that I don't think I said anything for quite a long time after that. 'In fact, she came in last Wednesday, Thursday and Friday. We haven't seen her since.' Well, I had all these questions, naturally. How were they sure it was her? Had they taken an address for her? How was she? How had she survived? What about my father? The American lady was sorry. My mother had been very secretive. She had just drifted in and then out of the centre, refusing to leave any details. The American lady said that she had seen her herself on the Friday. My mother, she said, looked like most survivors: as if they had already lived three lives, each one harder than the other. She said I could remain there as long as I wished. She was sure my mother would return. I stayed there for all of that Tuesday, but there was no sign of her. I arrived before the centre opened on the Wednesday, and waited outside for long after it closed, and still no sign. I did the same on the Thursday.

On the Friday I again arrived early, but there was already a large queue: food was being handed out to help tide survivors over through the weekend. The guards were checking everyone's papers so I decided to move away until things quietened down at the entrance. By now, I had reasoned that this was all a mistake. If the woman really had been my mother, and she knew I was alive, why had she not returned to the centre? And why had she not come back to the apartment in Mindener Strasse, which was surely the most obvious place for her to go? Anyway, I decided to go for a walk: up Oranienburger Strasse and then down Friedrichstrasse, heading in no direction in particular and feeling taunted at having my mother dangled in front of me only to be whipped away like some cruel trick. I was just approaching the bridge over the Spree when an elderly woman appeared by my side, her thin hands gripping my elbow. This happened all the time, people were desperate for anything they could get. I reached into my pocket for some coins when I heard her whisper my name. 'Georg.'

I would never have recognised my mother. She had aged and was painfully thin, and her hair was a dirty grey. We fell into each other's arms and I was astonished at her strength, not letting me go for many minutes.

We walked slowly back to the centre in Oranienburger Strasse, hardly saying a word to each other. They gave us a room where we could talk, but we were both too much in shock to say very much. I recall we both kept asking if the other was all right, and reassuring each other that we were. I realised that we needed to get out of the centre and back to the apartment. Fortunately the centre had access to a car and after an hour or so we were driven back to Mindener Strasse. When I told her we were getting a lift back to the apartment, she got very agitated. 'What about the soldiers?' she kept saying. When she'd returned to Berlin in early September, she said, she'd gone straight to Mindener Strasse, but when she got there she saw a soldier on guard outside the apartment block and assumed he was waiting to arrest her, so she went away. She returned that night and the following day, but he was still there so she never returned. I explained that the soldier had been there to protect us.

It must have been late morning when we returned to our apartment. We began to talk. By the time we finished talking, it was dark – that is how long we talked for. First of all, I told her my story. She made me promise to tell her everything, which I did. I told her about the Webers, how they had been killed, how I had been recruited into the SS and had joined this special unit. I told her about our training, about how I managed to escape in Essen and had eventually returned to Berlin. I even told her that I had been ordered to kill a prisoner.

She reacted very calmly, as if I was talking about school, to be honest. When I had finished she said that I had made it through because of my own instincts for survival, and I should be very proud of that. She made me promise that I would never recount my story to anyone else, ever again. There could be repercussions, she said. As far as the world was concerned, I should say I'd gone into hiding and survived. I had been lucky. No one need know about the Webers or the SS or anything like that. I had to promise her. We would never discuss it again, she said. Not with each other and not with anyone else. And that is what happened. This is the first time since 1945 that I have shared my story with anyone.

Then she told me her story – how they were arrested the morning after I left and taken to a police station, and from there to Sachsenhausen. All of that time and for the next few days, Horst didn't say a word. Thinking now about the way my mother described his reaction, I would say that he was in a state of shock. But then, one night, he told one of the SS officers he was not Georg Stern and that he wasn't Jewish. My mother, father and Horst were summoned to an interrogation room. They told Horst to repeat his story. Apparently he never gave his real name: he obviously wanted to do what he could to protect his parents. But he insisted that he was not Jewish, and the real Georg Stern was being hidden by non-Jews. The next part of this story is truly appalling. An officer ordered Horst to remove his trousers and pants. Right there, in front of everyone, can you imagine? My mother said he just froze on the spot, as if he realised what was going to happen. A guard went over and pulled down his trousers and pants. They all laughed because, unbelievably, Horst had been circumcised. My mother said she remembered Frau Weber

227

telling her, when he was about four or five, that Horst had this procedure because of a medical problem. The officer apparently said something like, 'So, you're trying to tell us that you're not Jewish, are you?' And with that, he shot Horst in the penis and then said, "Well, you are now!" My mother said it was worse than a nightmare; Horst was writhing on the floor in sheer agony, blood everywhere. The SS were laughing their heads off, and she and my father had to act as if their son had just been shot. She said my father stood rooted to the spot. She felt she had to go over to Horst but, as she did so, she was kicked out of the way. After a few minutes one of the guards shot him in the head.

My mother said her overwhelming emotion, for which she felt very guilty, was relief that at least I was now safer. They remained in Sachsenhausen for well over a year. My father was in much demand repairing the spectacles of SS troops, while my mother worked as a seamstress. They had skills, you see. This was how they survived − until they were sent to Auschwitz. My mother told me that the last time she saw my father was when the train arrived at the camp, and they encountered the notorious selection. He was sent one way, she was sent the other. She never saw him again: he'd been sent to a gas chamber as soon as he arrived. My mother survived because when the female guards heard that she was a dressmaker, they took her to a special barracks and put her to the test. After that she spent every hour of every day making beautiful dresses for the female camp guards and for the wives of SS officers. Her unusual existence continued until the autumn of 1944, which was when the Nazis knew that the game was up and they started to destroy evidence of what had gone on at the camp. From then on, my mother was a 'normal' prisoner, if that is the right word. Because she was less exhausted than the average woman prisoner, she survived until the January of 1945, when she was sent on a so-called death march. She ended up at the concentration camp at Flossenbürg, in

Bavaria. She was still in Flossenbürg when it was liberated by the Americans towards the end of April. She was very ill by then. She had caught typhoid and heaven knows what else, so she was sent to a hospital for liberated prisoners at Dachau, which was quite nearby, and then to a convalescent hospital in northern Bavaria. After that she came back to Berlin.

She was very calm, very factual. She was almost devoid of emotion, even when she talked about the murders of Horst and my father. Occasionally she would shrug her shoulders or look down, but her tone was steady and she never cried. When she had finished speaking, she said that was that. We had both told each other our stories and we would never repeat them to anyone ever again. That was an instruction. And then a remarkable thing happened. She stood up and no longer seemed so old, so hunched. She ruffled my hair and said I needed a haircut. My mother had been through Sachsenhausen, Auschwitz and Flossenbürg and had just been reunited with me, and she was worried about the length of my hair. But actually, that was how she survived – by putting the past out of her mind. It was as if, in that instant, she went back to normal. From that moment on, she never again discussed what had happened during the war. I went to university, qualified as a lawyer, married a woman whose family had been hidden by friends in Grunewald, had two children and… here I am. My mother died in 1969. She was seventy-two, and never moved out of the apartment in Mindener Strasse. In fact, she rarely left it.

I certainly recognised Otto in 1968 in Frankfurt: I was as shocked as he was. I do not dispute anything in his version of the story. In fact, I was so convinced he was going to report me to the authorities that I returned immediately to Berlin, half expecting the police to be waiting there. I decided to wait a day or two before doing anything. Otto – Bernhard – was correct: I do remember ringing the firm

he worked for the next day to ask if an Otto Schröder
worked there. They insisted they had never heard of him.
I then came to much the same conclusion as he appears to
have done – namely that it would not be in his interests
to inform on me. We were as guilty as each other. Having
read his story, I feel desperately sorry for him. It would have
been good for us to meet and talk. I could have helped him.
I am truly sorry about how he died.

'You are the first person I have shared my entire story with, since
my mother,' said Georg Stern when Viktor returned to the office.
'I can only hope you appreciate how circumstances forced me to
do many of the awful things I have described. It was the war, and
terrible things happened in it. Did you fight in the war?'

'Yes, if "fighting" is the correct word.'

'And which side were you on?'

'The same side as you, I suppose.'

Stern laughed sarcastically. 'The same side as me? Even now
I'm not sure which side I was on. Look, I don't want to be
undignified and start pleading but since the war I have led – I
hope – a decent and respectable life. Now, all that—'

'I promised you yesterday, Herr Stern – if you co-operate
with me nothing more will come of this. It is enough that you
have confirmed Otto Schröder's story, which in turn corroborates
another account we have. I have no interest in punishing or
exposing you. All I wanted was for you to tell me the truth, and
now I will ask one more thing of you.'

'Which is?'

Viktor removed an envelope from his bag and emptied its
contents onto Georg Stern's desk: half a dozen photographs of
the same man, some in close up, others taken from a distance. He
watched Stern carefully as he spread the photos out and thought
he spotted a flicker of recognition as one or two tiny beads of
sweat gathered on Stern's upper lip.

'Do you know who this man is?'

The lawyer picked up one of the close ups, and then another photograph.

He nodded. 'It's Erich Schäfer.'

'You're sure, Herr Stern? It is thirty years since you've seen him.'

'It's Erich Schäfer, I'm telling you. What happens now?'

'Nothing as far as you're concerned, Herr Stern – I promised. It is enough that you have confirmed this is Schäfer. I do have one further question for you though: Wilhelm Richter, tell me about him.'

'In what sense?'

'Otto Schröder says he was the worst of the lot.'

'He most certainly was.'

'I myself interviewed an SS officer who witnessed Richter committing war crimes at the end of the war.'

'That doesn't surprise me in the least. He was the most evil person I've ever encountered. But why are you asking these questions about Richter?'

'He's still alive, Herr Stern – and in West Germany.'

For the first time, genuine fear crept across Georg Stern's face. 'Oh my God.'

Chapter 21

'Here we are. Christ, Viktor – this one lived even further away. This could be your man!

'A Heinz Fleischhauer, fortytwo years old. According to the notes I made this was his third divorce, he'd been accused of being cruel to his wife. You'll never guess where he lives.'

'Go on, *synok*.'

'Cologne, Viktor. And this is interesting: against profession Herr Schmidt wrote "Government" and then, in brackets, along-side that, "BfV"! You know what the BfV is, don't you, Viktor?'

–

As soon as Viktor had finished his conversation with Peter the previous evening, he'd hurried out of his hotel on Budapester Strasse. The revelation that Richter was a BfV officer called Heinz Fleischhauer had unnerved him. He needed to think, he needed to plan – and a warm hotel room was no place to do either of those things.

He mentally ran through what he knew about the situation, and it all made sense. Reinhard Schäfer had an agent in the BfV, codename Goalkeeper, who was almost certainly Wilhelm Richter. But until this evening Viktor hadn't known Richter's current identity – he could have been any one of the thousands of people working for the German security service. Now every-thing pointed to it being 'Heinz Fleischhauer', the man Bernhard Krause had spotted in April 1968 and had been convinced was

232

Richter. If Fleischhauer was forty-two years of age in 1968 he'd have been have nineteen in 1945, making him the right age to be Wilhelm Richter. And Cologne, where 'Heinz' lived, was the headquarters of the BfV.

And then there was the question of Reinhard Schäfer: what was this KGB officer doing running a Nazi war criminal as an agent? Could Reinhard Schäfer and Erich Schäfer really be the same person? Georg Stern had confirmed as much, but Viktor couldn't make sense of it.

Most importantly, 1968 was eight years ago now. He needed to know if Fleischhauer was still alive and, if he was, whether he was still working for the BfV. Viktor walked slowly along Lützowufer, by the Landwehr Canal, and by the time he reached Lützowplatz he was sure he hadn't been followed. He found a telephone kiosk and from there rang Irma's apartment in East Berlin. He'd taken as many precautions as possible in securing her phone, including a device that was meant to indicate if a call was being listened to, but he was still running a big risk. It was one he had to take.

'It's Joachim, about your electric problems...'

'You've taken your time, Joachim! It's all fixed now.'

They could talk.

'Get a pen and paper... ready? OK: Heinz Fleischhauer. He could be Goalkeeper. Everything points to it. See if he's still working for them in Cologne.'

'When do you need to know this by?'

'First thing tomorrow morning.'

She knew better than to argue: they'd picked up on the intelligence grapevine a rumour that the Stasi for some reason became interested in calls once they exceeded two minutes and forty seconds, which was very Stasi in its precision. That was, if they were monitoring her phone, which he didn't think they were.

'I'll go back now. I'll find an excuse. Don't ring again tonight.'

'Of course not...'

'Seven o'clock.'

He rang her back as promised at seven the next morning, from a telephone kiosk inside Zoo Station, which was beginning to fill with commuters.

'It worked out well. I told the duty officer I'd left my migraine medication in my desk. He was delighted to see me – he needed some help with something, which meant I could access the files without any suspicion.'

'Go on, this needs to be quick...'

'The list of BfV staff we have was last updated in February. There's a note which says that we only have about sixty per cent of the names, and only about half of those are complete names. However, there is an H. Fleischhauer listed. No first name, just an initial with "Herr" in front. He's based in the Cologne HQ but the list doesn't say what he does.'

'Did anyone see you what you were up to?'

'No. The duty officer was distracted. When are—'

'I have to go. I'll see you soon.'

Viktor leaned back against the glass divide of the kiosk, holding the phone under his chin with two hands, his eyes closed tight in thought. He was interrupted by an impatient knocking at the door, someone wanting to use the phone. Viktor indicated he should wait and dialled again, after checking he had enough change to see him through the next conversation.

'Ring me in half an hour at the hotel I told you I was staying at. I'll be in room twenty-six.'

He rang when he'd been told to. 'You know what time it is in England, don't you Viktor? We're a bloody hour behind you. You rang me at ten past six. The dog's never had such an early walk. It's deserted round here and I'm in a bloody phone box outside a bloody pub. Christ knows what anyone will think if they see me. I'm getting too old for this.'

'Listen, Edgar, Krause was right: it sounds like he did see Richter in 1968.'

'Have you identified him?'

'I believe so: everything points to him being a Heinz Fleischhauer who lives in Cologne and probably worked for the BfV in 1968. There is currently a Herr H. Fleischhauer with the BfV in Cologne.'

'I'd better get over there. Our people in Bonn are going to need to know there's a KGB agent—'

'Just wait, Edgar. Wait until I tell you when to go. I still have some matters to sort out here first.'

–

Viktor had first met Piotr Vasilyevich Kozlov in the mid-1950s. At that time Kozlov was a student at the Higher School of the KGB, after an unremarkable but unblemished dozen years in the army, and then a spell at one of the technical colleges in Moscow the KGB tended to recruit from. 'Unblemished' was how they described someone who didn't cause trouble, obeyed orders and had a modicum of intelligence. Viktor had been giving a course at the Higher School on interrogation and Kozlov was a diligent enough student, but not one who seemed destined for stardom: more a time-server than a high-flyer.

Viktor had come across Kozlov intermittently over the years, and each time was surprised at how well this somewhat unsophisticated man from Vladimirskaya Oblast was doing, which made Viktor realise he should perhaps be less dismissive of time-servers. Kozlov had worked his way through the usual departments in Moscow and then, rather surprisingly, was posted to Athens, followed by a series of increasingly important European stations.

After a spell in Brussels, Kozlov was posted to London, with diplomatic cover in the trade mission where, as far as Viktor could gather, Kozlov was ranked number three or four in the KGB station, which was quite impressive. Kozlov was one of the ninety Soviet diplomats expelled from London for espionage in September 1971. Being part of that group became something of an exaggerated badge of honour back in Moscow, where they behaved as if they'd been involved in the defence of Stalingrad.

So Viktor was not too surprised when, a year after being expelled from London, Piotr Vasilyevich Kozlov turned up in East Berlin as the KGB Head of Station. But by now Kozlov was in his fifties. His diligence was not as keenly applied as it once had been. Within just a few months, he began to behave as if he had reached the pinnacle of his career. He discovered distractions he'd hitherto avoided, including a taste for a certain type of German woman: young and very well-built, with a specialist interest in discipline. He began to drink heavily, and became increasingly lazy.

Moscow's reaction was to give him a high-flying deputy, which was how Viktor's protégé Yevgeny Yefimovich Mironov had arrived in East Berlin. Mironov was an altogether different proposition to Kozlov. He hailed from Leningrad, with the assurance and sophistication bordering on arrogance often associated with natives of that city. It didn't take him long at all to discover what a mess East Berlin station had become and he managed to persuade Kozlov – whose biggest fear was being removed from East Berlin and all its pleasures – to allow Viktor to come out and help.

Now Yevgeny Yefimovich Mironov had been promoted to Vienna, but even Kozlov knew better than to dispose of Viktor's services. The older man was too experienced and too wise, and he helped compensate for Kozlov's laziness. This did not mean Kozlov liked Viktor, if anything it caused a resentment which explained the current tension in Kozlov's office on the fifth floor of the Soviet Embassy in Unter den Linden. It was late in the afternoon on the last day of August, and the heatwave that had gripped Europe showed no signs of abating.

'Where have you been anyway, Viktor Leonidovich? I've hardly seen you for weeks.' Kozlov was one of those people who spoke far louder than necessary. Not shouting or sounding angry, but just at an unnecessarily high volume: as if he were addressing someone at the back of a large and noisy room.

'I told you, Piotr Vasilyevich, Mironov needed me in Vienna. You agreed.'

'I agreed to one visit. You seem to have moved there! And what's this I hear about you in popping up in Budapest?'

Viktor shrugged. He'd made the mistake of underestimating Kozlov's network of contacts and informers. 'A woman. You of all people, Piotr Vasilyevich, you'll understand.'

'But you have that woman here in Berlin! You should do what I do and keep her in Moscow. Now, maybe it would be better if you're honest with me... is there something going? You've not been anywhere else I should know about, have you?'

Viktor stared at Kozlov, unsure of how much more the other man knew.

'Because if you have... well, you know your role here is supposed to be advisory, and the last thing you're meant to be doing is running agents and suchlike. If I have to send you back to Moscow you'll never leave that city again, not even for your *dacha.*'

Viktor studied Kozlov's face and his expressions, his general demeanour. He knew something. Certainly not everything, but probably enough to require Viktor to be a bit more honest with him than he'd intended to be.

'Just say, Piotr Vasilyevich, hypothetically... if as a result of my work here – work you have sanctioned, I should add – I came across intelligence which, if true, could expose an operation working against the interests of the Soviet Union. And say – and this is hypothetical, remember – I used contacts going back many years to investigate this intelligence and as a result was able to confirm a plot from the depths of the Second World War. And say this hypothetical plot involved desperate measures taken by the Nazis as they faced defeat and compromises – even now – the integrity of this embassy and the Soviet Union...'

Kozlov said nothing, but raised his eyebrows, a mixture of astonishment and incredulity. Viktor had the impression Kozlov had struggled to follow him but was intrigued nonetheless. The thin red lines on his face seemed brighter and now he looked uncomfortable, pulling his earlobe.

'But as you say, Viktor Leonidovich, hypothetical.'

'So what I need to know, Piotr Vasilyevich, with this hypothetical case, is if I were to bring it to your attention, would you be grateful?'

'I'm not sure what you're on about to be honest, Krasotkin, but remember – this is fucking Berlin! Both sides of the city are full of former Nazis. Anyone over the age of fifty – give or take a year or two – would have been involved with them in one way or another, despite what they may tell you. I'd be more surprised if you came and told me you'd found someone who hadn't been a Nazi.'

'But if—'

'But if nothing, Viktor Leonidovich. Look, everyone knows what a hero you were in the war, but you also spent the following ten years interrogating Nazis. I'm not surprised you imagine they're about to take over the world.'

Viktor made to get up. 'Very well, Piotr Vasilyevich, but it's a shame. If anything came of this hypothetical case and it transpired you'd been aware of it but ignored my warnings – it would reflect very badly on you. But there we are... you're the boss, you obviously know better than me.'

Kozlov anxiously gestured for Viktor to sit down. 'Wait, wait, wait... maybe we don't play games, Viktor Leonidovich. Maybe we drop this hypothetical nonsense and you tell me what you want.' He was still speaking far too loudly, but now making an effort to sound less hostile. He looked worried.

'I want to interview one of your officers.'

'Who?'

'Reinhard Schäfer.'

Kozlov raised his eyebrows in surprise. 'Schäfer, why?'

'I believe he may have been involved with a Nazi plot at the end of the war and is still involved in it here... running it from this very building.'

Kozlov shifted uncomfortably in his chair and fidgeted with something on his desk. He had the appearance of a man who needed a drink. While he considered his response he tugged his earlobe again. 'Schäfer is a good Communist. His loyalty is unquestionable.'

'I thought you just said that anyone over the age of fifty in this city would have been involved with the Nazis? Don't forget, Schäfer was a police officer in Berlin during the war.'

'Yes Krasotkin, Kripo – a bloody detective, not exactly Gestapo. He was never a Nazi. He passed all the checks after the war. He'd been KPD in the '30s and when the KPD exiles returned from Moscow, a couple of them vouched for him personally: I've seen the bloody file. As far as I know, Ulbricht himself knew him. I understand where you're coming from, Viktor Leonidovich. You operated behind Nazi lines in the war and you spent years interrogating the bastards. You don't like Germans, but—'

'I have no problem with Germans – I had some outstanding German agents. I do have a problem with Nazis.'

'You'll need to give me facts, Krasotkin. Are you sure this isn't just a hunch?'

'I need to question him, Piotr Vasilyevich. Then I can provide you with evidence.'

'That's not how it works, you know that, Viktor Leonidovich. Schäfer is one of our top guys here: he runs some first class agents. One of them in particular – what we get from him is so good that Schäfer sends his reports straight to Andropov in Moscow. Even I don't know his true identity.'

But I do.

'Very well, Piotr Vasilyevich. I'll sort out the evidence, then come back to you.'

–

Viktor was now a hunter, and Reinhard Schäfer was his prey.

He'd decided to ignore Kozlov even though he knew there was a chance he'd warn Schäfer. He suspected Kozlov wouldn't risk it. When he'd warned Kozlov of the fallout of ignoring what he was saying he'd seen the flicker of worry in the other man's face, clearly turning over in his mind the career-limiting consequences of what could happen if what Viktor was saying were true. Warning Schäfer would be too risky. Viktor decided the most Kozlov would do was check the German's files and wait for Viktor to come to him with the evidence.

But Viktor could not risk waiting. He needed to get to Schäfer.

Chapter 22

England, September 1976: The Monday

'You MI6 chaps are like the proverbial London buses.'

'And in what way would that be, Paget?'

Detective Superintendent Martin Paget drummed his fingers in the little space available to do so on his desk and paused, hoping his brief silence would signal his irritation at being addressed by his surname alone. He didn't know what was worse: Lassiter talking to him like this, or Edgar using his first name. He couldn't see what was wrong with using his rank. Just because they didn't have them in MI6...

'Because one can go months without hearing from you lot and now I've not only had you hammering on my door and barging in, but Edgar too. When we in the Branch want something from you we have to crawl on our knees and wait patiently to be granted an audience, but when you want something from us – well, we're expected to drop everything and deliver it straight away. Don't forget, we're in the front line of fighting an actual war against the IRA. In case it's escaped your intention, it was only a couple of weeks ago they blew up our ambassador in Dublin. And then there are the bloody KGB, who somehow seem to have a free run in London...'

'Of course I'm aware of all that, Paget, and we're terribly grateful for your help. You say Edgar has been to see you: he's not one of ours any longer, you know, hasn't been for years.'

'I thought he was still involved?'

'Hardly. Don't forget, he left the Service years ago. He certainly shouldn't be going around claiming to be acting on behalf of the Service in any kind of official capacity: that would amount to misrepresentation.' Lassiter paused and when he resumed it was in a more of a 'matter-of-fact' tone. 'What did he want anyway?'

Paget hesitated. He didn't especially like Edgar, whom he had always found to be brusque and demanding, but nevertheless he respected him. It was clear that Edgar did not view the Branch as traffic wardens, which he was well aware some in MI6 called them, and Lassiter would certainly be one of those. He didn't like his rudeness or his sense of entitlement.

'I had always understood, Mr Lassiter, that there is a well-established protocol which governs the relationship between MI6 and Special Branch, one element being the confidential nature of discussions between officers. Edgar came to see me to discuss a sensitive matter of interest to both our Services. It would be quite wrong for me to discuss it.'

'Did he go through Room 21?'

'No, not as such, but—'

'But that's protocol, isn't it, Paget? In fact, Edgar is why I'm here. Anything official involving our two Services has to go through Room 21, where one of your chaps sits opposite one of ours in an unventilated room and in between drinking tea, eating digestive biscuits and failing to complete the Telegraph crossword they consider matters one service wants to discuss with the other. I think the word in vogue is "liaison," which I assume they picked up from the Americans. So you see, Paget,' Lassiter was leaning menacingly across the desk, 'if this didn't go through Room 21 and give those chaps in there something to do, then your precious protocol doesn't apply, does it? And you certainly don't have any duty of confidentiality to Edgar. It's not as if you're some bloody priest taking confession from him, eh? So perhaps if you share with me what he wanted...'

'How do you know he wanted anything?'

'I am aware that Edgar has accessed old MI9 files at our place, and found some information of interest to him in them, possibly names.'

'Last month Edgar approached me and said he had some information which could be of interest to Special Branch. He gave me a list of four names and asked me to see if any of those names popped up in our system. I think these names may have come from the files you mentioned. I can't recall if Edgar mentioned MI9. I didn't think there was anything improper in this request. I checked the names out and sure enough one of the names did indeed crop up – in a letter written years ago. The letter writer's solicitor was to pass the letter on to the police in the event of him dying from anything other than natural causes and, as it happens, he died a few weeks ago.'

'And the name?'

'Christopher Vale, but his original name was Lothar Meier. M-E-I-E-R.'

'I see... and were there any other names in this letter?'

'In what sense?'

'Names, Paget! For fuck's sake, this need not be difficult. This is quite a serious matter actually. There is every chance Edgar may be fouling up an ongoing MI6 investigation and you have been assisting him, however inadvertently. What I mean is: you said Edgar gave you a list of four names. Other than Lothar Meier's, did any of the others crop up in your system?'

'Not that I recall.'

'I'll need to see the letter – and it's the original I want, not a bloody copy. I'm not going to leave without it. I also want Edgar's list of four names.'

'Shouldn't we clear this with Room 21?'

'No need, Paget, you seem to have established a very convenient precedent for bypassing Room 21.'

Paget copied the names onto a sheet of paper and passed them to Lassiter. 'Here you are, but as far as Meier's letter is concerned, I'm afraid we only have a copy. I gave Edgar the original.'

Lassiter looked at Paget as if he were a school pupil who had admitted to a serious misdemeanour. 'Really? We'll have to see about that then. Obviously I'll read this carefully, but can you think of any other names that came up in it, even if they weren't on Edgar's list?'

Paget closed his eyes and thought carefully. This whole business was becoming messy and the very last thing he wanted was to be caught in the middle of some bloody turf war in MI6. He was beginning to think that if he could pass the whole matter over to Lassiter, as unpleasant as he was, he could forget everything and return to less stressful tasks such as hanging out in noisy Irish pubs sympathetic to the IRA.

'There was one, actually.'

'Go on.'

'Quite a few references to a Captain Canterbury… You'll have to excuse me, Lassiter, but I didn't actually read this letter in too much detail. Once I'd spotted Lothar Meier's name I was in hurry to pass it on to Edgar. From what I could gather, Captain Canterbury was some kind of Nazi sympathiser whom this Meier had had contact with over the years. His name kept cropping up.'

'And did you follow that up?'

'Meaning?'

'Meaning, did you try to find out who or where this Captain Canterbury is?'

'No, I assumed that was something Edgar would be doing. Look, I know I've not been terribly thorough, but this was Edgar's case. I have more than enough on my plate as it is. This isn't really my business…'

'No, Paget, it certainly isn't.'

–

'When you first came to see me about this whole wretched business, Edgar, I asked you whether this was all above board – I seem to remember that was the very phrase I used – and you assured me it was. You promised I wasn't going to get into trouble and that, rather than this being a favour for you, you were actually providing me with valuable information. Well…'

They were sitting in Paget's car, parked in a turning off a country lane not far from Edgar's home in Dorset. It was early evening and despite the open windows it was stifling in the car. Edgar raised his eyebrows, encouraging Paget to answer his own question. He was not going to help him out.

'Well, where do I start Edgar? Lassiter came to see me this morning. Jesus Christ, Edgar, he pretty much threw the book at me. He implied you have at best a tenuous connection with the Service, that you're on what amounts to some kind of freelance operation, and that you are fouling up an ongoing MI6 operation – his words, Edgar, not mine – and therefore I'm some kind of accessory after the fact.'

'Which is why you've driven all the way down here?'

'I left work as soon as I could. I need to know what the hell is going on, because I need to have my defence ready, so to speak. I would not put it past Lassiter to go to the top with this, and the last thing I need is to have the Deputy Assistant Commissioner on my back.'

'What did Lassiter actually want?

'He wanted to know what you were after.'

'How did he even know I was after anything?'

'He implied he has a source in the Branch, which wouldn't surprise me in the slightest.'

'Tell me what you told him – and don't worry, you're not going to get into any kind of trouble for this.'

Paget had been staring ahead out of the windscreen at the field of gently swaying wheat in front of them. He turned round and gave Edgar a sceptical look. 'Really, Edgar? You'll excuse me if I don't share your confidence. I told Lassiter the truth: how you gave me a list of four names and asked me to check in our systems whether any of them cropped up. I told him about the Christopher Vale letter and that Lothar Meier – his original name – was one of the names on your list.'

'And did that satisfy him?'

'Satisfy would be the wrong word, Edgar. He insisted I give him Vale's letter and your list, which of course I had to do. He actually asked for the original letter but I'm afraid I felt obliged to tell him you have that. He was not very happy. And something struck me as very odd about Lassiter, more so as I look back on it. Nothing I told him seemed to surprise him very much – especially when I told him about Lothar Meier. I made it clear that his letter was only to be passed on by his lawyer if he died from something other than natural causes. But Lassiter didn't react to this. He didn't ask me when he had died, or how. That struck me as odd; such an obvious question to ask.'

'Strange. And that was that?'

'There was something else he wanted to know. He asked if the letter contained any names other than the ones on your list. There was one other name, which I did tell Lassiter about.'

'Go on.'

'You'll have seen in the letter, Meier mentions a Captain Canterbury. When I told Lassiter this he seemed very interested, even momentarily shocked, if that's not too strong a word. He was very keen to know whether I'd looked into this man and I assured him I hadn't. But this rather intrigued me so, when Lassiter left with his copy of the letter, I did some checking on this Captain Canterbury. He turns out to be a most fascinating, if unsavoury, character.'

Paget turned round, scanning the lane and the empty fields around them. 'Look, I hope I'm not being unduly jumpy, Edgar, but I wonder if we're a bit exposed here?'

'There's no one around here, Paget. This is my part of the world; it's deserted even when it's busy.'

'A dark-coloured Jag drove past the entrance to the lane about five minutes ago, I caught it in my driver's mirror. What looks like the same car has just driven past again, this time going in the opposite direction and far more slowly. It's probably nothing, but I'd feel somewhat easier if we drove on into a bit more cover.'

The policeman had started the engine and drove the car down the lane. Eventually they came to a small wood and he reversed into it, giving them the cover of the trees. Both men opened their doors and removed their jackets. Paget took out his notebook.

'Christ, Edgar, I don't know whether I've ever known such a hot summer. Some of the younger chaps in the office have even taken to not wearing ties, but I think that's a step too far.' He fanned himself with his notebook. 'I'm wondering what you've got me into, to be quite honest, Edgar. Though you could be right, maybe after all this will be a case for the Branch. There was nothing on Captain Canterbury in our main filing system, but I dug around. Lothar Meier's letter said that the first time he saw Canterbury after the war was in 1956, when he turned up in Nottingham and said he'd recently been released from prison. My hunch was that he could have been court-martialled. I don't know how much you know about this subject, Edgar, I imagine more than me, but during the war a number of British prisoners of war went over to the German side, collaborating with the enemy in various ways. All rather shameful. They were known as renegades. My hunch was right, and it appears Captain Canterbury could well have been one of them.

'Everything points to his real name being Bramley Arthur Sefton Bevan, more commonly known as Arthur Bevan. Bevan was born into a wealthy family in Berkshire in 1905, went to public school and then Sandhurst, got a commission in the King's Own Regiment and then ended up in the Royal Air Force where he became a pilot. He left the RAF in 1934 and went into estate management, as far as we can tell – the records are a bit vague at this point. However, they are not vague about the fact that by 1937 Bramley Arthur Sefton Bevan was an active member of the British Union of Fascists, Mosley's lot. We know he was living in the Worcester area at the time because the local constabulary there had begun to keep an eye on him. According to them he chaired some meetings and subscribed to fascist newspapers.

'When Bevan left the RAF he automatically became part of the RAF Reserve, and so when war was declared, he was expected to rejoin the RAF. He was a qualified pilot after all, and they were much in demand at the time as you can imagine. Extraordinarily, Bramley Arthur Sefton Bevan refused to join. He wrote back to the RAF saying that this was a war he didn't believe in, and he felt this country was making a big mistake siding against Germany. Can you imagine it, Edgar? Personally I'd have thrown the book at him at that point, but the RAF must have been pretty desperate because they persisted and told Bevan that if he didn't join up he'd be conscripted, but as a non-commissioned officer.

'So Bramley Arthur Sefton Bevan rejoined the RAF with his old rank of Pilot Officer. According to the files he was flying transport aircraft, and was captured by the Germans in Belgium in May 1940. It is rather unclear as to what happened: Bevan claims his aircraft's engine seized as he was about to take off when the Germans approached the airfield. But there is also some suggestion that he may have deliberately surrendered. Anyway, Bevan ended up at a prisoner of war camp for Allied air crew near Frankfurt. While he was there he caused no end of trouble. According to the ranking RAF officer at the camp Bevan didn't stop going on and on about how the Allies were going to lose the war, and how we were on the wrong side. He blamed the Jews for everything and got into a number of scrapes with fellow prisoners. The prisoners managed to get word of this back to MI9 through the usual channels and told the German commandant they could no longer guarantee Bevan's safety, such was the ill feeling against him.

'Sometime in 1942, possibly in March, Bevan disappeared from the camp and there are no records of him turning up at another British prisoner of war camp. However, MI9 did receive reports from Berlin that Bevan had turned up there, and was working for the Germans in some kind of propaganda capacity. It seems for a time he worked with William Joyce – you know, Lord Haw Haw – and then went to work at the German Foreign Ministry. Shockingly, he was not the only British person in Berlin working for the Germans during the war. It seems there was a little community of them. Hard to imagine a more unpleasant group, don't you think?

'MI9 ensured he was put on something called a "British Renegades Warning List" and, sure enough, he was captured by a

Canadian unit in May 1945 in Belgium, going by the name of Stephen Sefton.

'He was arrested, brought back here and court martialled at RAF Uxbridge in the December of that year. Now, at the time the RAF was unaware of the claims of what Bevan had been up to with the SS and Nazis. The only evidence they had against him was his behaviour in the camp, and working for the Germans in Berlin. He was charged with acting contrary to Section 40 of the Air Force Act – in my opinion he was bloody lucky not to be facing a treason charge. Frankly, he ought to have swung for what he did, like Joyce and Amery. As it was, he was found guilty and sentenced to twelve years in prison. He served his time in civilian prisons and was released from Wormwood Scrubs in June 1956, which ties in with what Christopher Vale said in his letter. Everything points to Canterbury being this chap, Sefton: age, physical description, important dates. There are no other renegades matching that description.'

Edgar nodded enthusiastically, genuinely interested. 'And what has Bevan been up to since 1956?'

'Well, there's the thing, Edgar. No one knows.'

'Eh?'

'Within days of being released from prison, he disappeared. His wife was living somewhere in Kent in rented accommodation and she moved out the day after his release. Bevan was, rather strangely, entitled to some kind of pension from the RAF, but he's never drawn it. There has been no sign of him at any of the addresses with which he was previously associated. His name appears on no records anywhere. The reason we know this is because in 1961 – which is when the name Captain Canterbury is first linked with Bevan – allegations were made against him that he had joined the Waffen SS. Efforts were made to find him to interview him about this, but there was no trace of him anywhere...'

'Family?'

'Parents were dead by then, he was an only child, and he had no children of his own. His wife had a brother, but he insists he's not heard from her since 1956.'

'They could have emigrated... I imagine South Africa would have appealed to them?'

'Nothing in any records – they must have assumed new identity. It's expensive, Edgar, building a new life from scratch, or at least one that will withstand some scrutiny. His wife had taken most of her cash from their bank account, but there wasn't much there. He must have had money from somewhere.'

'And help.'

'Indeed. I say Edgar, I know I'm being a bit jumpy but did you see something moving down the lane?'

'I can hardly see anything through the trees, surprised you can.'

'Like a vehicle. I'm sure I saw something.'

'Could be a tractor, we get those in the country you know. It's interesting about the real identity of Captain Canterbury, but it doesn't get us anywhere near finding him, does it? If he's been living under a different identity since 1956, all I can say is it must be a damn robust identity to have kept him safe for twenty years. Can't see how we would crack it now.'

Paget did not appear to have heard what Edgar was saying. He was looking nervously around, peering through the trees and cupping his ears to pick up any sound. 'You are correct of course; all this is academic if we have no idea where Bevan is now and what name he goes under. But this is where I had a lucky break: there was a note on Bevan's file – it had been requested two years ago by our colleagues in Gloucestershire. A woman had turned up at the police station in Cinderford and made allegations against her husband, claiming he'd beaten her up; she was very distressed. She also told the police that her husband had been a Nazi, and his real name was Bramley Arthur Sefton Bevan, which is why they approached Special Branch. The file was returned a week later with a "no action" note against it. I telephoned the officer who dealt with the case at the time and he told me the woman had withdrawn her allegations, so there didn't seem to be any point in pursuing the matter. Of course, someone should have followed it up.'

'I don't suppose you…'

Paget took a wallet out of his trouser pocket, extracted a slip of paper and handed it to Edgar, who looked at it carefully and then took a road atlas out of the passenger door compartment.

'It will take us three hours if we set off now, you'll need to put your foot down. If we can stop at a call box I'll tell my wife I've been called away on an urgent matter. I imagine you will need to do the same.'

'Tonight, Edgar, really? It will be getting on for ten o'clock by the time we get there. Can't this wait until tomorrow?'

'No, it can't. From what you've told me, it seems Lassiter knows a lot more about this business than he's letting on. It's as if he's involved in it. He was far too interested in Captain Canterbury, and the fact that he never asked about Meier's death is significant. We need to get to Gloucestershire before anyone else does.'

Paget had started the car and turned into the lane. Both men looked around them to see if they were being observed.

'There's another reason to get a move on.'

'What's that, Edgar?'

'I fear you were right. We may have been watched.'

–

As soon as they caught wind of what was going on, Lassiter was summoned.

The day before he was to meet Paget he'd taken his normal route home: the Central Line as far as Holland Park, turning left out of the station and left again into Lansdowne Road, apparently en route to his flat. But he'd made half a dozen checks since leaving the train and, as he was sure he hadn't been followed, turned right and crossed the main road into Holland Park. They'd be watching over him now, able to tell whether he was being followed. He walked at his normal pace, which was quite brisk, through the park and out at the southern end, into Ilchester Place. There was a wooden bench covered in peeling green paint just by the exit and on it a copy of the Evening News. Lassiter paused to adjust his shoelaces and glanced at the masthead. The newspaper was from two days previously. All was well. He hadn't been followed. The meeting was on.

He crossed Kensington High Street and from there walked through a warren of side streets until he came out at Cromwell Road, where he hopped on a bus, staying on it only as far as the next stop and then walking towards the Natural History Museum.

He'll have a camera hanging round his neck and a big blue camera bag over his shoulders. He'll ask you where the Science Museum is. You'll say you are going in that direction, and offer to take him. That will give you five minutes together, more than enough.

'We have just five minutes. Perhaps we walk a bit slower.'

Lassiter dropped his pace. Why did they always send someone with such a pronounced foreign accent? He felt nervous. Everything was as he'd been told to expect, apart from the foreign accent and the fact that the man was wearing sunglasses, which ought to have been mentioned. Small details mattered. So Lassiter walked a bit slower, as the man suggested. Despite this they were already turning into Exhibition Road. It was too quick.

'You have the package for me?' Lassiter made it look like he was giving directions and pointed ahead.

The man nodded, patting his camera bag.

'And it's straightforward?'

'Yes,' said the man, gazing up at the entrance of the Science Museum. 'He is quite old, I understand?'

'Seventies.'

'And with a history of heart problems?'

'So I believe.'

'Well then,' said the man with the camera, smiling. 'As I say: straightforward.' The man explained how it worked.

As Lassiter made to leave, the man held him by his elbow. Wait. 'There's one other thing: they want to know if you're definitely meeting Paget tomorrow?'

Lassiter moved closer to the man with the camera, appalled that he'd seen fit to use a name in public. He was, he replied.

'They say you should deal with this matter as soon as possible after that,' patting the briefcase. 'The same day.'

Lassiter sat opposite Captain Canterbury in what the latter described as his 'library': a few uneven shelves of books in no particular order – cheap novels, plenty of P.G. Wodehouse and G.K Chesterton, and a worn *Shakespeare's Tragedies*.

A silence had descended heavily onto the room, in keeping with the tense atmosphere which had greeted his arrival at this rather run-down house on the edge of an isolated village. The older man had appeared put out when he'd turned up. He was busy, and couldn't understand why the younger man hadn't told him he was coming. 'Not even a telephone call! Fortunately my wife's in Bristol and won't be back until late.'

Now the older man's mood switched from annoyance to being quite courteous, even friendly. His eyes brightened when Lassiter produced a bottle from his briefcase. He held the bottle carefully in front of him with a twinkle in his eye, turning it slowly, admiring its qualities.

'A pure malt, eh? Twelve years old!'

Lassiter went into the kitchen and returned with a couple of glasses, pouring a much larger measure for Captain Canterbury, who downed it in one go. Lassiter offered him an immediate refill.

'Why the hell not, eh?'

Lassiter limited himself to a few sips from his glass. He wasn't really a whisky man, but at least this helped steady his nerves. The older man's mood had changed again, Lassiter was unsure if this was in spite of the whisky or because of it. Lassiter had seen the drink do this to him before. He became maudlin and had a tendency to express his thoughts a bit too frankly. It was one of a number of reasons why Lassiter had come to distrust him.

'We were right you know. We were always right. I never doubted it for one minute, even when they locked me away for all those years. The bastards would never accept I was a political prisoner.'

'What makes you bring this up now?'

'Now, Lassiter? I've never stopped believing in the cause, and I hope you haven't either.' He looked at Lassiter accusingly.

'No, of course not...'

'Earlier in the year I had to take my wife to Bristol for a hospital appointment, you know – stomach.' He was patting his own ample stomach in case Lassiter was unsure of where the stomach was. 'And do you know what? The clinic she attended had four doctors: two Jews and two blacks.'

He spread his arms in front of him in the manner of a barrister resting an unanswerable case. 'Even in this village there's a family of bloody Indians, and as for Stroud, well... And that chap who's just taken over from Harold Wilson – James Callaghan – wouldn't surprise me if he's a Jew. Marvellous isn't it, a Communist replaced by a Jew. This is why our cause is so important, and why I have never failed to believe in it and have dedicated my life to it, even though that life has been difficult and stressful. I'll have a drop more whisky please, Lassiter... it will all work out, won't it Lassiter? Bit more than that please... I know it's been a long time now, more than thirty years, but even so...'

But now the mood had changed again. Lassiter waited until there was a pause in Canterbury's rant, and started his questions. He was forceful, making the older man defensive, shifting uncomfortably in his seat, fiddling with his frayed cuff, removing his watch and then putting it back on. A band of perspiration had gathered across his bald head and his hands were shaking.

When the older man finally replied to Lassiter's questions it was in such a weak and uncertain voice that the younger man had to urge him to speak up.

'I said I had no idea how Edgar found all this out. Clearly if I knew he knew I'd have…' He paused, unsure of what to say, unsure of what he'd have done. He coughed noisily. The very early signs of fear were beginning to appear about him, like a heavy suit weighing him down.

'How the hell did you allow things to slip so much?'

'Haven't we been through all this? The breach of security was at not at my end, Lassiter. I've kept things under control for more than twenty years now, and I can't tell you what a strain it's been. The breach of security came with the appearance of the Otto Schröder document in Frankfurt in 1969, which was quite evidently not my fault. I know Edgar's been sniffing around again recently but I have no idea what got him onto things after all these years. Jesus Christ, Lassiter… we managed to dispose of all four of them without arousing any suspicion. Do you not appreciate what an effort that was?'

'You didn't do it all on your own.'

'Which I have acknowledged and thanked you for. But how the hell was I to know Meier had written a bloody letter? Jesus Christ…'

'In which,' Lassiter was once again waving it in front of Canterbury, 'he said you had been menacing and making all kinds of threats.'

The older man shrugged. 'That was six years ago, soon after we'd found out about Schröder's document. Things were a bit… tense at the time.'

Lassiter leaned over and poured another generous measure into Canterbury's glass. He seemed too distracted to notice how much he'd been given.

'And from the enquiries I've been able to make,' said Lassiter, 'in the short time since I got this bloody letter from Paget and first came to see you, it appears Edgar has been asking questions about the others. How the hell does he know about them? They're not even named in the bloody letter! And yet he somehow seems to have discovered that Christian Schäfer was living as Tom Hartley in Huddersfield – we know because he approached the police there. Likewise with Bauer, he's on to that one. The only one I'm unsure about is Hartmann. The Kent police haven't come back to me yet and I can't afford to be too pushy: don't want to alert them. This is a precarious enough situation as it is.'

Lassiter paused to catch his breath and calm down. The moment was approaching. He needed to find out one thing first. 'Drink up, here…' he poured another measure, not as big as before, the whisky was clearly beginning to have the desired effect. Canterbury had slumped a bit in his armchair and his eyelids drooped. There was a wistful smile on his face for no apparent reason.

'Look, I'm not blaming you…'

'Rather sounds as if you are, Lassiter.'

'I just want to be sure we've got matters as tight as possible. Tell me, do you have any paperwork to do with all this. You must have some documents, some notes, things you've written down over the years…'

'A few papers and suchlike – no need to worry though, they are as secure as possible.'

'Where are they?'

Captain Canterbury sat more upright and looked at Lassiter suspiciously. 'I said they're safe, Lassiter. You don't need to worry.'

'But I need to be sure: just tell me where they are and then I can tell "them" that all is in order. One other thing. I've agreed that we will transfer a special payment to you, a one off for all the trouble you've been put to recently.'

'Really? That would be splendid. May I ask how much?'

Lassiter hesitated for a moment longer than he ought to have done. He'd noticed how run-down the house was. The carpets were threadbare, some of the window panes were cracked and the sills rotting, the wallpaper peeled at the edges and the garden was overgrown. Canterbury's shoes were scuffed, with holes in the soles. The cuffs of his shirt were frayed and his trousers looked shiny – well worn.

'A thousand, we can have one thousand pounds in your account tomorrow. How does that sound?'

There was a long enough pause to show Lassiter how desperate Canterbury was. 'Very acceptable Lassiter, thank you very much. I was thinking though – without wanting to appear in any way ungrateful – whether there could perhaps possibly be a little bit more, to cover some incidental expenses, you understand?'

'Another five hundred – but I want to check those papers.'

Captain Canterbury hauled himself out of the armchair and dropped slowly to his knees next to a patterned rug that covered much of the empty space in the room. He pulled the rug away, liberating a number of flies.

He had now exposed the floorboards and asked Lassiter to pass him a large pewter tankard from one of the shelves. It was stuffed with pens, pencils and a ruler which had snapped at the ten inches mark. He removed a long screwdriver from the tankard and pushed it into a gap between two of the floorboards. There was a click, and the floorboard sprang up.

'You're younger than me, Lassiter. Reach under there and grab the metal box, you'll need to stretch.'

The box was no more than three inches high but a good eighteen inches square, and jammed full of documents: identity papers, photographs, bank details, a couple of passports, a dozen pocket diaries, and notebooks bound together by rubber bands.

'There you are. Satisfied?'

Lassiter said he was. He was ready now. His heart beat hard in his chest. 'Yes – it all seems safe enough to me. And this is all there is?'

Canterbury nodded. Lassiter knew that this was his opportunity. As Canterbury put the papers back in the box, Lassiter went to the small table and reached down into his briefcase next to it.

It's a special syringe. It's just been developed but we have used it a couple of times already to great effect. Very straightforward: just push it in and it will do the rest itself.

Captain Canterbury was on his knees, returning the box to its place under the floorboard. Lassiter went to help him up and led him over to his armchair, keeping hold of his left arm.

Potassium chloride is ideal, but you need to inject it into a vein. The hands are good, older people's veins tend to stand out in them.

Lassiter acted fast: he clamped Canterbury's left arm to the side of the chair and jabbed the special syringe into one of the veins standing out like a piece of gnarled string across his hand. By the time the older man realised what was happening, it was too late.

'I say, Lassiter. What the hell are you doing?'

Lassiter said nothing, still holding Canterbury down by the arm. The older man tried to stand up but it was a forlorn attempt. He was flushed and breathing rapidly, his eyes having trouble focussing. After a few more seconds Lassiter felt the other man's body slump into the chair, and he stepped back. Canterbury's eyes were now glazed over, beads of perspiration pouring from his forehead. His flushed appearance had been replaced by a pale, grey demeanour, and his shirt collar was turning dark with sweat.

'I say, Lassiter… What have you…'

Lassiter stood in front of the other man, watching him closely. He saw his hands grip the armrests, as if trying to haul himself up, but he was too weak. He looked as if he was endeavouring to move his legs, but he couldn't manage that either.

'I think you'd better ring someone. Please…'

You say he's around fourteen stone? Give or take? There's ten grams there; more than enough.

Lassiter knew Canterbury would be confused and disoriented now, but he nonetheless managed to fix him with a pleading look. Lassiter glanced at his watch – it had been three minutes.

It can take up to ten minutes but I'd be surprised if it takes longer than five – a man that age and weight, with his history of heart problems.

It took a minute or two longer than that. Canterbury slumped further into his armchair, slipping in and out of consciousness, his skin turning a blue-grey and his breathing getting slower. He moaned loudly, moved both hands across his chest, and then it was over.

Potassium chloride causes the heart to stop beating, so will make this all look natural. No one will suspect a thing, especially given his history. Even if they bother with a post-mortem examination, they'll just find potassium in the body, which occurs naturally anyway. And the puncture from the syringe will be so tiny…

Lassiter checked Canterbury's pulse and, once he was satisfied, moved fast. He took a pair of thin gloves from his pocket, removed all the papers from the metal box, and stuffed them in his briefcase. He then replaced the box, putting the floorboard back in place and positioning the rug over it. He topped up the older man's whisky glass and made sure it was on the table next to him, taking care to wipe the bottle. He took his own glass into the kitchen, emptied the contents down the sink, rinsed and dried it and placed it back in the cupboard. Nothing else was out of order, no signs that he'd been there.

He noticed Canterbury's mouth was open, as if he were about to speak. Did that look suspicious? He felt no emotions other than satisfaction at a job well done, along with a sense of relief. With Canterbury and the other four now gone, it was almost all over. The strain, he was only just starting realise, had at times been unbearable. He would get the message to Berlin, and that would be that.

He left through the back door, standing by it for five minutes to acclimatise to the sounds outside, in case there was anything unexpected waiting for him. He felt sure he was being watched, so stood very still, scanning the garden with his eyes. Ahead of him, sat on a high crumbling wall and peering through the branches of an apple tree, was a large black cat, its yellow eyes assuring him it knew what he was up to.

Once he was sure it was safe he left through a gap in the overgrown hedge, into the field. He'd removed the gloves now and taken a cloth cap out of his jacket pocket, one which lay low over his face. He moved quickly round the field, sticking to what shadows he could find, then into the copse at the far end of it, through that and to the road where his car was parked in a lay-by. It was odd, he thought as he reversed the car and started his journey back. Canterbury could have led a privileged and comfortable life but chose instead the path of a fanatic. It was, in the end, a meaningless existence: a futile and dangerous one, unrewarding, always in the shadows.

That's what happens when you sign up to an ideology. Or maybe it's what happens when you start down a path and are simply unable to stop, however much you may want to – as he knew all too well himself.

–

They'd stopped after half an hour to fill the car with petrol and for each of them to telephone home. Urgent business.

They picked up the A350 at Blandford Forum and headed north. Around Warminster, Edgar suggested he'd be happy to drive, which Paget understood was a request rather than an offer. Edgar pushed the Rover 3500 hard, driving far too fast at times and then suddenly at a more leisurely pace. They spoke little for the first part of the journey. Around Newbury, Edgar opened the car up on the occasional stretches of dual carriageway and then slowed down after roundabouts, driving well within the speed limit. Paget noticed that Edgar was constantly glancing in the rear-view mirror, though his head was angled firmly ahead.

'You think we're being followed Edgar?'

Edgar did not reply at first, glancing constantly between the rearview and the wing mirrors. 'Well, if we were, we're not now.'

They had made it to Gloucestershire and a series of winding and precarious roads through the Stroud Valleys, the lush green countryside sweeping above them to one side, below them to the other, any sign of habitation coming as something of a surprise.

'I should have been more frank with you, Martin,' said Edgar. 'You took a copy of the Meier letter and gave me the original – in case I wanted to have the type or paper checked. What you wouldn't have spotted on the copy, of course, and I could only just see on the original was this, on the back of the last sheet. Here, have a look.'

Edgar had taken the letter from his jacket pocket and passed it over to Paget, the car veering slightly as he did so. The policeman took it all in. 'And I imagine you checked out these names?'

'All three – plus Christopher Vale of course – have died in the past month: one that looked like suicide, the other two apparently accidents. But unsatisfactory nonetheless.'

'Jesus, I can see why you—'

'On their own, perhaps not suspicious, but connected… and of course once we have the link with Captain Canterbury, and Lassiter's interest in the case and knowledge of it…'

'You think Lassiter is a Nazi?'

'Nothing would surprise me at this stage. But if we can get to Canterbury, then I'm sure we'll find out – assuming no one else has got to him first.'

–

The village where Captain Canterbury – once Bramley Arthur Sefton Bevan, now Dennis Field – lived was halfway up the side of a valley, south of Stroud. The village was hidden behind a wood and was so isolated and quiet that Edgar and Paget agreed it reminded them of an abandoned film set.

They parked in the lane about fifty yards from the house, and watched it for ten minutes. The wind carried the sound of church bells from a few miles away striking ten o'clock, but otherwise the uncanny quiet in the village meant they could be sure of hearing any extraneous noise.

The doorbell wasn't working but lights were on upstairs, and soon after they knocked the door opened, with much undoing of bolts and chains. A thin, elderly lady with a cardigan wrapped tightly round her despite the heat stood behind the half-open door. She was deathly pale, and her eyes were slightly red.

'Mrs Field?'

She nodded.

Paget flashed his warrant card. 'We have come to see Mr Field. Dennis Field.'

'Have you now?' She took half a step back into the doorway and allowed an unsmiling and bitter laugh to briefly pass her lips as she tried to close the door. 'I have no idea what time it opens, but I can give you the address of the mortuary.'

–

'He died this afternoon: heart attack… Why are you here? … He has been under a lot of pressure recently.'

'What sort of pressure?'

'That would be his business. Now if you don't mind, tell me why you're here. You're sorry for my loss? I'm not sure I am…'

They left after she asked them to do so for the fourth time.

'Drop me in Bristol, Paget, I need to be on the first train to London.'

Before they parted, Edgar extracted a promise from Paget that he'd do nothing until he heard from him. A day at the most. He'd promised Viktor he wouldn't go to Bonn until he got word from him, but with the four men dead and now Canterbury, he couldn't wait. Viktor would have to understand.

Chapter 23

East Berlin, The Monday

Viktor waited a week.

Reinhard Schäfer lived in Prenzlauer Berg in the northern part of East Berlin and Viktor – with the help of Irma – had been watching his journeys home from the embassy. Surprisingly, Schäfer never varied his route and by the Monday – which was the sixth of September – Viktor was ready.

It was just after six thirty and although there was still a decided air of summer about the city, there were also the very early hints of the nights drawing in. Viktor watched as Schäfer walked up the east side of Schönhauser Allee, and fell in behind him. He was just a metre behind Schäfer when they came alongside the cemetery gates. He moved swiftly to the German's left and put his large right arm around the other man's shoulder, gripping it quite firmly. To anyone watching, it was the greeting of an old friend. His left hand held a pistol in the inside of his jacket, which he allowed to open just enough so that the gun was visible to Schäfer.

'We'll go in here, Reinhard. Here we can talk, no one will disturb us.' Viktor was using his height and weight to steer the much smaller German into the Jewish cemetery. They exchanged not a word as Viktor led the German past the damaged building at the entrance, and along a network of paths. He had reconnoitred the cemetery twice in the previous week and knew precisely where to go. Every small strip of land between the graves seemed to be taken up by a tree, giving the sense of being in a forest.

Viktor had found an area in the middle of the cemetery which appeared like a small clearing. It was a family plot, long neglected. Somewhat incongruously, a pair of park benches had been placed on either side of a large black tomb, covered in moss and with faded writing in Hebrew on the top, rather than a headstone like the others around it. Viktor pointed at the bench Schäfer was to sit on. He had chosen it carefully. From the other bench, where he'd sit, he had a good view of where they'd come from, the only way in or out.

Schäfer had chosen to sit in the middle of the bench, and appeared dwarfed by his surroundings. The linden trees stretched high into the Berlin sky, their canopies allowing little light in, meaning the two men were facing each other in the graveyard in a premature gloom.

All this time – since being stopped in Schönhauser Allee, forced into the cemetery and marched to this spot at gunpoint – Schäfer had said nothing and nor had Viktor, other than his initial instructions. The Russian now leaned forward, and was able to make out Schäfer's face surprisingly well. The little light which did permeate the trees came in the form of bright shafts, which dappled the graves, and one of them was illuminating Schäfer. He seemed remarkably calm, almost relaxed about his predicament. He removed his glasses and polished the thick lenses, breathing heavily on them to help him in his task.

'Are you carrying anything?' Schäfer shook his head. Viktor had patted him down as they entered the graveyard, but he wanted to check. 'Open your jacket so I can see... and your waistband.' He held his own pistol up and showed it to Schäfer.

'I've been in here a few times recently, looking for somewhere we could chat. This was one of the first Jewish cemeteries in Berlin, you know, more than 25,000 graves. Not many new graves here for around a hundred years. Somehow, it survived more or less intact during the war. Apparently a gang of deserters hid here but the Nazis caught them and hung them from the trees. You probably knew that.'

'You've abducted me in the street to bring me here to deliver a history lesson?'

'I brought you here so we wouldn't be disturbed, although when I came yesterday afternoon there was a woman tending a grave at the front. Apparently they did bury a few people here after the liberation. You don't mind me using that word?'

'What word?'

'The liberation... of Berlin.'

Schäfer looked confused. 'Why on earth would I mind?'

'Maybe you didn't see it as a liberation?'

Schäfer frowned and adjusted his glasses as if to improve his view of Viktor. He had what looked like a genuinely puzzled expression on his face. 'Stop being so ridiculous, Krasotkin. I have no idea what you're talking about. All this... grabbing me in the street – with a gun – and bringing me here and then rambling on about Jews and graves. If you are unwell then I am prepared not to make a fuss about this and have a quiet word with Piotr Vasilyevich instead: I am sure he'll arrange treatment for you. Our sanatoriums for senior party members are really very good – and most discreet. I'm not an unsympathetic man, Viktor, I've seen it before. Men feel under pressure, then they crack.'

'You're not even asking me what all this is about? You don't feel... angry?'

'I'm sure you're going to tell me, as soon as you calm down.'

Viktor was unsettled, not a feeling he was used to and certainly not one he expected to have now. He should have been in control of the situation, but Schäfer was so calm it disconcerted him. He took a deep breath and loosened his tie. He wondered how much he should tell Schäfer, how much he should reveal. 'You won't interrupt me, Schäfer, let me finish what I have to say and then I promise you'll be able to respond. You understand?'

'Is this an interrogation?'

'Keep quiet and listen to me.' Viktor paused as he heard a rustle somewhere behind Schäfer. 'Rats: this place is teeming with them, like in the rest of this city. After the war, Schäfer,

I investigated Nazi war criminals. It was a job which lasted for years – well into the '50s. I came across many war crimes that remained unsolved, but there was one which kept coming back to me. Cigar?'

The German shook his head.

'In June 1946 I was called to Gdansk, where the Poles were holding a series of trials for SS officers and others who'd been involved with the Stutthof concentration camp. They executed quite a few of the bastards.

'The reason I was called there was to meet a prisoner, an SS officer called Werner Krüger who'd been sentenced to death. One of the offences he was convicted for was his involvement in the massacre of some 5,000 Jews on the Baltic coast – they were prisoners who were being marched away from Stutthof ahead of the Red Army. Krüger had accepted his fate, but what he wanted to tell me was he had had a young SS *Untersturmführer* under his command and this man had defied his orders, and was responsible for the murder of all these women and children. This *Untersturmführer* had somehow avoided being put on trial, but instead had been taken to the Soviet Union as a prisoner of war. He wanted me to know about him. I think he felt it was unfair that the person responsible for this war crime was, in effect, getting away with it.'

'You mean he was trying to save his own skin perhaps, Viktor?'

'Possibly, but I have a lot of experience of prisoners trying to do that, and I do believe this man was resigned to his fate. He simply wanted us to be aware of this other officer. Krüger told me something else very interesting about this young *Untersturmführer*. Their commanding officer was *Obersturmbannführer* Peters. Peters and Krüger were very friendly, both were from Bremen. Peters told him that the young man was meant to be on a top secret mission, in that he meant to be captured by the British or Americans and sent to Britain, where he'd later be part of a Nazi resistance, or something like that. Peters was supposed to arrange this, but it was too late. They were captured at Poznan, where apparently Peters killed himself, and the young officer was taken to the Soviet Union, rather than arrested as a war criminal like the others.'

'What was this *Untersturmführer*'s name?'

'Wilhelm Richter.'

Viktor stopped speaking after saying the name, carefully watching Schäfer's face. There was no flicker of recognition or emotion, as far as Viktor could tell, though Schäfer looked away from him and removed his glasses briefly, putting them back on almost straight away.

'To my shame, I forgot about this case,' Viktor continued. 'There were so many others. But in 1949 I was called to a prisoner of war camp near Rostov, where a young SS prisoner had an unusual request. He wanted to be repatriated to the DDR rather than to the Federal Republic. He told me a familiar story: of how he and a group of other young men had been recruited to the SS for a special mission, the aim of which was for them to be taken prisoner, sent to Britain, then to escape and wait until they could take part in a new Nazi movement. They were trained at an isolated house near Magdeburg in 1944. This prisoner's name was Carsten Möller, and he also admitted that they had carried out some war crimes during their training.'

Viktor paused again, studying Schäfer in vain for any reaction.

'Möller gave me the name of one recruit in particular, who he said had been worse than the others and had murdered one of their fellow recruits. He described him as the most evil man he had ever met. That man's name was Wilhelm Richter, the same name given to me by the condemned SS officer in Gdansk. He also told me how, a few months previously, he had been taken to a special camp which he thought was just near Kazan, the purpose of which was to assess prisoners to see if they could work for the Soviet Union. He was only there for a week or two: he was deemed unsuitable but while he was there he caught a glimpse through a fence of Wilhelm Richter.'

Viktor paused to select another cigar. As he lit and smoked it he said nothing, instead observing the other man. Schäfer sat quietly, impassive, acting as if the Russian were still rambling on about the history of the cemetery.

'So I tried to find this Richter…' For the first time Schäfer began to appear uneasy, crossing and uncrossing his legs, running his hands through his hair. 'I discovered that Richter had definitely been held at a prisoner of war camp near Kazan in 1948. But before I could continue investigating I was summoned to Moscow, where I was ordered to drop the case. I was told that Richter had died in 1947, despite my having evidence that he was alive in 1948 and possibly in 1949. So I did what I was told. Don't forget, this was 1949; I was in a precarious position. I could have fallen out of favour at any time.

'I did nothing about Richter for twenty-five years, but recently he came to my attention again. I have now come across testimonies from two more of the recruits who were at Magdeburg: an Otto Schröder, who died in Frankfurt in 1969 under a different identity, and a Horst Weber, who is alive today and living in the Federal Republic, also under another name. They both tell the same story, they corroborate each other and the account Carsten Möller gave me in 1949, as well as tallying with what the SS prisoner told me in Gdansk.'

'And what – if anything – has this to do with me?'

'All three – Möller, Schröder and Weber – describe a short man with thick glasses who was one of the key people organising their mission and training them for it. That man's name was Erich Schäfer. I have good reason to believe you are that person: Erich Schäfer. I should add that very recently Horst Weber positively identified you.'

Schäfer frowned, as if having trouble understanding Viktor.

'And recently, I discovered that Wilhelm Richter is still alive. I think Richter and you are still… connected. Imagine that, Schäfer, a Nazi war criminal operating under the noses of the KGB?'

Schäfer neither moved nor reacted, but just stared at the Russian opposite him, waiting to see if he had any more to say.

'Oh Viktor, Viktor, Viktor,' Schäfer was shaking his head, looking almost bemused. 'You've got this so wrong, so wrong. You're putting together some hearsay, a few bits of tenuous evidence and one or two coincidences, and coming up with some kind of conspiracy. If only you'd come into my office at the Embassy. I'd have closed the door, we'd have had a drink and a friendly chat, and I'd have explained everything to you. Instead, you bring me here – at gunpoint – and treat me like a traitor!'

'It sounds to me as if you're not even bothering to deny that the Erich Schäfer at Magdeburg and the Reinhard Schäfer sat in front of me are the same person?'

Schäfer looked at Viktor in a genuinely puzzled manner. 'Of course they are. I don't deny it: if you'd bothered to asked me, I'd have told you! Hang on, Viktor; you believe I'm a Nazi too, don't you?' He began to laugh, amused at the very thought of it. 'I am what I've always said I was – a Communist. I was never a Nazi. I joined the KPD in 1928, when I was just eighteen, and was recruited into the police two years later. I was quite active in my branch in Wedding, not very far from where we're sitting now in fact. Walter Ulbricht was KPD chairman in Berlin at the time and I knew him well. In fact, it was he who suggested I should leave the party in 1932. As the Nazis came to power he advised quite a few people to do that. He targeted people in positions like mine – not too prominent, that is, otherwise our political affiliations would have been public knowledge. He wanted us to remain in jobs he thought could be useful to the party in case it went underground: policemen, civil servants, doctors... Everything I did was at the instruction of the party. I applied for a transfer to the Kripo because the party felt they had enough covert members in the uniformed branch in Berlin, but not enough plainclothes. When senior party members started to flee Germany, others remained behind. Some went underground, others had good cover. Of course, thousands of comrades in Berlin were arrested and murdered. It was truly terrible. I'm afraid it also has to be acknowledged that many Communists, and particularly those to the left of the KPD, like the Trotskyists, became Nazis – in many cases they became the most enthusiastic Nazis. It turns out this was not too much of a political journey for them.'

'Nor for you by the sounds of it, you—'

'Shut up, Viktor, and listen. If only you knew how wrong you are. I did everything I could to undermine the Nazi system, while being careful to give the impressions I was part of it. I rose through the ranks of the Kripo, I did well. My job was to investigate serious crime and I did what I could to overstate some crimes, understate others – at one time I'd arrest too many people, at other times I wouldn't arrest anyone at all. Berlin was a mess during the war you know, Viktor. There was so much crime around. Despite everything you read, under the Nazis there was a sense of lawlessness. You know what Berliners are like: they have an anarchic streak, and it was as if many of them believed they had a licence to break the law. I'm not sure if you're aware, but between the autumn of 1940 and the summer of 1941 there was a serial killer at work in Berlin. Almost all of his victims were attacked on trains or near to stations. He sexually assaulted and murdered eight women and attacked dozens more. Everyone knew about it of course, despite attempts to suppress what was going on. It's hard to keep a lid on something like that in Berlin. The Nazis' instinct was to blame the Jews for everything and, if not them, people like the Poles. I was one of the lead investigators on the case and encouraged the general hysteria that the serial killer was a Jew – or a Pole. I cannot tell you how many hours we wasted interviewing Jews and Poles – but no one was going to criticise me for trying to blame the Jews or for wasting hundreds of police hours by pulling in Polish labourers for questioning. In fact, all the evidence pointed in the opposite direction: what little we had to go on indicated the killer was a railway worker who spoke in a strong, working class Berlin accent. Sure enough the man we eventually caught was a railway worker, a Berliner and a Nazi Party member.

'In September 1944 my boss told me he had been instructed to provide one of his top officers to work on a top secret intelligence programme, and had chosen me. Obviously I had very mixed feelings: I didn't want to work on some Nazi intelligence programme, but then at least it meant I wasn't being sent to fight on the eastern front, like so many of my colleagues. My secondment was to a highly secret intelligence unit. There was an understanding, after Normandy, that Germany's defeat was inevitable, and so the purpose of this unit was to devise schemes to ensure the Nazi legacy lived on. My whole experience of this unit was how delusional everything was: people seemed to believe if we came up with a few hare-brained schemes then, after a few years, the Nazis would be back in power.

'There were a number of operations. This one I worked on was especially farcical – you touched on it, Viktor. The plan was to recruit around fifty seventeen or eighteen year olds who happened to speak English very well. They'd be trained and sent to SS units with instructions to be captured and, once in Britain, to escape and live undercover until we contacted them after a few years. I was happy to work on it because, firstly, it was so evidently doomed to failure and, secondly, it tied up resources which would otherwise be fighting the Red Army or the British and Americans.

'As you say, we had a house near Magdeburg and we trained the recruits there. From the outset, it was hopeless – almost laughable. For a start, we'd only managed to find ten suitable recruits and one of them was killed on the first night. One of the team was a British prisoner of war, an extremely odd RAF officer called Arthur Bevan – he was a passionate Nazi who'd been working at the Foreign Ministry in Berlin. He was involved in the training, and the idea was that he'd be a contact for the boys once they made it to Britain. His code name was Captain Canterbury... you can see how crazy this whole business was.

'We sent them off to their units in November or December 1944. To be frank, I thought most of them would be killed and that the others would abscond – I certainly would have done so had I been in their position.

'After that I returned to Berlin. I went back to the Kripo and during the battle for the city I hid in a bunker, waiting for the arrival of the Red Army. I was arrested, of course, but as soon as the KPD leadership returned from Moscow I was able to establish my credentials, and quite quickly I ended up working in intelligence at the Soviet Embassy, where I've been ever since. Incidentally, you mentioned my name and implied that it was careless to only change my first name. Well, there's no mystery there. I had always been Reinhard – certainly when I was in the KPD. I used the name Erich after I joined the Kripo, but reverted to Reinhard after the liberation. Think about it, Viktor: if I really was trying to conceal my identity, don't you think I'd have changed my surname at least, eh?'

'And Richter, what about Wilhelm Richter?'

'What about him, Viktor?'

'What is your connection with him now?'

'What makes you think I still have a connection with him?'

'Is he Goalkeeper?'

A long pause. 'What did you say?' Schäfer could not hide his shock: he turned around to check they were still alone and gestured with his hands for Viktor to keep his voice down.

'Goalkeeper. I asked if Richter is Goalkeeper.'

'Shut up, Krasotkin, you should know better than this. You have no idea how risky this is: you're endangering an operation that's been years in the planning—'

'And Defender and Winger, Schäfer, – who are they?'

'Shut up.' Schäfer was anxiously looking around. When he turned back to face the Russian he appeared panicked. 'We can't talk about this here, this is far too dangerous. I give you my word, Viktor, if you let me go now we can meet in the Embassy tomorrow. I will have to tell Kozlov about our meeting, but I promise I won't mention the way in which you invited me here.'

Viktor stood up, putting his pistol away as he did so. It was his way of signalling agreement, but he nodded his assent too. 'In any case, it's getting dark now. We've probably outstayed our welcome here.'

Chapter 24

East Berlin, The Tuesday

'Can you hear that, Viktor?'

Irma was prodding him in the ribs, but it was unnecessary: Viktor had long been awake. In fact he'd hardly slept at all, despite the now almost empty bottle of brandy by the bed. He'd been propped up on his pillows all night, going over and over in his mind what Schäfer had told him the previous evening. He was worried he'd accepted Schäfer's version of events far too readily and regretted letting Schäfer control matters before they left the cemetery. He was worried his intuition and sure touch was no longer as sharp as it had been. He was trying hard to think through the possible consequences of what he had done. As dawn approached, so too the gravity of the situation loomed larger.

'I hear nothing, *sova*, only the plumbing.' *Sova* was his nickname for Irma. It was Russian for owl and a tribute to her hearing, which was so acute he used to joke she should work at one of the listening posts in Siberia. They'd save money on equipment!

'I heard a car door close very quietly, at the top of the street, then footsteps approaching our building. Two people, both quite heavy. They're inside now, coming upstairs, one behind the other. Is this anything to do with last night, Viktor?'

So this is how it will be, after all these years.

He glanced at his wristwatch: it was a minute or two before six o'clock. Typical, obeying their instructions to the letter – the only way they'd know how to do things. Knock on the door at six – not before, not after. Sure enough, moments later, the knocking at the door. Quite, loud and persistent but not as heavy as it could have been, and at least no shouting or breaking the door down.

It was Kozlov's driver, a thickset Georgian called Giorgi who undertook his master's especially dirty work. Behind him was another Georgian, called Dmitry. Dmitry was Kozlov's body-guard and rarely left his side. Dmitry was even more thickset than Giorgi.

'You're to come to the embassy now. You have a minute to get dressed. Dmitry will stay with you while I bring the car to the front.'

–

Piotr Vasilyevich Kozlov had been waiting for him, in the corridor outside his office on the fifth floor. The KGB Head of Station looked as if he hadn't slept all night either. Viktor assumed Schäfer had had to interrupt some of his boss's specialist activities to fill him in.

Dmitry accompanied him up to the fifth floor and followed Viktor and Kozlov into the latter's office. He stood in the doorway, taking up most of it.

'Wait outside, Dmitry,' said Kozlov. He held off speaking again until the door had closed. Three chairs had been arranged in front of the desk, around a low table with cups and a teapot on it. Reinhard Schäfer was in one of the chairs, looking quite comfortable. Kozlov indicated which chair Viktor should sit in. Everything appeared, to all intents and purposes, quite cosy.

'What did I tell you?' Kozlov hadn't sat down yet. He was walking towards the chairs.

'When?' Viktor was trying to get a better feel of Kozlov's mood, gauging quite how much trouble he was in. It was best to assume Schäfer had told him everything.

Kozlov sat down, sighed, and leant back towards his desk to get his cigarettes, which he then offered around. The flame from Schäfer's lighter was unnecessarily high, causing the two Russians to pull back. Somehow Kozlov managed to speak in his usual loud voice, despite the cigarette wedged in the corner of his mouth.

'When you came to see me the other week, Viktor Leonidovich – that's when. You made these ridiculous allegations about Comrade Schäfer. You told me some fairy tale about Nazi plots, saying that it was all hypothetical, but you nevertheless wanted to interview Comrade Schäfer. I said you'd have to bring me evidence first, didn't I?'

The thick carpets and heavy drape curtains in Kozlov's office didn't prevent his very loud voice sounding as loud as ever. The word 'evidence' had been given particular emphasis. The conversation was in Russian: Schäfer's command of it was far better than Kozlov's German.

Viktor nodded as if he'd only just remembered, grateful to Kozlov for having jogged his memory. Ah yes.

'I could not have been clearer, Viktor Leonidovich. You were to get the evidence and then come back to me. But what do you do? You pull a gun on Comrade Schäfer in the street and then march him into a cemetery and proceed to interrogate him. Are you mad, Viktor Leonidovich, literally – mad? This isn't Berlin in 1944 you know. You don't treat fellow KGB officers like that. Officers more senior than you have been shot for doing half of what you've done...' Kozlov was now tugging his earlobe and pulling hard on his cigarette, his hands trembling. 'Comrade Schäfer is going to ask you some questions, Viktor Leonidovich: you will tell him everything you know. Understand?'

You will tell him everything you know. So Kozlov and Schäfer were unsure how much he knew – otherwise Giorgi and Dmitry would have broken down his door at midnight rather than knocking on it six hours later. And it was almost certainly the only reason they'd brought him here, rather than straight to Schönefeld where he'd have been bundled onto a military flight to Moscow with no return ticket.

'Last night,' said Schäfer, 'you asked me if Richter is Goal-keeper. You also asked me if I had a connection with him during the war.' Viktor nodded with a slight frown, again conveying the impression he was only just about managing to recall what Schäfer said he'd asked. 'You need to tell us how you know that Richter is Goalkeeper.'

You need to tell us. A long silence. A wisp of steam lifted from the teapot and Kozlov shuffled nervously in his chair. Schäfer didn't move.

'And you also asked me who Defender and Winger are,' Schäfer continued, 'I need to know how you know all this.'

Viktor allowed another silence to reign for a while before replying. 'I have no idea who Winger and Defender are.'

Schäfer looked confused at Viktor's response, and annoyed by his blatant obfuscation. 'Don't treat us like fucking fools, we're not amateurs. I asked you: how do you know that Richter is Goalkeeper?'

'So you are confirming he is Goalkeeper?'

Kozlov slammed the side of his chair. 'Answer the fucking question, Krasotkin. This is going to be one of those rare occasions in your charmed life when you answer questions rather than ask them, you understand?'

'A source, that's how I know. From a source.'

A loud sigh from Kozlov, followed by a muttered, 'This is ridiculous.'

'I'll tell you again what I told you last night,' said Viktor, 'and some of this may be news to you Piotr Vasilyevich. I became aware of Wilhelm Richter's war crimes as early as 1946. In 1949, I discovered he'd been in the Soviet Union. So, from my point of view, this is a case I never closed, and one I'm perfectly entitled to be pursuing. A few months ago it came to my attention that Richter was almost certainly alive and in the Federal Republic in 1968, so I stepped up my search for him again. I believe now he goes by the name of Heinz Fleischhauer, and works for the BfV in Cologne. I also believe he is an agent of yours, Schäfer – codename Goalkeeper. I believe he's still a Nazi and, if you are indeed running him, Schäfer, then you're picking up where you left off in 1944 – when you were involved in a Nazi plot,. How about that, Piotr Vasilyevich – a Nazi war criminal working for the KGB, here in East Berlin? I imagine Andropov will love that. When it all comes out it's going to do your career no end of good.'

Kozlov was turning red and glancing anxiously between Viktor and Schäfer, a panicked expression building on his face. The German was very calm though, leaning forward to pour tea for all three of them before he spoke. 'Of course Fleischhauer's a Nazi all right, and Carsten Möller was correct, he was – is – one of the most evil men you could ever have the misfortune to meet. As Wilhelm Richter, he was a committed and dedicated Nazi and, as Heinz Fleischhauer, he remains one. He's convinced he is still serving his cause, believe it or not.'

He sipped at his tea, taking one of the cigarettes Kozlov had offered. Schäfer smoked in the manner of someone who found cigarettes distasteful, but nonetheless smoked them as low as possible. 'My main role here at the Embassy has been to recruit Germans we can infiltrate into West Germany as agents, and run them. In the early 1950s I used to fly to Moscow every few months, to meet German prisoners of war who'd been identified as possible KGB agents. I'd interrogate them, assess them and if they were suitable – very, very few were – then they'd be set up as agents. Would either of you like more tea?'

Schäfer poured himself another cup, finishing off his cigarette as he did so. 'In 1953 I was in Moscow. When I looked at the list of people I was due to see, there was Wilhelm Richter's name. Now,' he took another sip of tea, 'if there's one thing I'm an expert on it is who's a Nazi and who isn't. No one has more experience of the bastards than I do, even you Viktor.

'I know you were in and out of Berlin in the '30s and operated behind enemy lines during the war, but I was here the whole time. I'd known them since they first crawled out of the gutter in the '20s and I worked with them for more than a dozen years. I had to pretend to be one of them. I learned the difference between the true Nazis – the fanatics, the believers – and those who went along with it as part of the crowd, you know the type. And in all that time, I doubt I met a more committed and fanatical Nazi than Wilhelm Richter. He was a fanatic among the fanatics, one of the few who genuinely believed Germany was going to win the war, right until the end. But, according to the file I saw in Moscow, as soon as he'd been arrested, in Poznan in 1945, he told anyone who'd listen that he was really a Communist and wanted to work for the Soviet Union.

'He was persuasive enough to be treated as a prisoner of war, rather than as a war crimes suspect. His youth certainly helped. He'd managed to convince them that he was just a very junior officer, obeying orders – the standard defence. But there were always doubts about him. For a start, he wasn't very convincing as a Communist: he had no understanding of Marxism and hadn't even heard of Engels. And then there was his sheer nastiness. He was always informing on fellow prisoners. All of the prisoners who were being considered as agents had to undergo psychological testing and he was, unsurprisingly, diagnosed as having psychopathic tendencies: an absence of feeling for other people and a heightened readiness to use violence, usually gratuitous and quite sadistic. But that was not in itself a drawback to being one of our agents. It could even be an advantage. He was sent to the camp near Kazan you mentioned. They decided to monitor him for a while longer, as they didn't think he was ready.

'A few years later, he was put on my list. I couldn't believe it when I first saw his name: Wilhelm Richter, the Nazi, wanting to be a Soviet agent? It was impossible. But then I had an idea and I spoke to the people in Moscow. Richter, I told them, was a Nazi: of that there was no question. He was desperate to be a Soviet agent because he saw that as a way of saving his skin. I had no doubt, I said, that as soon as he was in the Federal Republic he'd betray us. Well, the reaction in Moscow was as you'd expect – "Shoot him now" – but I persuaded them that we could be clever: we should harness his fanaticism and get him to work for us, without him realising it of course.

'When I met with him he was naturally shocked to see me, but I told him I was still a Nazi, and had infiltrated Soviet intelligence.

I managed to convince him that it was all part of the plan, that I was still running the clandestine unit from East Berlin which was gathering intelligence to serve the Nazi cause, and it was just a matter of time before we were called to action. And he believed me, he lapped it all up. There were two reasons for this. Firstly, he wanted to believe me, he was desperate to become an active Nazi once again And secondly, he was so used to doing what he was told that he just accepted my instructions.

'We continued his training, got him into the Federal Republic as "Heinz Fleischhauer" in early '54, and within a year he was working for the BfV in Cologne. Incidentally, his route into the BfV,' another pause while he finished his tea, 'was courtesy of the British. Their network in the Federal Republic was poor, and they were desperate for agents. We gave Fleischhauer a stream of low-grade Soviet intel to pass on to the British and they lapped it up, thought they'd recruited a top agent. They sang his praises to the BfV and that's how he got in there.'

Schäfer leaned back in his chair, looking for all the world as if he'd been enjoying reminiscing with friends. It was Viktor's opportunity to respond.

'He's been in the BfV since what – '55? And in over twenty years, he's not become at all suspicious? He still really believes he's part of some Nazi plot? I mean… in that time, even the most diehard Nazi would realise there was no chance of them being anything other than on the margins. It's hard to believe—'

'It would be hard to believe with a normal person, Viktor, but Richter does not come into that category. I told you how his assessment showed he was psychopathic, didn't I? Once he'd been in the Federal Republic for a year or so, this tendency came out. He got married and divorced within a year, and his wife reported him to the police more than once for cruelty. Then he got into debt, got a fifteen-year-old girl pregnant, defaulted on a loan, remarried… I could spend a day telling you about the trouble Richter has got into over the years. He's been married three times now; his last divorce was in 1968. We constantly have to bail him out. We fund him – to clear his debts, to pay off the people complaining about him. We've paid for four abortions at the last count.

'The last thing we want is for the BfV to see him as so unstable they sack him, so we do what we can to keep a lid on all his problems. It takes up a lot of our resources in the west, I can tell you. But if it wasn't for us he'd have been in very serious trouble a long time ago. He needs us and he knows it: the last thing he's going to do is question things.' The German clapped his hands. As far as he was concerned, the conversation was over.

'There you have it, Viktor Leonidovich!' Kozlov had sprung up from his chair with a suddenness that surprised both Viktor and Schäfer, his voice as loud as ever. 'Comrade Schäfer has told you what an important agent Richter is. He may be a Nazi but he's working for us, and his material goes straight to Andropov himself. That's good enough for me and it should be good enough for you. From now on, we will hear no more of it; you can forget this nonsense about a Nazi plot here at the embassy. I'll overlook what happened last night, but only if you accept your time here in Berlin has come to its natural end. Go back to your office while I think things over.'

–

Viktor had gone to his own office at the rear of the embassy and just sat at his desk, gazing out of the window over Behrenstrasse while trying to collect his thoughts. The meeting in Kozlov's office had ended far too abruptly: something was not right. Schäfer was too smart to let him off the hook like that. He'd told him too much and not asked enough questions in return. Viktor would have expected him to push him harder on how he knew about Goalkeeper. Maybe they were saving that for Moscow. And as for Kozlov saying he was prepared to overlook what had happened, and that his time in Berlin had come to a natural end... all Viktor could think was that he surely didn't look that gullible.

He was an old man: he hadn't handled Schäfer with anything like his usual guile – either this morning or especially the previous night. He had been outmanoeuvred, allowing the German to gain the upper hand in a situation he ought to have been in control of. If he really was to return to Moscow, allowed to retire, to spend the rest of his days at his *dacha* along with Irma, that would be fine. But he somehow doubted a rural idyll was what Kozlov had in mind. Maybe everything Schäfer had said was true after all: Goalkeeper was a top agent, and all Viktor had done was put him at risk.

At ten o'clock Viktor walked quietly over to the door, opening it just enough to be able to check the corridor. Apart from a clerk moving from one room to another it was empty. Neither Giorgi nor Dmitry were hanging around as he'd feared they might be. He'd get hold of Irma in her lunch break. He'd given her an excellent set of Federal Republic papers, a really first class identity. She could cross the border later in the afternoon at Bornholmer Strasse, before it closed. Then he would attempt to get out the next morning, through Friedrichstrasse station. He'd get word to Edgar, who'd help him.

Viktor's door opened silently, and the short figure of Schäfer slipped into the room. Without acknowledging Viktor he moved to the front of the desk and pulled up a chair. His eyes darted around the room, checking that all was in order: no sign of bags packed or of imminent flight. When Schäfer finally spoke it was just one word. 'Kozlov.'

That had to suffice for a while, as if it explained everything.

'There's a lot that Kozlov just doesn't need to know. And I will give you the benefit of the doubt, Viktor: you declined to tell me how you know so much because you felt inhibited in front of Kozlov. Is that correct?'

'You were going to tell me about Winger and Defender?'

'Well, let's see. Somehow you've managed to pick up a few bits of intelligence, but by no means the whole story. I don't know how you've managed even that. A little bit of knowledge can be a dangerous thing. In this case, it is more dangerous than you perhaps realise: the fact you even know about Goalkeeper puts one of our most important agents in the west in danger. He's on the verge of a major intelligence coup. When I tell you the whole story perhaps you'll appreciate how important this is, and then you'll drop everything. If you stop now, at least you'll have done so before any major damage is done. If I tell you who Winger and Defender are, in return you tell me everything, you understand?'

'I understand.'

'And when I've finished, you tell me what you've done with the information you've chanced upon?'

Viktor nodded very slowly.

'As an added incentive, Viktor, consider this: at the moment, I'm all that's stopping you being sent back to Moscow this afternoon. I've told Kozlov I need you here... for the time being. I hope you understand that.'

'Yes, I understand.'

'Very well then. You've asked who Winger and Defender are. I told you last night about Arthur Bevan, the British prisoner of war known as Captain Canterbury: the man who helped train the recruits. He is Defender. Not surprisingly, he was arrested and court martialled by the British after the war. More surprisingly, he wasn't executed, though he was sent to prison for quite a while. London Station kept an eye on him, so when he was released I went over to meet him. He was never in any doubt that I was still part of the Nazi mission and was picking up where we'd left off. As with Richter, it wasn't hard to persuade him to believe me – he was desperate to do so. That's the measure of a fanatic: you tell them what they want to hear and they lap it up like a thirsty dog.

'My overriding concern was to protect Richter. He'd been with the BfV for a year by then and we could not risk anything about his background coming out, even though he was operating under a different name. So we funded him, and used London Station to give Bevan and his wife new identities. He became Dennis Field and, to all intents and purposes, disappeared. He had one job: to keep an eye on the four recruits in England. They were leading very ordinary lives, and it was essential that things stayed that way. Canterbury never questioned why the mission wasn't taking place: whenever he moaned, we just gave him more money.'

'But if your priority was to protect Richter then wouldn't it have made more sense to dispose of them – and of Canterbury for that matter?'

'In hindsight, yes. As you know, Viktor, we're certainly not averse to measures like that. But disposing of them ran the risk of alerting people. If their deaths were investigated it was always possible something would be discovered which could have led to Goalkeeper. We felt that as long as none of the four in England, nor Canterbury, were causing any trouble it would be safer to leave them alone.'

'How did you keep in touch with Canterbury?'

'At first it was through London Station, dead letter drops and the like. But that wasn't satisfactory. Then we recruited another agent, and his main job has been to be my link with Defender, who believes this man is a fellow Nazi.'

'This is Winger?'

'Yes – and don't forget, Viktor, in a moment you are going to tell me how you came to find out about Goalkeeper, Defender and Winger. I recruited Winger myself, in 1964. He was a student at Oxford University and was spending a term here in East Berlin at Humboldt University, studying linguistics. He was more or less a walk-in: he asked one of his lecturers if there was any way he could help the Soviet Union. Apparently he'd discovered he was a Marxist, which is not an uncommon occurrence with the English middle class – one of our English agents told me it's what happens to them in between losing their virginity and getting a mortgage. This lecturer naturally reported the contact and fortunately came to us rather than the Stasi. I met with the student. He was bright, though I did have some doubts about him. He was very impulsive, and talked too much, and I'm always sceptical about walk-ins; but he passed all our checks and so we recruited him, steered him towards the Foreign Office and he ended up in MI6. He's run by

London Station of course, but I retain an interest in him – his main role is to watch Defender, Captain Canterbury. As far as I was concerned, if Defender was doing his job making sure the four recruits weren't causing trouble, then Goalkeeper was safe. That's before you came charging in, of course.'

'Winger is in MI6 and that's all you're using him for? Bit of a waste, eh?'

'It may seem like that, but in fact we also think he'll be useful as a sleeper. So we want him not too active for us in terms of providing intelligence – to keep as clean as possible in that respect, and then we'll wait until he gets higher up the organisation. He's still young, only in his thirties.'

Viktor was beginning to experience a sense of dread, a realisation of being in the wrong, of having badly messed something up. Throughout all his time as an agent – in the field, in Nazi-occupied Europe, in Stalin's post-war Soviet Union, which was almost as dangerous, and then in the DDR – he had never made a serious mistake. That was how he survived: by being brighter than the rest, more intuitive and certainly one step ahead of them. He'd been convinced he'd discovered a Nazi plot in the Soviet Embassy. Last night he became unsure. And now he was realising he'd made a serious mistake, and the consequences were too terrible to contemplate. Not only was there no Nazi plot, but he could be inadvertently helping to destroy a KBG spy ring. If he had one hour he could try to contact Edgar, and maybe stop any damage being done – but he sensed it was too late.

'What is it, Viktor? You look worried. Are you not pleased that I've been able to clarify matters and reassure you?'

'I am going to be frank with you, Schäfer. I heard about Goalkeeper on the grapevine and then chanced upon Richter's name in some old files of yours in Registry, and was able to make the connection. On reflection, of course I should have approached you, but I was convinced Richter was the Nazi war criminal I had been looking for. After all these years, I still think he should face justice. I contacted a source of mine, a man who had connections in the past with British Intelligence. He—'

'Hang on—'

'Let me finish. Through this man I obtained the testimony of Otto Schröder. He had lived as Bernhard Krause since the war and died in Frankfurt in 1969. In his papers, he—'

'You don't need to tell me, Viktor. I read it in 1969.'

'How did you get hold of it? It went straight to MI6.'

'Exactly!'

'Winger?'

'Viktor, this is—'

'What is Winger's name?'

'After all this, you expect me to tell you the name of a key agent?'

'Schäfer, I fear I may have been indiscreet. If we are to protect Goalkeeper, we have to tell each other everything.'

'Hugh Lassiter.' Schäfer stared at the ceiling, as if it was about to cave in.

Viktor gripped the arm of his chair tightly. He felt unwell: it was beginning to dawn on him that he could well have compromised Soviet intelligence. He was unable to think of a response, he had no idea what to say, of how to break it to Schäfer. The German sensed this. Like Viktor, he'd conducted enough interrogations to know when the subject realises the game is up and needs a few moments to compose themselves before confessing. A good interrogator allows them time, as Schäfer was doing now.

And then Viktor told him almost everything: about Edgar, about Georg Stern in West Berlin, about how his intentions had been good, but... Schäfer listened patiently. He kept any anger he was feeling under control. He was almost friendly. He knew he had to tease every last shred of information from Viktor.

As Viktor talked he noted that Schäfer repeatedly but almost imperceptibly shook his head, signalling his resignation to the situation – because he believed that Goalkeeper was still safe. The Russian realised he was keeping back just enough from his account to allow the German to believe this was indeed the case.

He told Schäfer how, after finding out about Richter, he had approached Edgar to see if he had any information, and how

Edgar had produced Bernhard Krause's testimony. He admitted that both he and Edgar had, for reasons of nostalgia as much as anything else, been intrigued by the case.

But he omitted to tell him how they had continued to pursue it; how Edgar had found out the names of the other recruits, and how Lassiter was on his trail. And nor did Viktor tell Schäfer how he and Edgar had met quite recently in Vienna, where under the protection afforded by the giant shadows in the cathedral the two old adversaries had agreed a plan: that Viktor would go to West Berlin to seek out Georg Stern. And how Edgar had returned to England to find out what he could there, and how Edgar knew that Richter's new identity was Heinz Fleischhauer. And that Edgar would wait for word from Viktor, but that the Englishman would not wait too long before travelling to Bonn. And in Bonn, he'd tell the authorities about Goalkeeper, before no doubt heading to Cologne.

But, glancing once more at his wristwatch, Viktor was resigned to the fact that it was probably too late. Edgar would be on his way to Bonn by now, if he was not there already. Viktor had been too slow; he had made too many mistakes. It would be his fault that the KGB's main agent in the Federal Republic was about to be exposed. Of course he could admit all this to Schäfer, they would probably pull Richter in. But then the damage would be irrevocably done, and if he admitted his mistakes then Viktor himself would in Schönefeld within the hour – if he made it that far. Alternatively, if he could find an hour's grace from somewhere... somehow... then he could muster all his skill and cunning for one last time and endeavour to get himself and Irma to safety.

When Viktor finished speaking Schäfer went over to the door and checked it was shut. He gestured for Viktor to join him by the window, where the Russian had to bend down to catch the German's quietly spoken words.

'I didn't want to say too much in front of Kozlov: the word from Moscow is that Andropov no longer trusts him, you know – the women, the drink... What I tell you now is in utter confidence. Goalkeeper has had mixed results as an agent, I have tended to talk him up to be honest. But he has been concentrating on one very important task in recent years. The plan was to get him inside the Military Liaison Office at the BfV. We thought it would take two or three years, actually it's taken a lot longer. But he's almost there. Once he's inside it will be a goldmine for us: we'll get access to the NATO defence plans for Western Europe. Andropov has made it a priority. We think Goalkeeper's transfer is imminent.'

Schäfer turned to look at Viktor. 'So, you can see why my main concern has been keeping Goalkeeper safe. At least you have been able to reassure me. We'll talk later.'

Chapter 25

Bonn and Cologne, West Germany, and East Berlin, The Tuesday

Edgar struggled against the hypnotic effects of the wheels flying over the tracks on the first train of the day from Bristol to Paddington. He hadn't slept for nearly twenty-four hours and was finding it hard to think properly.

He'd caught a train at five thirty and, by the time they'd reached Swindon and he'd finished his second cup of coffee, he was able to think slightly more clearly. He was sure they'd not been spotted in the village, and doubted they'd been followed as Paget drove him to Bristol and dropped him off near the station. But he couldn't be sure whether Paget would say anything once he was back in London.

They could be waiting for him at Paddington, and in his exhausted state he was no longer too sure who 'they' were. So he left the train at Reading, only alighting as it pulled away from the platform to be certain that no one left the train after he did. It was seven o'clock and a bus was leaving just ten minutes later. He was at Heathrow by eight.

He was travelling on his own passport, the only one he had on him, having left Dorset in such a rush. There was ample opportunity for him to be picked up: as he bought a ticket, as he checked in, as he went through passport control and then as he boarded the plane. But no one gave him so much as a second glance and the flight allowed him two hours of sleep.

It was midday when the Lufthansa flight landed at Cologne Bonn airport. Once he'd cleared customs, Edgar found an Italian coffee bar near the exit. The mirrored walls and ceiling meant he could be certain he wasn't being watched, and the espresso was so strong he could be sure of remaining awake for a few more hours at least.

–

Indecision must have been thick in the air around the Soviet Embassy on the Unter den Linden that Tuesday in September.

It hit Viktor when Schäfer left his office. He was uncertain whether to go and find Irma and flee East Berlin, or to wait where he was and hope they believed him.

Indecisive was certainly how both Kozlov and Schäfer could be described as they met in the former's office. 'Do you believe him, comrade Schäfer?' Kozlov was pacing unsteadily around his office in his stockinged feet. A bottle of vodka, which had been full when they'd met first thing in the morning, was open and half empty on his desk.

'I'm not sure, Piotr Vasilyevich, I'm really not sure. He is absolutely correct in saying that Goalkeeper was a war criminal, and I believe him when he says that was his motive in pursuing him. But to contact this Edgar amounts to treason. And how much he's told Edgar... I just don't know.'

'But everything is sorted in England, yes?'

'Apparently so, but it is not a good situation. My main concern, sir... my only concern really, is Goalkeeper. As long as he's protected, that's all that matters. I have to concentrate on him – whether he's been compromised in any way. I may have to tell Andropov...'

'So what do we do with Viktor Leonidovich?' Kozlov was sounding exasperated now, his voice even louder than usual. Mention of the Head of the KGB had unsettled him. His hand inched towards the bottle.

'I was hoping you would be able to advise me in that respect, sir.'

Kozlov slumped into his chair, holding the vodka bottle, proffering it in Schäfer's direction.

The German shook his head, a gesture to both decline the offer of a drink and to indicate his frustration at his superior's indecision. 'As I see it, sir, we have three options. I will explain them and then perhaps you could indicate which course of action we should follow?'

Kozlov poured himself a generous measure before pointing the bottle at Schäfer. Carry on.

'The first option is to arrest Viktor for treason immediately, and let Moscow deal with him. If there's anything he's not told us, the specialists at the Lubyanka will get it out of him. The second option is to keep him here in Berlin, but take him into custody ourselves – either here or we can ask the Stasi to help out. It—'

'No!' Kozlov slammed the bottle down on the desk, his voice booming around the room. The desk top now had a small pool of vodka on it. 'I am not having the Stasi going anywhere near him – those fucking Nazis knowing our business…'

Kozlov grabbed his cigarettes, managing to spill the whole packet over his desk before selecting one. 'And the third option?'

'We do nothing: leave Viktor here while I concentrate on checking that all's well with Goalkeeper. Of course we'll put a tail on him, which may produce interesting results. You need to decide which option is the most preferable, sir.'

'Or the least undesirable. Just as I don't want the Stasi anywhere near Viktor, nor do I fancy Moscow knowing too much of what's going on. If he goes back to Moscow then Andropov will hear about it and have me transferred: I'll end up in some miserable town in Kazakhstan. How long will it take for you to check all is well with Goalkeeper?'

'Possibly twenty-four hours, Piotr Vasilyevich.'

'Make it twelve – and whatever happens, don't lose sight of Viktor.'

The espressos in the airport coffee bar were so strong that they'd been accompanied by glasses of cold water, a combination Edgar hadn't come across before but which resulted in a remarkably clear head. He needed it. He knew that Richter – Heinz Fleischhauer – worked in Cologne, but he had no idea where he lived. He'd been relying on Viktor for that information but, worryingly, hadn't heard from the Russian for a while now. The death of Canterbury and the other four men had made this trip urgent: he couldn't afford to wait to hear from Viktor, despite the Russian telling him to.

Satisfied he wasn't being watched, Edgar found a bank of phone booths in a dimly-lit area behind an information desk. He dialled the West Berlin number Martin Winter had passed on to him back in March, when Viktor had first made contact – it was how he'd made the initial approach, for the message to be passed on to Viktor that he'd arrived in Berlin.

'*A female voice will answer. She will repeat this number. You are to ask if Klaus is there.*'

Edgar expected the phone number to be disconnected. Viktor would have been careful like that – using a number then burning it was standard procedure. But surprisingly it rang, and was answered very quickly: a man's voice, which didn't repeat the number, just a muttered, 'Yes?'

Edgar hesitated: 'Is Klaus there?'

A pause, three or four seconds – the response ought to have been far quicker, three or four seconds was too long. 'Klaus is not here,' and then the man in West Berlin put the phone down.

Back in March, Viktor's instruction had been clear enough. If she replies and says there is no Klaus, then do not attempt to cross over. That would have been a straight warning then. Edgar did not know if he should take it as a warning now. There could be an innocent explanation, but the pause was too long and the man didn't say exactly: 'There's no Klaus here.' *Klaus is not here.* Edgar didn't know what to do. Should he abort his trip now? But

Viktor's advice in the cathedral in Vienna had been explicit. Go to Bonn regardless.

–

Edgar hired an Audi 100 at the airport, choosing a dark brown one, the colour of wet, clay-heavy mud: its drabness would, he hoped, help it to be unobtrusive.

It was a short drive from the airport to Bonn and Edgar parked on Adalbert-Stifter-Strasse, just around the corner from the British Embassy, a drab four-storey affair on Friedrich-Ebert-Allee. There was heavy security at the front of the building, no doubt due to the Red Army Faction attacks. He managed to get as far as the main reception, where he was able to persuade a reluctant clerk to put a call through to Clive Cowley. An old friend.

Clive Cowley had been a bitter man when Edgar first met him in the early 1950s. He was a relatively new recruit to the service then, in his mid-twenties, an age when he ought to have been brimming with enthusiasm. But he'd just been turned down for a posting to Washington which he reckoned he'd been promised, and was spending a year at HQ, which was then at Broadway in St James's. After that he was to be sent 'somewhere in Africa.' At the time, Clive Cowley was Tarquin Cowley-Scott. He decided that his first name and double-barreled surname were the only impediments to an otherwise glittering career, so he dropped the Scott and promoted Clive from its previous middle-name status. Those adjustments didn't have the desired effect: Kenya, Uganda, Nigeria… a spell in London, a couple of marriages, school fees for children he rarely saw. Saudi Arabia, where the alcohol prohibitions proved to be a problem which should have been foreseen. Then an undistinguished journey through Europe: Romania, Italy, Belgium… not even a Deputy Head of Station, and certainly never a sniff of Washington.

Now he was in Bonn, counting the days to his retirement. Hopefully he'd be able to point Edgar in the direction of Heinz Fleischhauer: an address maybe.

It had been a few years since Edgar had last seen Cowley, who now had a stooped posture and an altogether raddled appearance. His heavy tweed jacket was too small for him, while his shirt was too large and his faded tie was dotted with stains.

Cowley had been pleased enough to see Edgar, but curiosity at this unannounced visit made him guarded. The two men walked down to the State Park on the banks of the Rhine. Edgar knew how carefully he had to play this: to get the information he needed from Cowley, without alerting him to the fact that he probably ought not to be giving it.

'I'd appreciate it if you kept it quiet I was in town Clive… very sensitive… senior Belgian army officer in Cologne suspected of shovelling top-secret stuff into the east… London terribly nervous because of all this Common Market business and NATO, you understand… they didn't want this to be too official, hence my involvement, best kept away from Bonn station… know I can trust you… and how are you keeping, being treated with the respect you deserve, I hope?'

That was all Clive Cowley needed: no he wasn't being treated with the respect he deserved, seeing as you mention it Edgar – never had been for that matter. He should have been given his own station years ago and, as for never being sent to Washington, well that was sheer spite, the fault of the socialists running the service… Ex-wives fleecing him for every penny they could get, children hardly communicating unless they wanted something, salary utterly inadequate… tolerated like some demented old time-server, out of the loop for anything important… 'Can't wait to retire. But the pension, Edgar…'

Edgar sympathised. He couldn't believe how badly his good friend was being treated. He wasn't promising anything, of course, but he had contacts in the City – very high up – the type of people who appreciated old-fashioned values like loyalty and decency. They'd be very keen to take on someone like Clive when he

293

retired. 'They call it consultancy, Clive. You'll double your salary, more with bonuses. Nothing too taxing… No promises, as I say, but if you're interested…'

Clive Cowley found it hard to disguise just quite how interested he was. It was getting on for evening now, the sun sinking over the Rhine, and what had been a pleasant breeze was now whipping off the river with some force. The effects of the espressos had worn off and Edgar wished for nothing more than sleep: any bed in any hotel. But he couldn't allow himself such an indulgence.

'I say, Clive… don't know what made me think of him, probably being in these parts jogged something in my memory, but does Heinz Fleischhauer still work for us? You know, BfV chap…'

They'd left the park and were now walking on a path by the river. Cowley hadn't replied to the question, and Edgar looked over at him. He was walking along at a steady pace, his head bowed and a slight frown on this face. He began to speak but then stopped as a couple rode past them on bicycles. They had disappeared from sight before he replied.

'Heinz Fleischhauer, you say?'

'Yes, Clive, Heinz Fleischhauer. We started using him back in the '50s. Surely you know of—'

'How do you know of him, Edgar? He's after your time surely?'

'Well, I never really left the service did I, Clive? When Fleischhauer first came on board, Porter asked me to see him a few times, check he was what he said he was… you know the score.'

'He's still around, unpleasant chap – frightful manners. We don't get much from him these days, barely makes our Second Eleven if you get my drift, which is probably why he's in my team. We only get anything at all if we give him something in return – hardly worth the effort in my opinion. I told him as much when I last saw him. I said—'

'So you're running him are you, Clive?' Edgar tried to make the question sound as casual as possible.

Another pause. An elderly lady was approaching them, pulled along by a pair of large dogs, a lead in each gloved hand. Cowley waited until she was out of sight too.

Cowley nodded his head as he walked along. 'Rather sums it up I suppose: former top agent, drops right down the batting order so yours truly can run him. Give me something to do, nothing too onerous. There's no gratitude, no appreciation of my—'

Edgar no longer felt tired. 'How about an early supper, Clive? On me of course. Where's the best place to eat in Bonn these days?'

Every minute of the expensive dinner, and what amounted to a two hour monologue from Clive Cowley, was worth it. By the end of the evening Edgar knew where to find Heinz Fleischhauer. And he suspected that, by the time he went to bed, Cowley would even remember he'd told him.

—

Around the same time that Edgar arrived in the city, Heinz Fleischhauer was summoned to the Personnel Department on the second floor of the BfV's Bonn headquarters. This was no ordinary summons: it was to see Frau Schlösser, the woman who moved staff from department to department with the steely precision of a chess grandmaster.

'You have been with the Rotation Team for six years now, Fleischhauer. You have enjoyed it.' It was phrased as a statement rather than a question, so Fleischhauer just nodded. 'You have spent the past year in Technology Support. The reports on you have been very good.' Frau Schlösser gave the impression of delivering the compliment in spite of herself. She had not looked directly at him since he'd entered her office, as if she regarded eye contact as an indulgence. 'Now it is time for the next phase of your rotation. Are you aware of the Military Liaison Office?'

'I don't think I am, Frau Schlösser, no.' He tried hard not to react in any obvious manner.

'The Military Liaison Office is perhaps the most sensitive section within the BfV, which explains why you've never heard of it. They only take staff with a very reliable work record: six years on the Rotation Team has helped in that regard. They take very few people from Rotation, but they have some people off sick and a heavy workload so you'll go there for six months, which could be extended to one year.'

Frau Schlösser closed the file in front of her, wrote something on a piece of paper attached to the front of it and finally looked at him, delivering something which, had he not known better, could have been a smile.

'And when do I start, Frau Schlösser?'

She looked at him as if the answer was obvious. 'It's Tuesday today. You'll start next Monday. Maybe get a haircut before then, Fleischhauer.'

He found it hard to contain his excitement. He'd have to meet Schäfer in person to tell him such wonderful news. Tomorrow he'd leave a dead letter drop demanding a meeting: 'Most urgent.' Schäfer would be thrilled. He'd have his hands on the Operation Open River plans in no time, and then everything Schäfer had promised about a war in Europe and a new Reich... he had to stop, he was so excited. He realised he'd almost been laughing out loud as he walked along the corridor.

–

Viktor snapped out of his indecision just in time. For a while he had remained at his desk, thinking about his life and awaiting whatever fate Kozlov and Schäfer had in mind for him. Since becoming an agent, Viktor's existence had been so precarious he'd always had to see it in the short term. When he was twenty-five, he realised it would be an achievement if he made it to thirty. When he was thirty, he doubted he would live to thirty-five. He was operating in Western Europe then, the Nazis were coming to power and life was increasingly dangerous. He took little comfort in reaching either thirty-five or forty: Europe was first on the verge of war and then in the grip of it and it didn't serve any purpose to think of survival, to do so was far too indulgent. He turned forty-five as the war ended, but by then he was back in Moscow and couldn't see himself surviving to fifty: he doubted Stalin would allow that. But he did. And by the time Viktor reached fifty-five, Stalin was dead, and while he did not exactly allow himself the luxury of contemplating old age, he was at least able to feel he had beaten the odds.

Now he had passed seventy-five, an age he would never had dreamt of. Viktor's uncharacteristic mood of resignation and reflection ended with the arrival in his office of Irma. It was her lunch break. He told her how he had admitted making contact with Edgar, but had not told Schäfer that Edgar could be en route to Cologne to confront Goalkeeper. Irma shook her head.

'They'll see that as treason, Viktor, you must know that. I don't know what's got into you.'

'He seemed to accept my motivation was to find a war criminal—'

'Listen to you, Viktor! You, of all people… it sounds as if you trust them. You said this morning that we need to leave. Why are you sitting here like this? This is not like you, Viktor. You look like a man waiting to be shot.'

'I know how Schäfer works, Irma. His priority will be to check that Goalkeeper is all right. They'll probably pull him out of Cologne for a while, but in the meantime they need me around to see what I'm up to. I need to get word to Edgar… it would be a disaster if he did anything.'

'Viktor!' Irma was leaning across the desk and holding Viktor's chin, forcing him to look at her. 'Forget about Edgar. We have no time.'

Viktor stirred. Irma was right. 'You go over today, Irma.'

'On my own?'

'Of course, it's far safer that way. We've talked about this so many times. You have those Federal Republic papers?'

Irma nodded and opened her jacket, patting the lining.

'Go back to your office for a couple of hours and act normally. Maybe tell them you have another migraine. Leave at four, through the back. The crossing at Bornholmer Strasse closes at five o'clock. It gets very busy, as you know, between four and five. Aim to go over then, with all those West Germans who can't wait to get out of this socialist paradise before dark. You can't go back to the flat, you realise that.'

'I know, I understand.'

'Good. I'll get some cash for you now from the safe. Once you're through the crossing you know where to go. That way I'll know you're safe.'

'But what about you, Viktor?'

'I'll probably come out through Friedrichstrasse station tomorrow morning. Don't look so worried, Irma, it will all be fine. Trust me.'

Irma did trust him, she had little choice. She took just enough Deutschmarks for them not to appear bulky in the lining of her jacket, and said a hasty goodbye to Viktor. She knew it could be the last time she'd see him, but this was not so unusual. For all of their life together, she had understood when she said farewell that it might be for the last time.

But she had a strange feeling this time. The Viktor she had said goodbye to in his office looked like an old man: someone who was tired, who knew the game was up and was accepting his fate. She fought against tears as she sat down back at her desk, and two colleagues asked if she was all right. Her distress was fortuitous; her migraine could not have appeared more plausible. The only remark they made when she left at four was to wonder why she hadn't left sooner.

Viktor watched Irma leave, along Behrenstrasse, from his office window. As soon as she was out of sight, he hurried down to the front entrance. He knew full well he'd be followed: for the next hour he'd be a decoy, drawing them away from Irma. The Bornholmer Strasse crossing was in the north of the Soviet sector, in Prenzlauer Berg, so Viktor headed east away from it, strolling slowly like the old man he was, pausing frequently, stopping a few times to rest. He was buying time, as much of it as possible. He walked along the Unter den Linden and spent a while in the university bookshop before crossing the Spree into Karl-Liebknecht-Strasse, and from there up into Marx-Engels-Platz. No more stopping, no evasive measures, no tricks – nothing the people following him could regard as suspicious.

There was a bar here that he had always known would be a perfect place to head to if he was being followed. It had an open staircase leading down into a basement room which, as an experienced tracker himself, he knew would be a nightmare. It was small and open, with nowhere to conceal yourself. As he reached the bar he had six people following him. They did what he expected: a man and a woman came down to the bar, the other four covered the outside. Viktor knew a few of the men in the bar. It was a place where men of his age hung out, men who had fought against the Nazis – some with the Red Army, a few who'd been in the camps. Viktor had one particular friend there. Max was an enormous man, probably in his early eighties; a Polish Jew who'd led a partisan brigade in the Pripet Marshes during the war and settled in East Berlin at the end of it. Viktor waited for the best part of two hours, the couple keeping an eye on him looking increasingly conspicuous and uncomfortable. Viktor explained his plan to Max. He didn't need to tell Max why. The walls of the bar were painted black and there was no toilet, just the stairs, the room and a bar. But there was a door, one you'd have to know about to see: a person could be standing next to it and be unaware of its presence. It was about three-quarters of a man's height and the same colour and material as the wood-clad wall. Viktor stood against the wall, Max in front of him. After a moment he bent down and opened the door. Within seconds Viktor was through, and Max had closed it behind him.

By the time the couple watching him realised he was no longer there, Viktor had already walked through a series of connected cellars, up a narrow staircase, along a corridor of sorts and out into Dircksenstrasse, well away from anyone who was meant to be watching him.

And from there, he disappeared into the night.

Chapter 26

Franz and Konrad were standing in front of a wide desk in an office on the top floor of the BfV headquarters on Innere Kanal-strasse. Everything about the office reflected the importance of the man it belonged to. Large windows allowed sweeping views of the Rhine as it made its way through the city and beyond, to the east, could be seen the vast expanse of sweeping forests. The carpet was so thick it felt like soft turf; the desk was curved and clearly made from an expensive and highly-polished wood.

The man behind the desk was so important and his job so sensitive that he was known by neither his name nor a formal title within the organisation. People would refer to him, though never in his presence, as 'the Saxon', on account of his distinctive accent. In terms of hierarchy he came below the President of the BfV and possibly his two Vice Presidents, but no one doubted the heads of the various departments deferred to him. In truth, hierarchies, organisations, protocols and structures didn't matter much to him. He had far more important things to think about. His job was to stop the Red Army Faction, and as far as he was concerned the two men in front of him weren't helping matters: they'd just delivered news of a serious setback. When he broke the silence there was no pretence of measure in his tone: he was both furious and incredulous.

'You allowed her to just… get away. Seriously?'

Franz and Konrad exchanged glances, each anxious the other should have the opportunity to reply. It was Konrad, the confident Bavarian, who eventually did so.

'We didn't allow her to get away sir; obviously this was not our intention. But the key to following someone is to allow enough distance and I regret that in this case we quite possibly allowed too much—'

'Stop! You've been brought here to explain why you released a twenty-six year-old woman from custody and then managed to lose her in the middle of Cologne – and now you insult me by delivering a seminar on surveillance techniques. Maybe you have a better explanation?'

The 'you' was addressed at Franz, who looked shocked, as if he'd hoped the Saxon hadn't noticed he was there.

'The only firm evidence we had against Ute von Morsbach was that for a number of years – perhaps six – she had been using a false—'

'You'll need to speak up. Don't whisper.'

'For around six years, Ute von Morsbach had been using a false identity, namely Sabine Falkenberg. That was as much as we could charge her with. Although we had monitored her arriving and leaving the apartment on Ratinger Strasse in Düsseldorf on a number of occasions, and she admitted knowing the people there and their connection with the Red Army Faction, it was all a bit too tenuous. The state prosecutor said it was not enough. We had no chance of charging her with conspiracy in relation to the murder of Heinrich Albrecht. I—'

'But didn't she admit to knowing that this Horst character had Heckler & Koch MP5s – and we now know from ballistics that Albrecht was shot with a Heckler & Koch MP5? Surely—'

'It's not enough, sir, I'm afraid. However, she did offer us one very promising lead. She—'

'You really must speak up.'

'I am sorry, sir. According to Ute, from approximately April 1970 to sometime in June 1972 she was in a relationship with a wealthy businessman called Werner Pohl. The Red Army Faction had heard about Pohl and sent her to Aachen so she could meet him and—'

'She's an attractive girl, isn't she?' The Saxon was holding a photo, nodding very slightly in approval, a slight smile on his face. 'Does she use the fact she's so attractive, eh?' He was looking at Konrad.

'Yes sir, I think she is well aware men – some men – would—'

'Which is probably why you let her out of custody. Carry on.'

Konrad continued. 'She had an affair with Werner Pohl, during which he transferred many hundreds of thousands of Deutschmarks to different Red Army Faction controlled accounts. None of the money came to her. Pohl also apparently suggested targets for the Red Army Faction, which she passed on to the leadership. He also obtained military-grade detonators for their bombs. Within days of the arrests in June 1972 he disappeared. We can find no trace of him, none whatsoever. A Werner Pohl certainly rented a flat in Jesuitenstrasse, but there is no other trace of him. There are of course a number of Werner Pohls in the Federal Republic, but we've investigated all of them and none are the one she knew in Aachen. We even checked Werner Pohls in Austria and Switzerland, but nothing.'

'Did she not have photographs of him?'

'No, sir. And the description she gave was not very specific. When we discussed the matter with our colleagues in counter-espionage, the consensus was that there may be a Soviet connection. They've long suspected the Soviets of funding and resourcing the Red Army Faction, but haven't been able to prove it. However, she did give us a lead. She told us that in July this year she was here in Cologne, collecting something for this Horst. On her way back to the station she was on a bus, going down Innere Kanalstrasse…' Franz gestured out of the window. 'She is convinced – totally convinced, sir – that she saw Werner Pohl crossing Innere Kanalstrasse. She said he was wearing a suit and carrying a briefcase, like he was leaving work. It was around six in the evening.'

'So we brought her back here, sir,' said Franz, his voice more confident now the man behind the desk looked less angry. 'We brought her to Innere Kanalstrasse and she was absolutely certain of the spot where she saw the man she knew as Werner Pohl.' Franz paused and coughed. 'There is no doubt in her mind, sir, that this man had crossed the street from right outside this very building. Every indication is he worked here. Our headquarters is the only building he could have been coming from. We'd brought her here in a van and she watched people entering and leaving the building all day, but no luck.'

'So you let her go?'

'No sir. Because everything pointed to Werner Pohl being someone who worked here, we felt the obvious course of action was to show her photographs of all the men who work in this building. Obviously showing someone like her photos of our agents represents a high security risk, but these are extenuating circumstances and even then we needed authorisation from the President. He was away, and it was going to take a day or two for one of the Vice Presidents to approve the request. We felt it would be wise not to waste that time.'

Konrad continued. 'So this morning we allowed her to walk around the centre of town, in the hope she'd spot Pohl. Naturally we were following her, but she was determined to get away from us. We lost her near the main railway station. She just disappeared into a crowd of people.'

'And what time was that?'

'Nine thirty, sir – two hours ago.'

'And that was that?'

'Yes, sir. We called in the police and searched for her, but I'm afraid she's just disappeared.'

–

All she'd been able to think about was that they'd send her to prison, and she'd die there. It would be Stammheim Prison in Stuttgart, the terrible place where all the Red Army Faction prisoners were being held. She wouldn't cope with being locked in a cell, she'd be terrified. And the others would make her life there a misery; Baader had never understood why Werner Pohl had disappeared. She kept getting messages from him even after his arrest, to say that he blamed her for it.

She was certain someone would try and kill her: if not her Red Army Faction comrades then maybe the state. It was only four months since Ulrike Meinhof's 'suicide' at Stammheim, which everyone was insisting wasn't suicide. Whoever was behind that would do the same to her.

So she had every reason to distrust Franz and Konrad. They were quite clearly tricking her. They were going to charge her with having a false identity and with being involved in the murder of that Albrecht man. But they were also obsessed with finding Werner Pohl, and so she agreed to co-operate with finding him. She was happy to go to Cologne, happy to go round the city, happy to identify the precise spot on Innere Kanalstrasse where she'd seen him, happy to point out the direction he'd come from.

On their first day in Cologne they sat in a van with darkened windows, at the very spot where the bus had been when she'd spotted Werner a couple of months previously. Wedged between Franz and Konrad, she watched as hundreds of people streamed into a large complex of buildings on the south side of Innere Kanalstrasse in the morning, and watched as they streamed out again at the end of the day. Just before six she was certain she saw him crossing the road with a group of people, but she said nothing, concentrating instead on watching which direction he headed in.

That evening, back in the cell at the police station in Cologne, Franz told her they were going to show her photographs of all the men who worked in that building – more than fifteen hundred of them. This was taking a day or two to arrange, and so the next day she was to walk around the centre of town to see if she could spot Pohl, with them following her.

The next day she did as instructed, and as she wandered around the Innenstadt she spotted her chance. Near the station a large crowd of people was milling around the concourse, and then a train must have arrived, because the crowd swelled even more so she quickly slipped into it. As she did so she took out the dark silk scarf she had in her pocket and wrapped it round her head. She then removed her jacket and turned it inside out.

Franz and Konrad had been following a woman with long blonde hair and a red jacket. Now her hair was covered by a scarf, and tucked into the back of a white jacket. She hurried through the station and out through an exit on the opposite side. On Domstrasse she found a bleak coffee shop, the kind that made you wonder why the owners bothered. She had just enough money in her jacket for a cup of coffee and she found a table at the back of the basement where she hoped she wouldn't be noticed.

In the hours she spent there she was able to grasp just quite how desperate her situation was. She had no money, no papers and was a wanted woman. At one stage her desperation became so bad that she thought going back to her family in Augsburg might be an option. She'd certainly be safe there, at least for long enough to plan what to do and where to go next. Her parents had never pretended to understand her, but she knew they didn't hate her. They even assured her that they loved her, though she couldn't imagine why. For her part, she didn't even like them: she despised everything they stood for and, as Werner had said to her more than once, how can you love someone if you don't even like them? Going back there would be as bad as the prison in Stammheim. She dismissed that as an option, and another plan emerged: she knew who'd help her.

–

Once she felt she'd outstayed her welcome at the bleak coffee shop on Domstrasse, she'd found a busy restaurant round the corner. The toilets were in the basement, next to a cloakroom, from which she stole an elegant, light brown raincoat.

By five thirty she was in position: standing back from the road in the shade of some trees, and able to observe the part of Innere Kanalstrasse she'd spotted Werner crossing to the day before. She saw him at ten past six: the same quick, confident gait – she'd always had to ask him to slow down. She followed him as he turned into Niehler Strasse, and at the corner with Kuenstrasse he stopped at the entrance to what looked like flats above some shops. She followed him in as he opened the door.

'Excuse me.' He barely looked in her direction as he held the door open. She waited until it closed and could see that they were alone at the bottom of the stairway. She removed her headscarf.

'Werner – it's me, Sabine!'

He spun round and took a hurried step back, staring at her in utter astonishment. He opened his mouth and then closed it, gripping the bannister at the bottom of the stairs. When he spoke his voice was weak from shock.

'I'm, I'm not Werner… please go away, I'm not Werner.' And then he looked round in panic, trying to work out what to do. 'Look, perhaps you'd better come up. Be quiet though, please.'

There were few personal touches in the apartment. Like its carpets, the place was tending towards threadbare. The furniture appeared dated and the television in the corner was dusty, as was the rest of the apartment.

He pulled a wooden upright chair from behind the table and placed it in front of the rather raddled sofa she'd perched nervously on the edge of. He looked anxious, far more flustered than she'd ever seen him. 'You can't stay, Sabine.'

'So you do know me after all!'

'What do you mean?'

'Downstairs, you said you weren't Werner.'

'I was shocked… the entrance is not a safe place to talk.'

'Is that all you can say, Werner, after four years? You tell me to go? What happened to you? You just disappeared—'

'My mother was ill.'

'You told me your mother was in a home in Switzerland, and you rarely saw her.'

'She was taken ill and I spent time with her before she died. I was so devastated, I…'

'Seriously, Werner, you expect me to believe that? You never contacted me: couldn't you have at least let me know what was going on?'

He leaned forward, rubbing his hands together as if to warm them up. 'I know, but look… I also had serious business problems. I managed to lose most of my money and was too embarrassed to contact you. I felt ashamed. I mean, look at this place… And tell me, how on earth did you find me?'

'I saw you in the street.'

'Why are you even in Cologne?

'Do you work in that place, Werner?'

'What place?'

'The place I saw you coming out of on Innere Kanalstrasse, the BfV headquarters. Were you always a spy, Werner? Was that what it was all about? You were spying on me for the BfV? You're not really Werner Pohl, are you.'

He looked down at the thin carpet and closed his eyes for one moment. The shock of her turning up had been so profound that he hadn't known what to do at first other than get her into the apartment. Now he was clear what to do.

'It is much more complicated than you realise, Sabine. I'll tell you everything, but first you tell me why you're here.'

It was only when she began to reply that he realised she was weeping. 'Everything has gone wrong, Werner, everything. I should have stayed in Aachen, but I went to Düsseldorf a few months ago and got mixed up with the Red Army Faction again – which I didn't mean to. And then the police arrested me and handed me over to the BfV and they found out my real name and now they're trying to link me with the killing of that Heinrich Albrecht in Wuppertal and—'

'Hang on, Sabine, slow down. You said the police handed you over to the BfV?'

She nodded.

'So what are you doing here?'

'If I tell you, you'll not be angry? You'll understand the pressure I've been under?'

'Of course, Sabine. You must know I've always cared about you.'

'They interrogated me so hard in Düsseldorf that I'm afraid I told them about you. So they brought me here to Cologne to try to find you. I'd seen you in Innere Kanalstrasse, in July I think it was, and they got that out of me. We had to sit outside your office building in a van with special windows, but when I saw you last night I didn't say anything, I—'

'Jesus Christ, Sabine. Jesus Christ.'

'Please don't be angry with me, Werner. I promise I didn't say anything when I spotted you.'

Werner's voice sounded much calmer when he replied. It was as if he was back in control. 'I'm not angry with you, Sabine. I just need to know what happened. Do they know who I am?'

'No – I think tomorrow they planned to show me photos of all the men who work at the BfV headquarters, so this morning I managed to escape from them. I hid from them all day, waited for you near Innere Kanalstrasse and then followed you here.'

'They could have followed you too!'

'They didn't, I'm certain of that. I need money, Werner; I won't bother you after that. Just give me some money, enough to get to Frankfurt, and I'll find people there to help. I promise I won't tell anyone anything.'

'You're certain they don't know who I am?'

'Positive.'

He was now even clearer about what he had to do. He sat next to her on the sofa and put his hand round her shoulder, pulling her close to him, kissing her gently on the cheek and stroking her hair with a degree of affection he'd rarely shown her.

'Don't cry, Sabine, it will be all right. Of course I will give you money, enough to get yourself sorted out. Don't worry. But maybe stay here tonight. It will be safer to travel in the morning,

I'll think of a way. I've got some money here, enough. We can enjoy ourselves before you go… like old times.'

She was so relieved that she resolved to tell him how she felt about him. She'd come to realise – to her surprise – that she cared about him in spite of herself. She was sure he'd understand, maybe he'd even feel the same and then they could disappear together, though she was aware this was looking at a desperate situation in a perhaps ridiculously romantic way.

She never got the chance.

They'd only been in bed for a minute when he climbed on top of her. She feared he was going to slap her again, and she thought that if she told him now how much she loved him he wouldn't hurt her. But there seemed to be no need to say anything to him: he stroked her gently on the face and kissed her and promised her he'd treat her well. He'd missed her, he said.

So she didn't argue when he tied first one hand to the head-board and then the other, promising he was going to be gentle, that he'd never hurt her again. At that moment, she trusted him so much she began to speak. But he placed a hand across her mouth.

Quiet.

Both his hands caressed her cheeks, cupping them before moving gently down to her neck. By the time both his thumbs were positioned on her windpipe and when she realised what he was doing, it was far too late.

Chapter 27

Bonn and Cologne, West Germany, The Wednesday

Early in his career, Edgar had been given a particularly sage piece of advice which had stuck with him. 'Watch out for questions suspects ask you, they're far more revealing than their answers to your questions. Answers can be anticipated and rehearsed. Questions tend to be more spontaneous and unguarded: they are more of a reflex.'

The advice had come from an experienced interrogator who had learnt his craft in the Great War. 'And also watch out for the unasked question. I'll give you an example. Imagine you tell a man you're interrogating, "We found something very interesting in your briefcase." You'd expect him to ask what that was. An innocent person certainly would. But someone who is guilty will avoid asking you what it was, most likely because of course they know what you've found, and the last thing they want to do is draw attention to it. This approach is far more effective than saying, "How come we found a map of the Humber ports in your briefcase?"'

Edgar had woken up confused in the very early hours of Wednesday morning. He was on top of a bed in a Bonn hotel room, dressed in the same clothes he'd been wearing when he arrived at the hotel just a few hours previously, after spending the evening with Clive Cowley. The few hours' sleep he'd managed to grab had been fitful and disturbed. Something was on his mind, and as he lay on the bed it became clear what it was.

Clive Cowley: the unasked question.

Cowley's behaviour the previous evening had been odd to say the least, even allowing for the man's caseload of grievances. He'd managed to be both helpful and evasive at the same time, and Edgar had been too exhausted to spot the unasked questions. At dinner he'd gently pressed him about Heinz Fleischhauer. How often did Cowley see him?

'Very rarely, Edgar, really not very much I can tell you about him.'

'I thought you said you're running him, Clive?'

Cowley had shrugged and delicately spread a generous helping of foie gras onto a curled slice of toast. So Edgar had let it drop for a while, and talked once more of how well rewarded Clive Cowley would be in the City. Not just well rewarded, well regarded too – appreciated. Cowley liked that, just as he enjoyed most of the second bottle of Pomerol Edgar allowed him to order. He looked carefully at Cowley: eyelids drooping now, slightly rheumy, a lack of focus. When he moved to the next stage of drunkenness, Edgar felt it was safe to broach the subject of Fleischhauer again.

'The BfV, are they still based on Innere Kanalstrasse?'

Cowley's mouth was full and a wine glass was at his lips. He nodded, a bit of foie gras dropping from his mouth and settling on his tie.

'Last time I had any dealings with Fleischhauer he was living very near there I seem to recall,' Edgar continued, 'just south of Innere Kanalstrasse.'

Cowley's mouth was once again full, but he shook his head. 'No, no,' a pause while he digested his mouthful, 'don't think he was ever there, other direction actually. Niehler Strasse, just past the park – block on the corner of Kuenstrasse. He's above a pharmacy, pretty green shutters, like some Black Forest cottage. It's not too far from Innere Kanalstrasse though. He...'

And then Cowley shut up, stopped in mid-sentence, wiped some crumbs from his lips and filled his wine glass, drinking its contents in one go. He looked uncomfortable. 'Sorry, Edgar, I've got confused: Fleischhauer lives over in Porz, other bank of the Rhine. What I meant was I always meet him there – on the corner of Niehler Strasse and Kuenstrasse, in a bar opposite the pharmacy. Sorry, all this wine, eh?'

That was what had disconcerted Edgar; it was what he should have picked up at the time. Cowley's unasked questions: why was Edgar asking about Heinz Fleischhauer? What, for that matter, was Edgar doing in Bonn? Hadn't he retired? Why had he looked him up? These were all obvious questions, and Cowley had asked none of them. And then he'd made such a mess of telling him where Fleischhauer lived. He should have let that one go. And always meeting him in one location? No one meets an agent all the time in just one location, not even Cowley.

As he lay on the bed, Edgar remembered Viktor's warnings. In Berlin in March, he'd warned him to trust no one on his side and in Budapest in May, Viktor had been far more explicit. 'Just be careful, especially if you go anywhere near Bonn, which you may well have to. In the last couple of years your embassy there has been the source of very high-grade intelligence… possibly MI6. I can't be sure, but it is someone there who has links to Goalkeeper.'

Up to now Edgar had assumed the double agent to be wary of was Lassiter, always mindful of Porter's initial description: 'Disagreeable type, a very high opinion of himself, too clever by half… you'd absolutely detest him.' Notwithstanding his dislike of the man, he had ample reason to suspect Lassiter.

Lassiter, he had realised after Paget told him about their meeting, was a classic example of the unasked question. Paget himself had remarked how Hugh Lassiter hadn't shown any emotion when Paget told him Lothar Meier had died and, tellingly, did not ask about the circumstances of his death. And then there was the way he'd enquired about Captain Canterbury. Everything pointed to Lassiter being a double agent, no doubt working with Canterbury and his Nazis.

But Edgar's certainty about Lassiter had caused him to ignore Viktor's warning about the Bonn connection. More than one person in the Service was spying for the Soviets. Cowley, he now realised, was almost certainly a double agent too, this time serving the KGB. He was the source in the Bonn embassy Viktor had warned him about.

As Edgar stood under a cold shower he admonished himself. Years ago, despite his exhaustion, he'd have spotted this. He wondered to what extent he'd alerted Cowley: had the slightly drunken behaviour been a mask? They'd been together for around three hours, and Edgar doubted the exchanges about Fleischhauer had taken up more than five minutes of that time. Cowley had been drunk enough to let slip where Fleischhauer lived, covering it up too late with an unconvincing correction, but Edgar must have rung some alarm bells. Cowley would probably get word to Fleischhauer, and Edgar had to assume Cowley would have followed him to the hotel. From now on he'd be watched.

Edgar waited until four o'clock before getting dressed. Despite everything, a sense of thrill settled over him. He'd made some mistakes, but he'd still back himself to outsmart Cowley and the others. He'd paid for the room the night before, so he didn't need to check out. He imagined Cowley would have the reception area covered, he'd probably already found out that Edgar had booked a six o'clock alarm call.

He edged open the door: the corridor was clear. He left through the fire exit and, once outside, stood for ten minutes with his back to the door, making certain he wasn't being been followed or watched. He took in the fresh air as he planned his next move. He edged round the side of the hotel. From behind a bush, with no light on him, he could see the front of the hotel, the Rhine glinting behind it. The street appeared to be deserted, but there was a delivery van parked immediately in front of the hotel, and on the other side of the road, a figure in the driver's seat of a dark-coloured Mercedes.

They'd be waiting for six o'clock, when he was supposed to be waking up. It was now four thirty, and within ten minutes Edgar had walked to the rear of the hotel then through the shadows to his car on Adalbert-Stifter-Strasse. He was sure Cowley had no idea he was parked there, but he sat in it for ten minutes nevertheless, watching the street carefully until he was certain once again that he wasn't being watched.

–

That same Wednesday morning was the worst of Reinhard Schäfer's life. They were in Kozlov's office, the one with the panelled walls, the heavy drape curtains and thick carpet. The large clock, tilted at a slight angle next to the portrait of Leonid Brezhnev, showed that it was twenty to nine. The head of the KGB station was sitting at his desk, playing with a dozen or so cigarettes loose on his desk. For some reason he'd tipped them out of the packet and was now arranging them like toy soldiers.

Schäfer was standing at the front of the desk. He had not been invited to sit which, given his short stature, made him feel especially uncomfortable. Nor had the two people next to him: a man and a woman, both of whom had been among the group following Viktor the previous evening.

'Let me get this correct,' said Kozlov. He had now formed a square with four of the cigarettes and was in the process of creating another square alongside the first one. 'Six of you followed Viktor Leonidovich when he left here yesterday afternoon.' The couple both nodded. 'Six of you!' Kozlov shouted and banged his desk, squashing a cigarette. 'You followed him to a bar in Marx–Engels–Platz you say. Do we know anything about this bar?'

The three people standing in front of the desk looked at each other. The woman replied. She was German, on secondment from the Stasi. Schäfer had had high hopes for her, but suspected the end of her secondment was now imminent.

'It's a small basement bar sir. An older clientele, popular with people who fought against the Nazis.'

'Huh, can't be very busy then,' said Kozlov. The cigarettes were now being formed into a series of triangles.

'When the subject entered the bar, Wilhelm and I followed him down there. I instructed two of the others to watch the main entrance and the other two to go to the back, in case there was a rear exit. As far as we could ascertain, sir, the bar comprised just the one room, with the stairs the only way in or out. The subject remained in the bar for over two hours, drinking and talking with various people, most of whom he seemed to know. Then he vanished sir. One minute he was talking to a very large man who had his back to us, and the next minute he was gone. We waited a few minutes; we assumed he'd moved towards the counter, where it was quite crowded. When we realised we couldn't see him any longer we moved over to the counter, but he wasn't there. We questioned the large man who we'd last seen talking to him but he said as far as he could recall, the subject had just walked away.'

'Who was this man?'

The woman checked her notebook. 'A Max Lazerowitz, sir, of an address in Friedrichshain.'

'Lazerowitz you say? Typical…'

'Once we realised the subject was missing we instructed everyone to remain in the bar. I went upstairs and alerted the others. Wilhelm and I then searched the place. Near to where the subject was last seen, with Lazerowitz, was a small door in the wall which led through to a cellar. This led to other cellars and eventually to an exit on Dircksenstrasse.'

'And I assume none of you *idiots*,' the last word was shouted with particular feeling, 'saw him in Dircksenstrasse?'

The man and the woman shook their heads. Schäfer sighed and looked away from Kozlov.

'And the woman – Irma?'

'She left the embassy at four o'clock through the back, into Behrenstrasse. We were going to follow her but then Viktor Leonidovich left a couple of minutes later through the front. There were only four of us at that point – the other two joined a few minutes later – and I felt we all needed to follow Viktor Leonidovich as he was the priority. I called for help and told them to pick her up near their apartment, but she never got there.'

Kozlov slammed the table again, disturbing his cigarette arrangements. From under the desk he produced a bottle of vodka and poured himself a glass. 'You're fucking amateurs. Fucking amateurs. The oldest trick in the book and you fall for it like you're at kindergarten! Leaving from separate exits to confuse you, her not going to where you assumed she was going… When this is all over I'm going to have this written up as a case study in how to fuck up following an elderly couple!'

'I'm afraid, Piotr Vasilyevich, there is some further bad news.' Schäfer was shifting uncomfortably from foot to foot. 'Once we realised we couldn't find either of them I ordered the records for all the border crossings to be checked. A woman matching Irma's description crossed at Bornholmer Strasse at a quarter to five yesterday afternoon. She had Federal Republic papers and—'

'How can you be sure it was her?'

'We have since seen photographs, it was definitely her. She must have gone to Bornholmer Strasse straight from here with false papers. I wasn't aware she was not being followed. However, the good news sir is that Viktor Leonidovich did not pass through any of the crossings—'

'Well of course not, you idiot! All the crossings close at five in the afternoon and your so-called experts here saw him in the bar in Marx-Engels-Platz at least three hours after that.'

'But he hasn't attempted to cross this morning, either. I've had the guards doubled at all the crossings.'

'There'll be an inquiry into this, you all understand that? This is totally unacceptable. To lose a man and a woman in their seventies, here in Berlin…'

'I'm sure Viktor Leonidovich is still in the city sir, if that's any consolation.' Schäfer sounded like he was unconvinced by what he'd said himself.

Kozlov was scooping his cigarettes up and stuffing them back in the box, his hands trembling. 'Viktor Leonidovich will outsmart you, you realise that? Mind you, after what you've just told me, it seems that's not a hard thing to do.'

–

When Viktor emerged from Dircksenstrasse he knew he'd got the better of them, but doubted his advantage would last long. He headed west and then south in an arc wide enough to keep him away from Marx-Engels-Platz, crossed the Spree on Bodestrasse, and then went up into Clara Zetkin Strasse where he found a doorway to step into, from which he was able to watch the street and catch his breath. The place was deserted, no sound of footsteps breaking the silent night.

Further down Clara Zetkin Strasse was a small ironmongery. The owner was someone Viktor trusted – they did each other the occasional favour. He found the keys in their usual hiding place and let himself into the windowless storeroom at the rear. He knew he would be safe there: it was the perfect place to hide. But he still waited ten minutes before turning the lights on.

One of the favours Viktor had done for the owner was to pay for a special phone line to be installed. If you knew an engineer to whom you could be excessively generous – in Federal Republic currency – and you were near enough to the west it was possible, though quite illegal, to put in a line which connected with West Berlin. And it was a West Berlin number which Viktor was now calling. A woman answered.

'Yes?'

'It's me,' said Viktor.

'She's arrived.'

'What's the message?'

'To let you know she brought six roses with her.'

Irma was safe. 'Good, good. Is she with you?'

'No – she came here earlier this evening, left the message and went off. There's something else though.'

'Go on, quickly.'

'The Englishman called apparently.'

'Really? When was that?'

'This morning. Karl took the call.'

'What time was it?'

'Late morning: I was out.'

'And what did the Englishman say?'

'He said what he's supposed to say: "Is Klaus there?"'

'And what did Karl say?'

'He says that he replied, "Klaus is not here." If I'd been there I'd have used the exact form of words, you know that.'

'That's all?'

'Only that I was able to trace the call to a call box at Cologne Bonn airport. Are you still there?'

There had been silence as Viktor was thinking. 'You'd better stay by the phone for the next twenty-four hours.'

He'd feared that this would happen. He'd taken too long over confronting Schäfer, only to discover that Goalkeeper was an important, if unwitting, Soviet agent. If he'd been quicker and smarter he'd have called Edgar off long before he got anywhere near Bonn or Cologne. He'd been too hasty in revealing 'Heinz Fleischhauer' to Edgar, and now it appeared it was too late to undo his actions. It wasn't hard to guess what had happened. Edgar had given up waiting for word from Viktor and was now in Cologne, ready to tell the British about the double agent. Viktor shook his head and sighed. Goalkeeper was about to be exposed, and there was no hiding the fact it would all be his fault.

Viktor found a rough blanket, draped it over his shoulders and lay his head on the desk. He'd remain in the storeroom of the ironmongery shop on Clara Zetkin Strasse until the morning. He was just a five-minute walk from Friedrichstrasse station, where the warren of platforms, different tracks and subways were his best chance of getting into the west.

–

Reinhard Schäfer cut a dejected figure back to his office after the carpeting from Kozlov. It was ten past nine, and he didn't anticipate that his awful morning could possibly get worse. But his secretary was hovering anxiously in the corridor, wringing her hands and speaking in an urgent whisper.

'I didn't know whether to interrupt your meeting. Comrade Volkov rang from Paris, three times… you're to call him urgently, on a secure line.'

Because of their proximity to France, KGB agents in Cologne and Bonn were traditionally looked after by the Service's Paris station, based at the embassy on the Rue de Grenelle. Goalkeeper was an exception. Volkov was an ally of Schäfer's, they'd worked together in Berlin and were friends who did each other favours, trading information and gossip about what was going on in their respective stations. Schäfer had rung Volkov the morning after his encounter with Viktor: 'Let me know if you pick anything up, I may have to call Goalkeeper in…'

'I heard you were meeting with Kozlov. I didn't know whether you should be disturbed.'

'I appreciate that, Andrei. You have something for me?'

'I'm afraid so, Reinhard. You've called me on the secure line, yes?'

'Of course.'

'Sofia Rules nonetheless, Reinhard. It's about Julius.'

Schäfer nodded, as if Volkov was in front of him. Sofia Rules: referring to agents only by their code name, even on a secure line or in person. Julius was Clive Cowley.

'There was an urgent message this morning from Bonn – from Julius. He called at about six forty, and the idiot of a duty officer here waited before I got in at half eight before bothering to tell me. Why he didn't think to contact me at home I don't know. Apparently a man called Edgar turned up in Bonn last night. He was asking Julius about Goalkeeper, wanted to know where he lives…'

'Hang on, this was last night and he waited until after six thirty this morning to tell us?'

'I know, I know. The man's a fool, all I seem to deal with these days are fools. But listen, it gets worse. Edgar stayed in a hotel in Bonn last night, and Julius had it watched. He found out he'd asked for a six o'clock alarm call, but when there wasn't any sign of him by six thirty, he had his room checked. It was empty: Edgar had left during the night.'

'And has Julius told Goalkeeper?'

'Yes... but for some inexplicable reason not until seven this morning. He phoned him at his apartment.'

Reinhard Schäfer began to feel very cold. 'And what happened? Was Goalkeeper even there?'

'Yes, but Julius is in a panic, he was gabbling on the phone. He kept going on about how we're going to have to bring him in. He sounds terrified. We need to do something about him Reinhard; he's dangerous in that state.'

'I'll have a think what to do. What instructions shall we give Goalkeeper though?'

'Julius says he told Goalkeeper that he needs to go to ground, he should leave his apartment by eight o'clock at the latest.' A long pause. 'Are you there?'

'I know you run him, Andrei, but Julius is a liability. What makes him think he could leave it so late and then give such ridiculous instructions? This was two hours ago. Has Julius not heard any more?'

'He was wondering whether to go into work as normal. I told him he must. Things are enough of a mess as it is without him drawing attention to himself by being absent, but he can hardly call Goalkeeper from the British Embassy can he?'

'I don't see why not: after all he does run him for the British. You'd better leave it with me.'

Schäfer leaned back in his chair and closed his eyes, concentrating on taking deep breaths. The walls around him were crumbling, brick by brick. He sensed that it was too late to avert a disaster: Edgar would surely have arrived in Cologne already. He knew how to solve one problem though, and pressed the buzzer to his outer office. 'Get Samuel for me – on the secure line.'

The call came through a minute later. 'Samuel?'

'Uh huh.'

'Are you in the usual place?'

'Uh huh.'

'How soon can you be in Cologne?'

'By car, just over two hours – under two and a half. By train a lot quicker.'

'Get there as fast as you can. You'll need to deal with our nephew there.'

'Uh huh.'

'And after that, go to Bonn. The uncle needs to be dealt with too.'

'Uh huh.'

'Be careful though, someone will be trying to get there before you.'

'Uh huh.'

–

Viktor slept for perhaps three hours altogether that night, half an hour here, twenty minutes there. It wasn't the discomfort of sleeping sitting up, with his head resting on the desk, that was the problem. He was used to that, and could usually manage to sleep anywhere.

Viktor's code – one he had drummed into his agents and had lived by himself – was to never question, never discuss, never hesitate. But, as he got older, he had occasionally found himself harbouring doubts about these absolutes which had guided his life. And these doubts, as fleeting as they were, tended to come in the early hours of the morning: usually after two and before four – the time, his mother used to tell him, when people were most likely to die.

Never question, never discuss, never hesitate.

And what kept him awake that night was the realisation that he was about to turn his back on everything he'd stood for, the cause he had served for more than fifty years. He knew he could justify what he was about to do, but he also knew it would destroy him.

He left the ironmongery on Clara Zetkin Strasse at eight. He'd been ready and tempted to leave at six, but the streets would be too quiet and the station would be nothing like as busy as it should be two hours later.

His plan was one he'd had in mind for a long time, ever since he'd arrived in East Berlin and feared one day he may have to leave it in a hurry. Friedrichstrasse station was the border crossing for train passengers. It was hard enough for passengers from the west to get into the east through the station's tightly controlled checkpoints and heavily guarded barriers. For people from the east trying to get into the west it was even harder, though still possible. But there was another way, and this was the reason he'd chosen Friedrichstrasse rather than one of the street crossings. There was an entrance on the southern side of the station for railway staff. It was also used by the Stasi to smuggle their own people into the west, and bring people from the west into the DDR. Viktor had long cultivated the guards at this entrance. They knew he was KGB and that he would need to frequently pop in and out, sometimes on official business, at other times simply because he hadn't been out for a while and liked to keep his options open. It paid to be a familiar face.

But this morning something wasn't right. Even though he knew the guard on the first gate, he was reluctant to let Viktor through.

'There's something up today, sir, I don't know what it is. There's a real flap on, been like that since I came on at four. They've doubled the number of guards everywhere in the station and there are Stasi all over the place, even a few of your people as far as I can tell. By rights I should be clearing you with my boss and even then you'd have to stick to the railway staff corridor. I wouldn't go anywhere near the barriers leading to the western platforms.'

Viktor didn't need telling. Over the guard's shoulder he could see the area was teeming with guards. Through an open door to a control room he saw half a dozen men in civilian clothes hunched over television monitors.

'Just wait here a moment, sir – I'll check if it's all right for you to come through.'

'Don't bother. It's really not urgent, I'll come back later. You take care.'

He moved aside as three border guards pushed past him and walked slowly away from the station. For a few minutes he stood in the doorway of a shop on Georgenstrasse, overlooking the subway entrance outside the station. There was no way out of East Berlin. He needed a while to think.

He walked the short distance to the junction of Georgenstrasse and Friedrichstrasse, and headed south towards the Unter den Linden.

Never question, never discuss, never hesitate.

Chapter 28

Edgar arrived in Cologne just before five thirty on the Wednesday morning. The drive from Bonn had taken less than an hour on the deserted autobahn, and as he approached the city the sun was beginning to rise over it.

He negotiated his way round the city's complicated bypass system and onto Innere Kanalstrasse, driving past the headquarters of the BfV where Wilhelm Richter worked – apparently as Heinz Fleischhauer – before turning left into Niehler Strasse, where he lived. He recalled Cowley's directions: 'Just past the park… block on the corner of Kuenstrasse… he's above a pharmacy… pretty green shutters, like some Black Forest cottage…'

Edgar drove down Niehler Strasse, past the park Cowley had helpfully drawn his attention to, and slowed down when he reached the junction with Kuenstrasse. Sure enough there was a pharmacy on the left and, above it, apartments with an entrance on Kuenstrasse and green wooden shutters on the upper floor windows which – if you were drunk like Cowley had been – could be reminiscent of a Black Forest cottage. Opposite the pharmacy, on the other side of Niehler Strasse, was a bar which, like all the other shops, had its metal shutters down. He continued driving along Niehler Strasse, turning right at the end of the block into Beuelsweg and right again at the end of that road, bringing him into Kuenstrasse. Fleischhauer's apartment building was easily visible on the other side of Niehler Strasse.

He parked with a clear view of the apartment building, leaned back in his seat, and went over the plan which he'd begun to form on the drive from Bonn.

Once he'd flushed out Richter – found exactly where he lived and was sure of his new identity – he'd ring Charles Kemp in Bonn. '*Good news and bad news,*' he'd tell the young MI6 Head of Station there. '*I've found you a Nazi working at BfV who's spying for the Soviet Union: that ought to earn you some Brownie points with the West Germans? Fancy giving them a call, better hurry though, he'll be on the move soon…*' The bad news? '*Ah yes, your man Cowley, he's spying for the Soviets too.*'

Just after six there were early signs of movement in the area, and Edgar felt able to leave the car. He walked up to the apartment block: alongside the entrance was a brass panel with the numbers and buzzers for the eight apartments and the names of the residents in a tab next to them. Apartment number five had the initials 'HF'.

–

Edgar had spotted them earlier when he'd driven down Beuel-sweg: half a dozen men, spread out under dirty blankets and torn up cardboard boxes in a couple of shop doorways, one or two of them spilling into a narrow alley. When he went back one was awake – much younger than Edgar had expected, with long black hair and piercing green eyes. Edgar knelt down beside him and spoke quietly.

'I'm looking for someone to do a small job for me. It will take no more than a few minutes and I'll pay very well.'

'You've come to the wrong place.' He didn't speak in the Cologne dialect, and narrowed his eyelids as he looked suspiciously at Edgar. 'You won't find what you want here. There are boys you can buy but not at this time of the day and not in this part of town; the police look out for that. Try one of the parks after dark if you want that kind of thing.'

'No, no… you misunderstand me. That isn't what I meant, I'm sorry. Look all I need is someone who can come with me and then ring on someone's buzzer, not far from here. Then you can go. It will take no more than ten minutes of your time, perhaps less.'

The young man had appeared interested, and when Edgar had pressed two fifty mark notes into his gloved hand, he'd agreed to come. Now they were sitting in the Audi, watching the apartment.

'Tell me once more, just so I can be sure you understand.'

The man, called Andreas, sighed with the impatience of a child tired of being nagged. 'I am to go to the apartment building over there, the one on the corner with Niehler Strasse with green shutters. I am to press the buzzer to apartment number five, the one with the initials 'HF'. I am to ask if a Herr Fleischhauer is there. When the person replies I say, 'Are you Wilhelm Richter?' I am to repeat that.'

'Then you leave – quickly.'

'Don't worry; I'll leave quickly enough.'

'And then you forget everything. Understand? Carry on down Kuenstrasse and disappear from the area for a few hours, preferably all day. I want you to repeat all this to me once more.'

Andreas's reluctance was cut short by the sight of another fifty mark note Edgar was removing from his wallet.

'And when do you want me to do this?'

Edgar studied his watch. 'It's ten to seven now: we'll wait a few more minutes.'

—

'It's me. Are you awake?'

Heinz Fleischhauer was awake only in the sense that he wasn't fast asleep – but his alarm had sounded just moments earlier and he was still in bed, the curtains closed. He'd fallen asleep late; the excitement of killing Sabine had kept him awake for hours. Unsure who the 'me' was on the other end of the line he hauled himself up into a semi-sitting position and muttered, 'Who?'

'It's me – from Bonn. You… you need to see the doctor today.'

Cowley: the occasionally sober Englishman, a man seemingly too incompetent to be a spy for one side, let alone two. But the code – 'You need to see the doctor today' – was reserved for a real emergency. He was in danger. He was wide awake now.

'I think someone is on to you.' The Englishman sounded breathless and was clearly trying to keep his voice down. He paused to catch his breath. 'You need to get away from your apartment, don't go into work. Just get away.'

'Hang on, hang on…' Fleischhauer tried to sound calm, but the panic evident in the other man's voice felt contagious. 'Start from the beginning, tell me what on earth is going on.'

'I don't have time. Just get away. It's seven o'clock now. Get out as soon as you can, certainly before eight. There's a man looking for you. Do you have somewhere to go?'

'Yes, but…'

'Tell me where.'

'You've rung me on an open line. I'm going to leave as soon as I can. I'll try to send you a message…'

Fleischhauer jumped out of bed and pulled the curtain aside just enough to look up and down the street. Nothing appeared out of the ordinary, but he couldn't afford to leave anything to chance. In the twenty or so years since he'd arrived in the Federal Republic he'd anticipated this moment: a warning that his cover may be blown, the need to dispose of Heinz Fleischhauer in an instant.

He didn't trust the West Germans or the British, and certainly not the Russians. He knew who he could trust – the only people he had ever trusted: his friends on the farm. He felt some regret he was leaving Cologne on the eve of his transfer to the Military Liaison Office, which would have been the culmination of his career, what he'd been working towards all these years. But there was nothing he could do about that now.

If Heinz Fleischhauer had learned just one thing from a lifetime of subterfuge, it was the value of allowing a few minutes to think, even in the most perilous and urgent of situations – to never take the most obvious course of action, at least not before stopping to consider it. It was the reason he had avoided being caught and put on trial by the Poles in 1945. It was the reason he had survived captivity in the Soviet Union. And it was the reason he had thrived while working for many different masters since then. He went into the kitchen, made himself a coffee, and thought.

The obvious course of action would be to do as Cowley instructed: to leave the apartment as soon as possible and disappear. And it wasn't as if he didn't have somewhere to go. A place where he knew he would never be found, a place where he knew he'd be protected: the friends on the farm. He looked out of the kitchen window. His BMW motorbike was parked just below it – he could be at the farm by the end of the day. This life, of never knowing when he'd be found out, would be over. He almost felt a sense of relief.

But what if this was a trap?

'*Someone is on to you… just get away.*'

It could be Cowley trying to trick him, or someone else. He would, he decided, wait in the apartment. He would be surprised if Cowley did not call again soon, if only to check he'd left. He needed to ask him some questions. He would wait.

And then there was the body: trussed up on the floor of the lounge and wrapped in sheets and plastic. He'd had it all planned. He was going to take the next day off work, hire a van and then, when no one was around, take the body down to the basement. He'd even worked out where to bury it. Now it would have to stay here.

–

The buzzer rang less than five minutes later, causing him to jump. It hardly ever rang, and certainly never at this time of the morning. Cowley, maybe? Fleischhauer sensed he'd been calling from a phone box: maybe he'd done so from one nearby and was now checking he was going to leave the apartment.

But it would be out of character for Cowley to behave in such a manner, and in any case it was too soon. He decided to ignore the buzzer, hoping it was a mistake. When it rang again, moments later, he went to the kitchen window and looked down. He could just about make out the shoulder of man with long hair and wearing a light-coloured top. The rest of his body was obscured by the doorway.

The buzzer rang again – a third time.

'Is Herr Fleischhauer there?'

He hesitated, trying to work out who it could be: it certainly wasn't Cowley. It was a German accent, but not the voice of someone in authority – it was slightly hesitant and young.

'Yes, this is Fleischhauer. What do you want?'

'Are you Wilhelm Richter?'

He felt the apartment swimming around him, the walls moving up and down, and he had to lean against the kitchen counter. It took a considerable act of self-restraint to prevent him answering instinctively in the affirmative.

'What?'

'Are you Wilhelm Richter?'

'Who the hell…?'

He ran to the kitchen window just in time to spot the man walking quickly away from the entrance and up Kuenstrasse, away from Niehler Strasse.

From a hidden compartment in the base of the bedroom wardrobe, he retrieved three padded envelopes. They contained his new papers, plenty of Deutschemarks and a small fortune in Swiss Francs, along with his Walther semi-automatic pistol. A few clothes and toiletries were ready, as they always were, on a shelf in the wardrobe. He threw them into a grab bag along with the envelopes.

He had a quick look around his apartment. He'd lived there for a dozen years but had always assumed it could be raided and searched at any time, so there was nothing to give him away. Nothing which could be construed as political, let alone extremist, nothing personal, no photographs other than a few of someone else's family he'd bought in a flea market, because it would have seemed strange to have none at all.

So he felt no sentimentality in leaving the apartment, no emotion. He stopped only to sweep a careful eye over the place to check he was leaving nothing incriminating, nothing to provide even the slenderest of clues as to where he was heading. Under the instruction booklet for the oven and other papers in a kitchen drawer was a road map of Denmark, along with a Danish phrase book. He doubted they'd fall for it, but he'd reckoned it was worth a try and maybe send them in the completely opposite direction to where he was going.

–

Afterwards – later that day – at the insistence of Kemp from Bonn, Edgar had compiled extensive notes of what happened and when that morning.

At three minutes past seven he saw a light go on in one of the second floor apartments, one of the two he thought Richter could be in. Moments later the curtain opened, though not wide enough for him to see who had opened it. Six minutes later he sent Andreas over to the apartment, after he had run through his script with him one final time. As Andreas walked over to the apartment, Edgar eased the Audi out of its parking space and into one on the other side of Niehler Strasse, more or less opposite the entrance to the apartment building, although a short distance up the road from it. At ten past seven he watched Andreas press the buzzer and, soon after, a face appeared in a small window in what he took to be the apartment. It was too fleeting and distant for him to be able to make much out, the best Edgar could say was it was a man and could have been Richter. Moments later – at eleven minutes past seven – he saw Andreas speaking. A minute later – twelve minutes past seven, according to Edgar's log – Andreas moved away from the entrance and hurried up Kuenstrasse, much too fast for Edgar's liking.

At nineteen minutes past seven, the man Edgar assumed was Richter rushed out of the apartment building, pausing in the entrance to put on a motorcycle helmet. He looked up and down the street but didn't appear to spot Edgar in the Audi. He crossed the road and, in his mirror, Edgar saw Richter stuff a bag into the steel pannier of a BMW motorbike. As he did so he removed something from the bag and put it inside his leather jacket pocket. He then leapt on the bike, gunning the powerful machine into life.

Edgar had not factored a motorbike into his planning. He knew the Audi couldn't compete with a motorbike that had a top speed of over one hundred miles an hour. But Richter was not driving fast, he was too smart for that. Just before Kuenstrasse crossed Neusser Strasse, Richter slowed down, and Edgar wondered whether he'd spotted him following, so he dropped his own speed. Then he saw why Richter had slowed. Moving fast along the pavement was Andreas, his long hair flowing behind him. Richter swerved the BMW into position behind him and reached into his jacket.

By the time Edgar realised what was happening it was too late. A single shot rang out. Edgar watched as the back of Andreas's neck exploded in a mass of red.

The Englishman steered the Audi towards the motorbike, aiming to collide with the BMW, but Richter was too quick. As soon as he'd shot Andreas he swerved the bike back into the road and accelerated hard. For perhaps a mile Edgar managed to keep the bike in sight, but it was a hopeless task. The last he saw of the BMW was it turning sharp left into an alley, too narrow for a car. He'd lost his man.

He found a phone box. He'd have to call Kemp in Bonn. It was not going to be the conversation he'd thought he was going to have.

Samuel was in Cologne by eleven, less than two hours after the telephone call from Reinhard Schäfer. He doubted whether the KGB would appreciate quite how well he'd done to get there in that time, just managing to catch the nine forty direct train. From Cologne station he'd taken a taxi, telling the driver his destination was on Niehler Strasse, a block past Goalkeeper's apartment.

But when he walked back into Kuenstrasse there was a group of police officers milling around outside the entrance to the apartment building. He didn't stop, carrying on instead – west down Kuenstrasse. In the distance he could see more activity, and he headed in that direction. He came to a section of road that was closed. On the pavement was a tent-like structure, with police officers guarding it. A small group had gathered behind a cordon. Samuel only needed to listen.

'A man's been shot, they say he's dead... pretty much took his head off, must have been a high-calibre weapon... the person who shot him was on a motorbike, a BMW apparently... I heard one of the policemen tell someone else it's the Red Army Faction... I don't know what the world's coming to: Hamburg, Munich, Frankfurt – and now here.'

Samuel spent another half hour on Kuenstrasse; long enough to ascertain the man who'd been shot was young and certainly didn't match Goalkeeper's description. He was as sure as he could be that Goalkeeper was the assassin. He knew he had a BMW motorbike, and there was now no BMW outside Goalkeeper's apartment building.

Samuel walked another three blocks before he felt it was safe enough to telephone Schäfer. It was a complicated procedure: he had to call a Hamburg number and from there the call was patched through to East Berlin. He wasn't too sure how much he trusted the connection, but there was no alternative.

The KGB officer took the news calmly enough. 'You're sure it was Goalkeeper who shot the man?'

'Not one hundred per cent, but it looks that way.'

'And you have no idea who he is?'

'No.'

'Listen, Samuel… go to Bonn. Deal with Uncle. Go to ground after that.'

'Very well,' said Samuel. 'But I'll need you to make a phone call.'

Samuel took a tram as far as the ring road and soon found what he was looking for: a tall office building with a large car park wrapped around it. Down the side of the building he found a light grey Volkswagen Golf and had no difficulty breaking in and starting the engine.

Once he was in Bonn, he drove straight to the apartment building. He'd been there before on Schäfer's behalf and he knew exactly what to do, exactly where to wait. Just before arriving at the apartment he'd stopped to phone Schäfer.

'Telephone him now.'

'You sure?'

'You want me to do this job for you or not?'

—

Clive Cowley could have wept with relief when he took the call at ten to one. It had come through as a local Bonn number – he had no idea how Schäfer managed that – and the message was clear: 'Your suit is ready. Please collect it immediately.'

There was a time when that message would have terrified him, now it felt like an act of mercy: he was to leave Bonn. He'd spent a decidedly nervous morning at his desk in the British Embassy, convinced his fear was radiating throughout the office, expecting an arresting hand on his shoulder at any moment.

But no one in the office was especially interested when he explained that he needed to collect a suit from the dry cleaners. He would need to return to his apartment, collect a few things and then travel to Paris, which was five hours by train, with a change at Mannheim. He'd arrive at the Gare l'Est then walk a short way to the address on Rue La Fayette. It was a journey he'd known he'd take one day and he was well prepared for it. He had even been on a couple of dry runs, just to get a proper sense of it.

From Rue La Fayette he'd be taken to a new life – he'd be looked after. He would be treated with respect – he'd have nothing more to worry about.

So there was plenty to think about as he parked his car under the dreary apartment building in Friesdorf. Even the location of his apartment just about summed it up: he hadn't been allocated an apartment in Bad Godesberg or Konigswinter, where the more senior embassy staff lived. But it didn't matter now.

There were few cars in the basement car park at that time of day, and no sign of anyone about. Clive Cowley was slightly surprised to hear footsteps behind him as he approached the lift, but he had no time to do anything about it other than half turn round. As he did so he was bundled into the fire escape doorway and then shoved against a rough concrete wall, his face smashing against the pitted surface. And before he could react, before he could even cry out, a knife plunged deep into him.

Chapter 29

East Berlin, The Wednesday

It was approaching half eight when Viktor wearily headed in the direction of the Unter den Linden. He paused once or twice, wondering whether to go back to his apartment, despite the obvious risks. He stopped at a grim café on Mittelstrasse and sat for a while at the back, sipping a lukewarm mug of bitter coffee. Next stop was a news kiosk where he bought a copy of that morning's *Neues Deutschland*, a newspaper he rarely read and which towed the party line so cravenly that the joke in the Embassy was it made *Izvestia* read like a liberal western newspaper.

For no other reason than this was how he was trained, he went back on himself before turning into Neustädtische Kirchstrasse for a few yards, his destination soon looming ahead on the other side of the main road.

To his surprise no one stopped him at the entrance, just the usual grunt and whiff of alcohol as the thickset guards nodded him through once he'd shown his pass. Viktor decided not to go to his office: there was an advantage to be gained in appearing before they had an opportunity to arrest him. As it was, he found it difficult to believe he'd made it this far.

Avoiding the lifts, he climbed slowly up the rear staircase to the fifth floor, pausing to catch his breath on each landing. He walked through the first security door and past a dozing guard at the entrance to the corridor that led to the office. He quickly backed into a doorway when he spotted Schäfer, and a couple of the agents who he recognised from the previous night, at the other end of the corridor, but they were soon gone and he was able to stroll unimpeded into the office of the Head of the KGB in East Berlin.

Piotr Vasilyevich Kozlov stared at Viktor in apparent shock: his mouth halfopen, his eyes unblinking, no other facial muscles even twitching. Then he hurriedly removed his vodka bottle from the top of his desk.

Minutes earlier Kozlov had been chastising Schäfer and his other agents for allowing Irma to escape to the west and Viktor to become a fugitive. Now Viktor had ambled into his office, as if he didn't have a care in the world and had popped in to exchange gossip about who was in line for the Bucharest job.

'You look confused, Piotr Vasilyevich. Is anything the matter?'

Kozlov reached down and returned the vodka bottle to the desk top, pouring himself a large measure which Viktor considered to be ill-advised at any time of the day, let alone so early in the morning.

'Where the hell were you last night, Viktor Leonidovich?' Kozlov's normally booming voice was little more than an uncertain whisper. He was staring at the desk top, occasionally shooting a glance in Viktor's direction as if to check he was really there.

'I was at a bar in Marx-Engels-Platz, comrade.'

'Who with?'

'Various old friends.'

'Was one of them…' Kozlov checked a notebook open in front of him, 'a Max Lazerowitz?'

'Max? Of course, old Max is a fixture at that bar… You know Max?'

'And you think it is wise to trust this Max Lazerowitz?'

'Why, comrade?'

'He's a Jew.'

'A Jew who commanded a partisan brigade that fought the Nazis for four years. He has more decorations than—'

'And how did you leave this bar, Viktor Leonidovich?'

'Is that not in your notes, Piotr Vasilyevich?'

'Don't be so fucking insolent with me!' Kozlov's voice had returned to its normal volume. The portrait of Brezhnev appeared to shake.

'I left through a side entrance. It's not my fault your people were too busy drinking – there were enough of them.'

'And where did you go?'

'Well, you obviously know I didn't go back to my apartment. Even your people no doubt managed to work that one out. I met a lady and went back to her place.'

'Her name?'

'I don't know it. She was not the kind of lady with whom you exchange names.'

'And where does she live?'

'Nor was she the kind of lady with whom you exchange addresses, comrade. I just followed her there.'

'I assumed you'd left East Berlin and escaped to the west.'

'Obviously not, comrade. Why on earth would I do that?'

The conversation – and Viktor did his best to make sure it was more of a conversation than the interrogation Kozlov intended it to be – continued in that vein for a while. Try as he might, the Head of the KGB in East Berlin could not get Viktor to admit to any wrongdoing. Viktor answered all his questions politely and plausibly, repeatedly asking one in return: what proof did comrade Kozlov have that he had done anything wrong?

'What about Irma escaping to the west?'

'I know nothing about that, comrade. I wasn't with her. Our relationship has not been good for quite a while.'

'Really, after all these years?'

'Especially after all these years.'

'And all these questions you've been asking about Goalkeeper?'

'I was endeavouring to expose a Nazi war criminal, comrade.'

'And your contacts with people in the west?'

'Part of my job, comrade, any good agent in the field has contacts and sources…'

The most Kozlov could get out of Viktor was an apology for any misunderstanding and a grudging acceptance that maybe he should have brought his suspicions – as unfounded as he now accepted they were – to his superior's attention earlier. At the same time Viktor dropped heavy hints about Kozlov's own shortcomings, and how they were part of the problem.

'Perhaps the pressure of dealing with the… failings… of your department had a detrimental effect on my behaviour Piotr Vasilyevich, for which I apologise.'

It was enough to worry Kozlov. As far as he was concerned, he told Viktor, the matter was closed. It appeared no harm had been done. But in return for him doing nothing – for not telling Moscow – Viktor should leave Berlin, return to the Soviet Union and retire.

To Kozlov's obvious relief, Viktor agreed. It was a good idea, he told him. He had been considering this for a while now. He wanted no trouble; he just wanted to see out his days at his *dacha* – he was too old for all this now.

'And we understand each other, Viktor Leonidovich, you won't cause any trouble?'

'Not if you don't,Piotr Vasilyevich, not if you don't. I ought to mention that Irma took some files with her, just in case…'

Kozlov looked shocked, tugging hard at an earlobe. 'I thought you said your relationship hadn't been good?'

'Let's say, for old times' sake,' said Viktor, winking.

There was a strange atmosphere in the room as Viktor prepared to leave it. Both men appeared satisfied, as if they could not quite believe what they had got away with.

–

Wilhelm Richter headed west out of Cologne, embarking on one of three routes he had so carefully rehearsed in his mind over the years. On the outskirts of the city he pulled into the Königsdorfer Forest, cutting the engine of the BMW along a narrowing track, and then wheeling the bike deep into the forest. This was also the place he'd had in mind to bury her, he thought a van could just about get down the track. It would have been

339

a peaceful resting place. When he was certain he hadn't been followed, he unscrewed the front and rear number plates from the bike and snapped them into small pieces, which he then buried in the undergrowth. From the steel pannier he took out two new number plates and fixed them in place, rubbing them with earth to take away their sheen. There was nothing, as far as he could tell, to distinguish the bike from the other tens of thousands of dark BMW 900s on the roads of Germany.

It was peaceful in the forest so he allowed himself a few minutes to think and have a cigarette, sitting against a tree trunk, watched by a large audience of ravens gathered in the treetops above him. He had taken an enormous risk in killing the man who'd asked if he was Wilhelm Richter. He'd risked being caught, and he thought he may have been followed by an Audi 100 but he couldn't be sure, and in any case he'd managed to lose it by going down a narrow alley.

And the risk of allowing the man to walk away was even greater. He knew something. He'd tell people. He'd had to stop him.

Richter continued his journey, joining Autobahn 61 at Bergheim and staying on it as he headed south. Just before eleven he stopped at a petrol station outside Hockenheim and from there he made a call.

'I'll cross the border sometime this afternoon, possibly between two and three. Tell me where to meet you…'

The land around the petrol station was flat, allowing a clear view: no vehicles had pulled in after him, none slowed down as they drove past. He was as certain as he could be that he wasn't being followed. Soon after Hockenheim he picked up Autobahn 5.

He continued south, the Black Forest a looming presence to the east, the Rhine and France, both lay westwards. The roads and weather were clear and he made good progress so he stopped again, filling the bike with petrol and allowing himself a quick snack at a window table with a good view of the petrol station forecourt.

He stayed on the Autobahn for only a couple more miles, exiting to drive through the suburb of Weil am Rhein before coming to the border crossing at Weilstrasse, which tended to be quieter than the main crossing on the Autobahn from Germany into Switzerland. The single German police officer waved him through while two Swiss policemen on the other side were preoccupied with a truck from Yugoslavia.

It was a quarter to three and he was now in Basel, less than eight hours after fleeing Cologne. His journey was almost over. He crossed the river on Wettsteinbrücke and drove down Binningerstrasse to the zoo. He found the car park off Tiergartenrain and soon spotted what he was looking for: a fawn-coloured Mercedes van with Zurich plates.

Twenty minutes later he was watching the lions as they watched him, when an older man with the build of a weightlifter appeared close to him. Richter was so relieved to see him that he had to restrain himself from embracing his old friend. The other man looked bored, concentrating on taking photographs and not looking at Richter for a full five minutes.

'We've been watching: you're clean.' He'd waited until an elderly couple and what looked like their grandson walked away, moving closer to Richter and speaking quietly, his Berlin accent evident even after all these years.

'I know, I wasn't followed, I'm certain of that.' Richter knew that had they so much as suspected he'd been followed, he'd have been abandoned at the zoo.

'You saw my van, yes?'

Richter said he had. He'd parked within sight of it.

'So I saw. Give yourself until half four to look around – and don't forget to appear interested. Then go back to your bike. When you set off, I will too, so allow me to overtake you and then follow me. I'll wait until we're away from the city and pull in when I think it's safe, then we'll get your bike in the back of the van. We'll be at the farm by ten o'clock tonight, possibly earlier – the roads in Obwalden are good at the moment. You'll finally be able to relax, Wilhelm, after all these years. You'll never need to worry again. Your war's over, at last.'

Wilhelm Richter turned round. He knew they were on their own, but wanted to be certain. He inched closer to the man next to him. '*Heil Hitler!*'

By ten o'clock on the Wednesday morning, Franz and Konrad had been in the Saxon's top floor office for more than an hour. This time they had been permitted to sit and were doing so around an elegant table along with the President of the BfV, one of his Vice Presidents, two heads of Department and of course the Saxon.

But by far the most important people in the room were two women, the BfV's experts on tracing the movement of money. Elke was the younger of the pair, a nervous and intense type with three pairs of spectacles which she switched between as she selected different documents from a large stack in front of her. Her boss was perhaps in her fifties, an elegant woman referred to as Frieda, who did most of the talking, checking as she did so the paperwork and notes passed to her by Elke.

'Ever since you called us in yesterday at...' she glanced at her watch, 'noon I think it was, sir, we have been working on finding out what we can about this Werner Pohl. Of course there is no doubt that he was using a false identity, which took just a few minutes to establish.' With the word 'minutes' she flicked her hand to convey how simple that had been.

'But our expertise is in investigating financial matters, as you know, and in this respect we have made some significant progress. Please pass that document, Elke, yes, that one... here we are. We know this Werner Pohl rented an apartment in Jesuitenstrasse in Aachen.' She paused as she spread three sheets of paper in front of her and checked one of them.

'And this gave us our lead, from which we have built our investigation. We were able to establish that the rent for the apartment was paid from an account in the name of Herr Pohl. This was paid from a branch of Commerzbank in Aachen, though the account itself was at their main branch in Frankfurt. I'll need the second Zurich file please, Elke…

'We managed to speak with the security department at the head office of Commerzbank yesterday afternoon, and through him have followed a number of leads. It is a very complicated and convoluted trail, sir, quite the most difficult one we have come across for some time, especially given how little time we've had. We were able to establish – no, the other Zurich file Elke, that's it – we established that Commerzbank in Frankfurt provided Werner Pohl with official proof of identification to present at Bank Leu in Zurich. It was the kind of proof of identity that one bank issues to another bank. Normally a Swiss bank would not divulge any information but, through our colleagues in the Swiss security services, we did find out which account Werner Pohl had access to at Bank Leu. This account was opened in May 1970 and remained active until June 1972, when it was closed down. During that period large sums of money were transferred into it from the VP Bank in Vaduz, in Liechtenstein. Elke, perhaps you can explain now…'

Elke coughed and spoke quickly, in a confident voice. 'We have a source within VP Bank who we also contacted last night. They went into the bank first thing this morning and were able to access details of the account at VP Bank. This account was opened in 1969 and remains active. It is a numbered account. Our source has so far been unable to associate any names with it. However, between April 1970 and June 1972 – the period when Pohl's Bank Leu account was active – large sums of money, almost identical to the sums transferred to Zurich, were paid into the VP Bank account. Frieda, maybe—'

'These funds were transferred to the VP Bank account from Centro Internationale Handelsbank in Vienna,' interjected Frieda. 'So we have Pohl's Commerzbank account, associated with a Bank Leu account, which was fed by a VP bank account, which was in turn fed by an account at Centro Internationale

Handelsbank,' Frieda paused and there was some muttering around the table. 'Some of you may be aware this last bank has strong links with the Polish state. We believe it is one of a number of banks in Western Europe and the Middle East which the Soviet Union uses to disperse funds, which they channel through Gosbank, the Soviet State Bank. I am confident that the man calling himself Werner Pohl was facilitating the transfer of Soviet funds to the Red Army Faction.'

'So we have established an unbroken trail,' said Elke, 'starting with Werner Pohl in Aachen, leading to an account in his name in Frankfurt and directly from there to Zurich, Liechtenstein, Vienna, Poland and the Soviet Union.' She brought her hands together, as if in muted applause.

'But to what accounts,' said the Vice President, 'were the funds transferred to from Bank Leu?'

'A good question: all of them were one-off accounts here in the Federal Republic. They seem to have been opened for the sole purpose of receiving one large payment. When that payment arrived the money was withdrawn as cash, and the account closed down. To be frank with you, I don't know why we allow this to happen, especially in the current climate. We are far too liberal in this respect.'

As those round the table considered Frieda's views about the country's liberal banking laws, the telephone rang on the Saxon's desk. He said little other than: 'When…? Who…? Where…?'

When the call ended he returned to the table and spoke very calmly. 'There's been a shooting here in Cologne this morning. We'd better adjourn.'

—

When they reconvened an hour later there was much muttering in the room – a sense of confusion and anticipation.

'This is what we know for certain,' said the Saxon. 'At approximately seven twenty this morning a man was shot dead on Kuenstrasse. The state police are unable to confirm his identity.

They say they believe he was shot by a man on a BMW motorbike, who sped off. There is nothing to connect the shooting at this stage with the Red Army Faction. However, in the last few minutes there appears to have been a significant development. Konrad has been speaking with the North Rhine Westphalia state police, so perhaps you can update us – when you're ready?'

Konrad had come into the room just before the Saxon began speaking and appeared flustered, catching his breath and flicking through his notebook. 'Apologies, sir, I've only just come off the phone with the State Police, as you say. Franz is making further enquiries at the moment. The shooting took place at seven twenty. At nine fifty the department of the state police in Bonn which deals with foreign embassies received a call from a diplomat at the British Embassy in Bonn, he—'

'Name?' It was one of the heads of department.

Konrad turned a page in his notebook. 'Charles Kemp. He's a First Secretary.'

'And he runs the MI6 operation in Bonn. Carry on.'

'According to Charles Kemp, they have a man visiting Cologne, called Edgar. Kemp was somewhat apologetic and explained he hadn't known Edgar was actually in Cologne, let alone the Federal Republic. He said Edgar was making what Kemp described as "unofficial enquiries" about an officer here at the BfV. Apparently Edgar had identified one of our officers as a being Soviet agent run from East Berlin, who also happened to be a former SS officer called Wilhelm Richter, linked with war crimes in Poland—'

'Oh for heaven's sake, not another Nazi story: is there going to be a point to this?'

'There is, sir. Edgar arrived here early this morning to locate this agent, at which point we were to be informed...'

'I'm sure. I don't suppose you have a name for this agent do you?'

'I was going to come on to that, sir. He is Heinz Fleischhauer: he's on the Rotation Team here.'

'Goodness,' said one of the heads of department. 'He was due to move to the Military Liaison Office next week, I seem to recall.'

'Edgar revealed that he'd paid a young homeless man to confront Heinz Fleischhauer early this morning at his apartment, which is on the corner of Niehler Strasse and Kuenstrasse. Edgar was watching the apartment and claims he followed Fleischhauer as he left the building on a BMW motorbike, and watched him shoot the homeless man further down the street. He tried to chase him but he got away. He then rang Charles Kemp, who rang the state police and—'

The door opened and a white-faced Franz entered the room, just as the Saxon began to speak.

'None of which, of course, proves that Fleischhauer was a spy. And as for this Nazi nonsense, I—'

'If I may interrupt, sir?' Franz was speaking quietly but all eyes turned towards him. 'I think you need to hear the latest on this case. Once the state police were given Fleischhauer's name they entered his apartment. Ute von Morsbach's body was there, wrapped in a sheet. The initial assessment is that she's been dead for less than twenty-four hours.'

'At least,' said Konrad, sounding quite pleased with himself, 'we now know the identity of Werner Pohl.'

The Saxon shot him a dirty look before turning to the President. 'You seem to have a serious problem, Herr President: not only has one of your officers been assisting the Red Army Faction, but it would appear they may also have been spying for the Soviet Union. And they are a Nazi, for good measure.' The Saxon was gathering his papers as he said this, already distancing himself in more ways than one from the BfV. 'If I were you I'd make sure this Edgar character doesn't hang around.'

Chapter 30

'We don't approve of freelance operations, Edgar.'

That was it. After a lengthy and doom-laden silence, the hooded men of the Inquisition had finally pronounced: 'We don't approve of freelance operations.'

After he'd witnessed the shooting of Andreas and telephoned Charles Kemp, Edgar had spent a very uncomfortable few hours. The first hour was with Kemp, who was so angry Edgar genuinely feared the young man was about to have a stroke: Kemp seemed to be taking the whole business personally. Then he spent a couple of even more uncomfortable hours, first with the state police and then with the BfV. 'Be as helpful as possible, Edgar,' Kemp had advised. 'But whatever you do please don't land us in the shit: make them realise this was all your mad idea. In fact, while you're at it let them think you actually are mad. Things are bad enough as it is.'

Then it was back to Kemp, who'd now set up a safe house in Cologne. 'I'm not having you anyway near Bonn, Edgar. You've done enough damage already.'

Edgar shrugged. He could cope with being banned from Bonn.

'You met with Cowley yesterday, I hear?' The angrier Kemp became, the higher the pitch of his voice.

'Indeed.'

'And now Clive's dead. Stabbed to death – throat cut.' Kemp moved his fingers across his neck in a rather aggressive manner. 'Blood everywhere.'

'So you keep telling me. I say, you're not accusing me of killing him, are you?'

'Of course not. Apart from anything else, you have an alibi. You were here in Cologne. Jesus Christ, Edgar, what is this all about?'

'London's ears only I'm afraid.'

'But you saw Cowley for Christ's sake, Edgar, you—'

'London, Kemp. They'll hear all about it.'

A few hours later Edgar was driven straight onto the apron of the military section of Cologne Bonn airport, where an RAF plane was waiting for him. It was dark when they landed at RAF Benson in Oxfordshire, and Edgar spent the night in the officers' quarters. He was woken the following morning at seven: an RAF sergeant unlocked his door, handed him a cup of tea and told him to be ready to leave in half an hour.

It was only a short flight on the RAF Wessex helicopter. Edgar could tell they were flying west-southwest: he spotted the M4 motorway appearing and disappearing under them. Not long after they flew over Marlborough before descending, heading south-east, over Savernake Forest, and landing in the grounds of a large house on the edge of the forest.

Edgar had only just clambered down from the helicopter when he was met by Ronnie Castle, the first time Edgar had seen him since April when he'd turned up at his home in Dorset with young Lassiter in tow. Now his usual bonhomie was absent.

'You're in trouble, Edgar: deep, deep trouble. If it's any consolation, so am I. This is a complete bloody nightmare. Can't you tell, Edgar? They've brought you here in a bloody helicopter! Have you any idea how hard it is to get a flight from the bloody RAF these days?'

Castle carried on in this manner as they walked out of the field, over a small fence and down a long lawn towards the house – one of those requisitioned by the Service during the war, which they'd managed to hold onto.

And now Edgar was in a large room in the basement, lit only by a few inadequate wall lights, making the centre of the room

– where he sat alone – quite dark. Ahead of him, behind a large table, sat three figures in the shadows, like the hooded men of the Inquisition.

None of them had said a word when Edgar entered the room. Edgar thought he was far too long in the tooth for this to bother him, but after five minutes of silence he began to feel unsettled. As his eyes adjusted to the dim light he recognised two of the men: an Assistant Director of the Service, and a former ambassador to Moscow, a man who now had some kind of a disciplinary and troubleshooting role in the Service. The other man – whom Edgar did not recognise – appeared to be there in some kind of administrative capacity, making notes and taking sheets from the files in front of him and handing them to the other two.

It was the former ambassador who had broken the silence. 'We don't approve of freelance operations, Edgar.'

On the very few occasions when Edgar had felt someone he was interrogating had gained the upper hand – albeit never for very long – it was when they became assertive, grabbing the initiative and trying to wrestle control of the interrogation. During the long silence preceding the ambassador's words, Edgar decided this would be his best course of action.

'Oh come off it. You know full well that all our operations are, in effect, freelance ones,' he replied, managing to sound put out, even quite angry. 'That's how it works, isn't it – in our game? Any operation worth its salt has a degree of deniability attached to it: keep a decent distance from HQ and the embassies, most of all from Whitehall, so if it all goes pear-shaped they can turn round and say "Nothing to do with me, didn't know anything about it." Rather like you're doing now.'

The former ambassador shifted in his chair and glanced at the Assistant Director, who in turn concentrated on a sheet of paper passed to him by the other man.

'I mean,' said Edgar, feeling confident enough now to adopt a sarcastic tone, 'all this nonsense getting me here. A military escort in Cologne, keeping me pretty much under lock and key last night, a helicopter – a helicopter for Christ's sake – to bring me here. What on earth is this all about?'

'That, Edgar,' said the Assistant Director 'is exactly what we wanted to ask you.'

Edgar leaned forward and concentrated his gaze at a point just above the three men. 'Everything I've been doing was in the interests of the Service and – more importantly – this country. Earlier this year I was approached by a Soviet agent—'

'Hang on, Edgar – a Soviet contact? Surely—' the former ambassador looked appalled.

'All decent agents have contacts and sources from different sides. This agent is someone with whom I last had contact back in 1945, when we were on the same side, more or less. This time he was investigating a suspicion that Nazis had infiltrated his Service, and he had reason to believe that some may be operating over here. He warned me to be careful of traitors on our side. I made a few inquiries and together we discovered a BfV agent called Heinz Fleischhauer, originally Wilhelm Richter, was part of a crazy Nazi plot, as well as being a Soviet spy. I passed on what I thought was reasonable to my contact, and then was able to unearth what remained of this rather pathetic Nazi coterie in this country. In the process, I discovered that Lassiter was a Soviet agent, hence my reluctance to share what I knew. Before I could talk to anyone else I needed to travel to West Germany, where I met with Clive Cowley and some more pieces of this rather shabby jigsaw slotted into place. I realised that he too was a Soviet agent: my contact had warned me there was probably a mole in Bonn. I then went to Cologne to track down Heinz Fleischhauer, at which point I would of course have informed the Service. My idea was to make sure of his identity, flush him out into the open and then let Kemp have all the glory. But as we now know, events rather got in the way.'

The Assistant Director leaned forward, the light catching his face full on. He looked impressed at Edgar's performance in spite of himself.

'Of course, sir,' continued Edgar, his tone now much more helpful, 'this is condensing a rather long tale. Naturally I'll put everything in writing. Should you think I've been in any way disloyal, or broken any laws, I am quite prepared to explain myself to whomever—'

'No, no, no,' there was a hint of panic in the former ambassador's voice. 'We're not talking about blame here, Edgar. We're here to tie up loose ends.'

'You – we – are most fortunate,' said the Assistant Director, 'these days the press and indeed the public attribute any act of apparently political violence in West Germany to the Red Army Faction or the Baader-Meinhof Group, whatever one calls them. The West German press and their counterparts over here have already decided that what happened in Cologne and Bonn yesterday were acts of terrorism carried out by the Red Army Faction.

'It is plainly not in the interests of the West German government for it to be known that a senior officer in their BfV was both a Nazi and a Soviet agent. And I can assure you it is certainly not in the interests of Her Majesty's Government for it to be known that Clive Cowley also worked for the Soviets, or that we had links with this Nazi. Frankly, it's the last thing the Government needs at the moment. The West Germans,' the Assistant Director leaned forwards as if he were a judge delivering sentence, 'will say the man who had his head blown off in Cologne was Heinz Fleischhauer, and he was a victim of the Red Army Faction. Everyone will forget about the poor young man you pulled off the street who ended up being shot by Fleischhauer.

'I understand his body has already been disposed of. We're getting some leeway from the fact that we've assisted in exposing a Soviet agent in the BfV. Notwithstanding your methods and singular lack of co-operation, they are nonetheless grateful. If the truth got out about Heinz Fleischhauer, it could bring down their Government.'

'Likewise,' said the former ambassador, 'we are happy – if that's the correct word – to brief the media that Clive Cowley was also killed by the Red Army Faction. I'm not sure whether this will stand up to a terrific amount of scrutiny – but we'll just have to ride that storm.'

'And what if the Red Army Faction turn round and say these killings were nothing to do with them? That would rather queer the pitch, wouldn't it?'

'I suppose they could do, Edgar,' replied the Assistant Director, 'but it's highly unlikely – if you think about it, it's quite a coup to have the scalps of a BfV agent and a British diplomat attributed to them. Meanwhile, there'll be lots of tributes Cowley doesn't deserve. Callaghan was going to make a statement himself in the House this afternoon, but I believe they've now managed to persuade him it ought to come from the Foreign Secretary rather than the Prime Minister, so Crosland will deliver it.'

'And that's that?'

'More or less, Edgar, more or less,' said the Assistant Director. 'Of course your role in all this… well, quite unconventional and you broke countless rules. But at the close of play both us and the BfV have fewer Soviet agents in our midst, so that offsets everything else. As for this Nazi business, well, no reason to complicate matters, eh? War was a long time ago after all. Perhaps it's time to retire properly, Edgar, even though we had reasonable grounds to assume you'd done that many years ago.'

'My role,' said the former ambassador, 'as you may be aware, is ensure nothing goes wrong and when it does, manage it. The Americans have a typically crude but tothepoint phrase I heard in Washington last month: "To stop the shit hitting the fan". Well, we've just about managed to keep the lid on this one, Edgar, but only just. The shit hasn't hit the fan. We got away with it. So did you. Take the advice you've just been given and call it a day.'

They were all standing now, the three judges of the Inquisition and Edgar: a man reprieved.

'But what about Lassiter' said Edgar. 'If he's a Soviet agent—'

'Lassiter?' The Assistant Director shook his head, in sorrow as much as anything else. 'That will all be taken care of.'

Around the time Edgar arrived at Savernake that Thursday morning, Lassiter had been escorted from his office on the eighth floor of the MI6 headquarters and taken to a room deep in its basement.

He confessed surprisingly quickly, though he was anxious to play down what he was actually confessing to. 'Nothing really, the odd snippet... had every intention of reporting it all in due course... more a misjudgment than anything else.'

No one believed a word he said, not that they showed Lassiter how they felt. It was the Assistant Director who found himself alone with Lassiter in his cell that evening.

'Tell us everything, Lassiter – and I mean absolutely everything – and we'll regard that as sufficient mitigation. You'll have to leave the Service, of course: we'll concoct a plausible enough reason and you'll disappear from view. We'll want to keep tabs on you, will need to know where you are and what you're doing and all that. You'll need a job, something harmless.'

Hugh Lassiter found it hard to disguise his relief, though he wondered what kind of job they'd regard as 'harmless' – as long as it wasn't something manual. 'And that would be doing you a favour too, I suppose.'

'In what way would that be, Lassiter?'

'Well,' Lassiter lounged back in his chair in a louche manner, crossing his legs so the right foot was resting on his left knee, and chuckled. 'A court case would be in no one's interests, would it?'

The Assistant Director pushed a thick pad of A4 paper towards Lassiter. 'Start writing, Lassiter, and don't stop until you've put everything down: how you were recruited, who your contacts were, operations you've been involved in. Everything. As far as we're concerned, no detail is too minor. Once you've done that we'll ask you a few questions.'

Later that night the Assistant Director admitted to the former ambassador that he'd found something odd about Lassiter's reaction.

'What do you mean?'

'I told him that if he told us absolutely everything then we'd regard that as sufficient mitigation…'

'As we agreed.'

'As we agreed, indeed. But he never bothered to ask me what the consequences would be if he didn't tell us everything. I'd have thought that was the obvious question to ask.'

'Ah,' said the former ambassador, 'the unasked question. We know all about those.'

—

Lassiter had underestimated what was expected of him. He was kept in a bleak cell in the basement with a bed, a toilet and sink, and a desk for him to write at. For the next week Lassiter was subject to a strict routine: the harsh lights would go on at seven in the morning and, after breakfast, two interrogators would come in for a session which would last at least three hours. They would leave him with a series of questions to answer and topics to cover, and he'd be alone with his writing pad for a few more hours before the next round of questioning began. There were four interrogators altogether, two teams of two, and despite his best attempts he was unable to build a rapport with any of them. They would point out flaws or gaps in his account and raise questions they wanted answered. The process continued for a week.

Hugh Lassiter told them how he had been recruited in 1964 while he was a student at Oxford University, and in East Berlin for a term. He described how he became a Marxist, an act which on reflection was little more than a passing interest, a juvenile affectation – except in a drunken moment he let it be known to one of his lecturers in East Berlin that he'd be willing to help the Soviet Union. He imagined this would mean putting up posters on College noticeboards of tractors and happy workers on the banks of the Volga. He most certainly hadn't imagined this would involve actually committing espionage, but by then it was too late. He told them how he'd been instructed to apply for the Foreign

Office and from there was recruited into MI6. And how he had been controlled by a succession of handlers at the Soviet Embassy in London – 'Names, Lassiter, we want every single bloody name' – and that his main role, one he was never terribly happy with or even fully understood, if he was honest, was to look after a group of old Nazis.

His final interrogation took place on the Thursday, one week after he'd been arrested. On the following Monday, eight men gathered in a secure room a dozen floors up from where Lassiter languished. The four men who had been interrogating him were there, along with the former ambassador, the Assistant Director of the Service, Ronnie Castle – Lassiter's erstwhile boss – and a younger man with long hair and a dark complexion, who sat behind the Assistant Director and the former ambassador and was introduced as Richard but did not speak once during the meeting, spending most of it toying with his spectacles.

'I read your report over the weekend,' said the Assistant Director. 'In essence, he's a fucking traitor.' The four interrogators looked surprised at their boss's choice of vocabulary. 'Has he told us everything?'

'He's told us everything he's going to tell us, sir,' replied one of the interrogators.

'Meaning?'

'Meaning we have no doubt there's plenty more he knows, but which he's not going to tell us. He's a real pro, a proper KGB spy. This "reluctant spy, not really a traitor" stuff is all nonsense – it's a front. Standard Moscow stuff. He's too smart to give us low-grade, useless material, but nor is it top grade. It's names of people who've already been burnt or who are back in the Soviet Union, that kind of thing.'

'How much,' said the former ambassador, 'of what he knows do you think he's told us?'

'We doubt he's told us half of what he knows, sir – and the half he's keeping back would be the most important part, obviously.'

'And if we were to give you another week?'

'I doubt, sir,' said the main interrogator, 'we would get much more out of him at all.'

'How about,' asked the former ambassador, 'if we were to sanction less conventional methods of questioning?'

Awkward coughs around the room.

'That doesn't work, sir, in our opinion: you can't put too much trust in anything someone tells you in those circumstances.'

The Assistant Director closed his file and looked up at the four interrogators. 'Thank you very much for your efforts, gentlemen. You may leave now.'

When they had left the room the Assistant Director addressed Ronnie Castle, thus far a shocked but silent observer.

'Tell us where we are with his letters and all that business, Ronnie.'

'We have his letter of resignation from the Service here sir, dated one week ago. His colleagues have been told he's resigned because of ill health: we've alluded to a rather sudden and upsetting diagnosis. Lassiter's sent them all a rather nice card with a picture of a chap playing golf on it, wishing them all the best for the future. He's written to his parents explaining that he is being sent abroad on a long and most sensitive assignment – he's sure they'll understand and be discreet et cetera – and it may be many months before they should expect to hear from him. We allowed him to follow this up with one phone call to them, very tightly controlled, but it's helped convince them. Can I just say, sir, not for one moment did I suspect Lassiter of…'

The Assistant Director held up his hand. 'Of course, Ronnie, we know that. You may leave now.'

They waited for a few moments after Ronnie Castle had closed the door.

'I suppose,' said the Assistant Director, 'those letters and the phone call buy us some time?'

'Indeed,' said the former ambassador. 'A good few months I'd have thought.'

'More than enough time, more than enough.' The Assistant Director and the former ambassador nodded at each other before turning round to the younger man who was sitting behind them, still fiddling with his spectacles.

'Very well then, Richard: over to you.'

–

In the trade they're known as one-night stands: properties taken on as short-term rentals by the Service and used as one-off safe houses, often for just one day – or night. This one-night stand was a recently rented modern detached house on the outskirts of St Albans, just north of London. The house was at the end of a road on the edge of a new development, with fields to one side and behind it. Most importantly, the house boasted a large garage which the estate agents helpfully described as being 'integral to the house.' It was, in Richard's opinion, ideal for the task in hand.

Hugh Lassiter had been driven there on a Tuesday, the day after the meeting in the secure room. They'd waited until nearly nine o'clock in the evening before taking him up a floor to an underground garage, and into a Rover with blacked out rear windows. An hour and a quarter later the Rover drove straight into the integral garage of the detached house near St Albans, no neighbours or passers by any the wiser about who had just entered it.

As dinner was being prepared, Ronnie Castle sat down with Hugh Lassiter at the dining table, going through all the paperwork pertaining to his new life and showing him an attaché case stuffed with used banknotes, enough to ensure a comfortable future.

'There's a place we've found for you not very far from here, six months' rent paid. You'll be taken there in a couple of days. After that, you're on your own – understand?'

There were two other men in the house: Richard, and a very tall young man called Andy, who was in the house when they arrived. Andy, as far as Lassiter could tell, was the cook.

Andy brought Lassiter a large whisky, placing it on the table next to the attaché case. Lassiter wouldn't have chosen to put ginger ale in the whisky, and certainly no ice, but he was preoccupied with the attaché case, which Castle had now turned in front of him so he could see quite how much money was in it.

Within a minute, whatever they'd put in the whisky took effect. Lassiter became flushed and was overwhelmed by a sudden tiredness, slumping forward, his head resting on the table. Richard approached him from behind, indicating to Ronnie Castle to remain where he was.

Ronnie Castle was surprised just how much noise Lassiter's neck made as it snapped, and he knew he'd never forget the fleeting look of fear on his face as he appeared to anticipate his final moment.

'I thought what was in the drink was going to be enough to kill him?' Ronnie Castle sounded shocked, even upset.

Andy and Richard had already laid Lassiter on the floor on a tarpaulin and begun to undress him.

'Always best to make sure sir.'

Chapter 31

London and West Berlin, October 1976

The shit, as the former ambassador had put it, began to hit the fan early in the afternoon of the first Wednesday in October, a fortnight after Lassiter's death.

The first hint of trouble came when the MI6 duty officer at the British Embassy in Paris rang London. The DST – the French equivalent of MI5 – had an agent inside the left wing newspaper *Libération* and, according to this agent, the paper was planning to run a story the next morning claiming that the murders in Cologne and Bonn were nothing to do with the Baader-Meinhof Gang. Not only that, but the paper was also saying, rather than being a victim of the shooting Cologne, Heinz Fleischhauer was actually the man who'd carried it out. And he was a Soviet agent, who'd been a Nazi war criminal – who also had links with British intelligence. And he was on the run. The report would further claim that Clive Cowley was an MI6 officer who'd also been working for the KGB. And just in case all that was not enough, the body of a young woman had been found in Fleischhauer's apartment. She'd been murdered, and was a member of the Red Army Faction.

No sooner had this news reached the Assistant Director than Washington was on the line: *The Washington Post* had the same story. The Assistant Director called in the former ambassador but before he arrived, word came through from Bonn: *Stern*, the mass circulation German news magazine, was putting the story on its front cover.

Most reluctantly, the Assistant Director spoke to his counter-part at MI5. Would he be so good as to find out if any British papers had the story, please? The answer came back just as the former ambassador arrived in the Assistant Director's office. *The Guardian* had the story, according to MI5. 'Splashing with it tomorrow morning,' the head of MI5 reported, with ill-concealed schadenfreude. 'Fancy trying for a D-Notice to stop it? You know we're always happy to give you chaps a hand when you're struggling.'

The former ambassador wondered whether this would be pointless.

'Quite right,' said the man from MI5 – the Assistant Director of MI6 could hear him smiling. 'Nothing *The Guardian* would like more than for us – you – to try a D-Notice on them. Would do wonders for their circulation.'

'Serves us right, I suppose,' said the Assistant Director to the former ambassador when he'd put the phone down. 'We thought we'd got away with it.'

'More to the point,' said the former ambassador, 'is who the hell has given them this story? It's obviously all coordinated. Edgar?'

'No, no, no – not Edgar's style, and remember we've been watching him like a hawk. He knows his antics should have landed him in a lot of hot water, and even he must be relieved he got away with it. No, this story has come from someone in West Germany – but Christ knows who. It's all timed to be published tomorrow, and *Stern* comes out on a Thursday. Half of West Germany reads that bloody magazine and then tells the other half about it. The whole plan's been designed to make the biggest impact.'

—

The staff at Rostt Legal had remarked how Herr Stern hadn't seemed himself in recent weeks. Normally such a composed man, since the end of August he'd appeared distracted: arriving an hour or even two later than he normally did, leaving early, and cancelling far more appointments than he was keeping.

The consensus in the office on Fasanenstrasse was that he must be ill – seriously ill, quite possibly with a terminal diagnosis. Among the secretaries this became the source of much speculation. One secretary had recently lost an uncle to a brain tumour and she recognised many of the symptoms. Another was certain it was lung cancer – she had noticed Herr Stern coughing on more than one occasion. Herr Stern's own secretary was reluctant to be drawn into anything so unseemly as gossiping, though she did confide in anyone who'd listen how Herr Stern barely ate his sandwiches these days and left his coffee cups half full. 'Stomach cancer,' she'd confidently whisper.

On the morning of Friday 1st October, Georg Stern was sitting at his desk. It was half eleven in the morning and in front of him was an array of newspapers and magazines, the murders of Heinz Fleischhauer and Clive Cowley three weeks previously still dominating the front pages. The consensus was that the murders showed how the Baader-Meinhof Gang was an even more dangerous threat than before. They seemed to murder at will, not enough was being done to stop them. It was bad enough that they targeted American servicemen and German police officers, but murdering a BfV officer and a British diplomat on the same day showed what they were capable of.

Georg Stern was sceptical at the ease with which the murders were attributed to the Baader-Meinhoff Group and, when he saw the photograph of the dead man the papers all published – and he knew for sure this was Richter, he was furious that no mention had been made of the man's Nazi past. He wanted Fleischhauer to be exposed as Wilhelm Richter.

He had some excellent contacts which he'd developed over the years, people who trusted him and owed him favours. These contacts included lawyers who represented Red Army Faction prisoners being held at Stammheim Prison near Stuttgart. He avoided the lawyers of the more prominent members. But he knew one of the other lawyers and, through her, a meeting was carefully arranged for the following morning.

Stern was to go to the Tiergarten and there, by the statue of Lortzing, he would meet a very tall man called Frederick who'd have a dog with him. If Frederick was wearing a long black scarf, then all was safe. The dog turned out to be a black and tan coloured Doberman, pulling hard on its short leash, eager to protect his master from Georg Stern. The dog's pointed ears were pricked up, as if in shock at what was going on.

'Let's walk now. Keep half a pace in front of me and don't turn round. When we reach the end of this path I will go to the right and you will turn left, so you don't have long. What do you want to know?'

'The killing of Heinz Fleischhauer in Cologne and the British diplomat in Bonn…'

'What of them?'

'Were the Baader-Meinhoff Group responsible?'

There was no reply for a while, although Stern could still hear the man's footsteps and the dog breathing noisily behind him, like it was choking. It occurred to Stern perhaps he shouldn't have said 'Baader-Meinhoff'.

'No. The Red Army Faction was not responsible.'

'But according to the press the Red Army Faction was—'

'The press prints many lies about the Red Army Faction.'

'So why not deny it?'

A pause, the dog panting hard. 'Why should they? But if you're so interested in this case, there is something you should know: the police found the body of a young woman in Fleischhauer's apartment. He'd murdered her. The authorities made the body disappear. She was involved with the Red Army Faction.'

'Do you know her name?'

'There's a family called von Morsbach in Augsburg – ask them. Your time is up.'

They'd reached the end of the path now, and Georg Stern heard the man's footsteps drop away, then heard him call out. 'Wait!'

Stern slowed down, allowing the man to catch up, still not looking at him.

'And you should ask the authorities in Cologne for the identity of the man shot in the street.'

'I thought it was Heinz Fleischhauer?'

The man gave a derisory 'Huh'. 'The Red Army Faction has contacts everywhere, Herr Stern,' he continued. 'The man who was shot in the street in Cologne was in his twenties and did not match the description of Fleischhauer, even with most of his head blown away. If you want to find out the truth ask why the autopsy lasted less than ten minutes and his body was cremated that afternoon, eh? The woman from the apartment, her body was cremated at the same time.'

'So Heinz Fleischhauer...?'

'Heinz Fleischhauer got away.'

And with that, Frederick's footsteps and the Doberman's panting faded quickly into the distance.

–

There'd been no hint in any of the newspapers that the man shot in Cologne was anyone other than Heinz Fleischhauer. Little personal information about Fleischhauer had been divulged: divorced, no family, many years of public service, the omission of the word 'distinguished' was possibly revealing, if you noticed it.

The meeting with Frederick suggested a course of action which Georg Stern could not take lightly, so he'd first called a contact in Cologne – a Federal Prosecutor he considered to be a friend. Are there photographs from the shooting? What is this about the body being cremated that afternoon? Was there no autopsy? And a woman's body in his apartment?

'Drop it, Georg, drop it. No questions.' And his friend had then put down the phone.

So the following morning – the Sunday – he tried one more contact, a senior diplomat at the United States Embassy in Bonn.

The diplomat sounded helpful: 'Leave it with me, call me first thing in the morning.'

But the diplomat called back that night, at almost midnight, and he sounded uneasy. 'If I tell you, Georg that I'm calling from a phone kiosk in a seedy bar in what passes for Bonn's red light district, and that to get here I drove around the city for an hour to be sure I wasn't being followed, then maybe you'll get the picture. This is the last conversation we're going to have about this business, got it? I didn't realise I was going to be risking my fucking neck – probably literally.'

Georg Stern said he understood and was sorry if...

'...I spoke to my pal in the CIA here. He said three things: one, don't ask any questions about the Cologne murder, zero. Two, Clive Cowley was MI6 but also KGB for Christ's sake. He said the impression he gets is that the Brits are relieved he's dead.'

'And the third thing?'

'He said if I don't drop this I may as well start choosing where in Africa I fancy being transferred to.'

–

Georg Stern arrived early at his office on the morning of Monday 4th October, after a sleepless night. The realisation of what he had discovered kept him awake, as had so many memories.

He thought about the night he'd left his parents' apartment in Charlottenburg; of Horst Weber and his parents' terrible grief when they found out about his arrest; of the night he returned to the house in Wedding to find the Webers dead; and about the dreadful night when he arrived at the house near Magdeburg and of how willingly – even eagerly – Richter had shot Axel Werner. And then he thought about the terrible events that followed: the murders – the war crimes – they'd committed in Dortmund; his escape from the Gestapo in Essen; the months hiding in the cellars and sewers under the city, his return to Berlin, finding his mother and hearing about the murder of his father, the encounter with Otto Schröder in 1968. And finally, he thought about the mysterious man who had turned up in his office just a few weeks ago to confront him about his past, and tell him that Wilhelm Richter was still alive.

It clearly suited too many people – important people – for Wilhelm Richter to disappear, to be forgotten about, to get away with everything he'd done.

Georg Stern could not allow this.

He opened a small notebook he kept in the top drawer of his desk. His priority would be *Stern* magazine, and if they were going to get the story into that Thursday's edition he needed to get a move on. He had three other numbers too, of contacts he'd made over the years: French, British and American newspapers, ones he could trust.

Wilhelm Richter would not be forgotten about after all.

Author's Note

The Berlin Spies is a work of fiction, and any similarities between characters in the book and real people should be regarded as purely coincidental.

Having said that, there are references in the book to a few well known historical figures, and hopefully their identities will be obvious. For example, Walter Ulbricht was actually one of the leaders of the German Communist Party (the KPD). He spent the war in exile in Moscow and afterwards returned to Germany, where he eventually became the head of the East German Government.

Likewise, various references are made to Yuri Andropov. Although his role in this story is entirely fictional, he was Head of the KGB between May 1967 and May 1982, before becoming General Secretary of the Soviet Communist Party.

The Red Army Faction – or Baader-Meinhoff Group, as it is sometimes known – was active in the period 1971–1993 and was prominent in September 1976, when the killings in *The Berlin Spies* in Cologne and Bonn are attributed to them. Their role in this story is also fictional, though to aid authenticity the book does feature some actual members of the Red Army Faction (all now dead). Similarly, there was a spate of bombings carried out by the Red Army Faction in May 1972, though the bombing of the British Army base at Rheindahlen in Mönchengladbach is fictional. The base was attacked by the Provisional IRA in 1973 and 1987. The main leadership of the group were arrested in June 1972, around the time in the book when Werner Pohl disappears. The cell in Düsseldorf and 'Frederick' in Berlin are all fictional. By the time Sabine/Ute is arrested in August 1976, Ulrike Meinhof had already committed suicide at Stammheim prison, in Stuttgart. Baader, Ensslin and Raspe were among those who apparently committed suicide on the same night in October 1977: whether these deaths were in fact suicides is the subject of much dispute.

The BfV was founded in 1950 as the internal security service for the Federal Republic, and continues as such after German reunification. Its headquarters are on Innere Kanalstrasse in Cologne. All the BfV characters in the book are fictional (as are all the MI6 characters). The Military Liaison Office and Operation Open River are also fictional (as far as I am aware).

As *The Berlin Spies* is based on actual events in the Second World War and the Cold War, I have tried to ensure that the context of the book and the historical references within it are accurate, along with many dates and locations. I hope the reader will find it helpful if I refer here to some of these in more detail.

In Chapter 8 reference is made to Wilhelm Richter taking part in the massacre of Jewish prisoners on the Baltic coast. While Richter is a fictional character (as are all the other SS officers mentioned in this context), there was indeed a massacre on 29th January 1945, near the village of Palmnicken, of around 5,000 Jewish prisoners who were on a forced march from the Stutthof Concentration camp.

Reference is also made in that chapter to a subsequent series of trials held in Gdansk between April 1946 and November 1947, of SS members who were stationed at Stutthof. These trials did take place: Eighty-four of the eighty-eight people put on trial were found guilty of war crimes, and twenty-three of them were executed.

Viktor describes his work investigating German prisoners of war in the Soviet Union. The figures quoted are accurate: there were around three million German prisoners of war held in the Soviet Union, many of whom died in captivity. The majority of these POWs were released by 1950, but a number (perhaps more than 25,000) were classified as war criminals, and the last of these were not released until 1956.

In Chapter 22 reference is made to a serial killer in Berlin. This is loosely based on a Nazi Party member called Paul Ogorzow, the so-called S-Bahn killer, who murdered eight women between October 1940 and July 1941.

The existence of renegades – British prisoners of war who defected to the Nazi cause – is fairly well known. There were others who worked for the Nazis in Germany (William Joyce or Lord Haw Haw being perhaps the best known). The Captain Canterbury character in *The Berlin Spies* is loosely based on a real renegade called Benson Railton Metcalf Freeman. Freeman was a Sandhurst-trained officer who became a pilot in the RAF before leaving it and joining the British Union of Fascists. He reluctantly re-joined the RAF at the start of the war (he said he didn't want to fight against Germany) and was captured in Belgium. So pronounced were his pro-Nazi views that he did not last long as a prisoner of war, ending up in Berlin where he worked for the Foreign Broadcast Department of the German Foreign Ministry. At his subsequent court martial his former German boss described him as 'a confirmed fascist and of Anti-Bolshevik and Anti-Jewish ideas.' In 1945, Freeman joined the Waffen SS. He was prominent on a MI9 'British Renegades Warning List' and was captured at the end of the war. Back in the UK he was court martialled by the RAF in September 1945 and found guilty on three out of four charges, including serving in the Waffen SS, working for the Germans and accepting money from them. Freeman could have been sentenced to death for both of the first two charges, but for some reason was sentenced to just ten years in prison.

I've long been intrigued by the case of Freeman and have been trying to find out what happened to him after his release in or around 1956. Despite many hours of research at the National Archives, Freedom of Information requests and other research, I have drawn a blank. If anyone reading this knows anything about what happened to Freeman, I'd be most keen to hear it.

While the plot involving the recruitment and training of a group of young, English-speaking SS recruits is fictional, it is nonetheless true that a number of seemingly desperate plans were put in place by the Germans as an Allied victory became inevitable after D-Day in June 1944. One of these was Operation Greif. In October 1944 Hitler asked SS Colonel Otto Skorzeny to form a special brigade of English-speaking troops to be part of the Ardennes Offensive, the aim being to exploit confusion among British and American forces and operate behind Allied lines. Skorzeny formed a SS Panzer Brigade with a commando unit of around 150 English-speaking German troops, but by the time it joined the Battle of the Bulge, in December 1944, the course of the battle meant plans to use the English-speaking commandos were abandoned.

It was the policy of the Allies that all SS prisoners of war were brought back to camps in the United Kingdom. A number did escape, but they never got very far – they were on an island that was overwhelmingly hostile to them. However, the references to Nazi sympathisers in the UK are not as unlikely as they may seem. There were a few hundred such people, many of whom were interred at various stages of the war or who were active to varying degrees in supporting the Nazi cause, including aiding escaped SS prisoners.

In Chapter 19 Georg Stern recounts how his parents were transported to Auschwitz on 2nd March 1943. There was an actual transport of 1,529 Jews on that date from Berlin to Auschwitz. Georg's parents are, of course, fictional, but their story and fate would not have been dissimilar to many on that and other transports. More than 55,000 Jews from Berlin were murdered in the Holocaust.

Some readers may wonder about the Wilhelm Richter (Heinz Fleischhauer/Werner Pohl) character working at various times for the Nazis, the Soviet Union, Britain and West Germany. In fact, the idea for this character came when I was researching at the excellent Topography of Terror in Berlin (well worth a visit, it's the former HQ of the SS, just off Wilhelmstrasse). There I came across an exhibit on Heinz Felfe (1918–2008), who joined the Nazi Party in 1936 and became an officer in the intelligence wing of the SS. After the war he spied for the British, before becoming an officer in the West German Federal Intelligence Service. Around this time Felfe had also been recruited as a Soviet spy. He was arrested in 1961 and jailed for 14 years. He was released early in 1969 as part of a spy swap and settled in East Berlin. I ought to emphasise that the character in this book is not based on Felfe, although the concept of someone managing to work for four different intelligence agencies is.

The banks referred to in the book – notably in Chapter 28 – are all genuine, though of course there is no suggestion that they were involved in the channelling of Soviet funds to the Red Army Faction. That is fiction. The Centro Internationale Handelsbank in Vienna is no longer a separate entity. However a 2002 CIA report on 'Soviet banks in the west' described this bank as one of a number 'established with Polish participation'.

I'd like to express my appreciation to the many people who helped me with *The Berlin Spies*, not least those giving professional and expert advice in a number of areas. I'd like to thank my family for their support and encouragement, not least my wife, Sonia. And finally, the publication of this book would not have been possible without the support and expertise of everyone at Curtis, especially my agent Gordon Wise and Niall Harman.

About the Author

Born in Lincolnshire, **Alex Gerlis** was a BBC journalist for more than twenty five years. He left in 2011 to concentrate on writing and freelance journalism. *The Best of Our Spies* is his first novel and he is represented by the Curtis Brown literary agency. He is a Visiting Professor of Journalism at the University of Bedfordshire. Alex Gerlis lives in west London with his wife and two daughters.

www.alexgerlis.com

Spy Masters